Pathophysiology of the Splanchnic Circulation

Volume II

Editors

Peter R. Kvietys, Ph.D.
Louisiana State University Medical Center
Shreveport, Louisiana

James A. Barrowman, M.D., Ph.D.
Memorial University of Newfoundland
St. Johns, Newfoundland, Canada

D. Neil Granger, Ph.D.
Louisiana State University Medical Center
Shreveport, Louisiana

CRC Press, Inc.
Boca Raton, Florida

Library of Congress Cataloging-in-Publication Data

Pathophysiology of the splanchnic circulation.

Includes bibliographies and indexes.
1. Gastrointestinal system--Diseases--Etiology.
2. Gastrointestinal system--Blood vessels. 3. Regional blood flow. 4. Physiology, Pathological. I. Kvietys, Peter R. II. Barrowman, J. A. III. Granger, D. Neil.
[DNLM: 1. Gastrointestinal Diseases--physiopathology.
2. Splanchnic Circulation. WI 100 P29776]
RC802.9.P38 1987 616.3'3071 86-29910
ISBN 0-8493-4661-4 (set)
ISBN 0-8493-4662-2 (v. 1)
ISBN 0-8493-4663-0 (v. 2)

Direct all inquiries to CRC Press, Inc., 2000 Corporate Blvd., N.W., Boca Raton, Florida, 33431.

International Standard Book Number 0-8493-4661-4 (Set)
International Standard Book Number 0-8493-4662-2 (Volume I)
International Standard Book Number 0-8493-4663-0 (Volume II)
Library of Congress Card Number 86-29910
Printed in the United States

FOREWORD

Discovering and discerning detailed information about the pathology and physiology of the splanchnic vascular bed is not only a stimulating intellectual challenge, but also rewarding because of the usefulness of the knowledge. It is likely that advances in the diagnoses and treatment of gastrointestinal diseases will be based, in part, on the information presented in this monograph.

Studies of the splanchnic circulation have lagged behind studies of other regional vascular beds. This lagging exists in spite of the fact that an understanding of the pathophysiology of these blood vessels probably will allow us to improve regulation of digestion and absorption of food in a world in which hunger and obesity coexist. In addition, eating and drinking are important pleasures in most peoples' lives.

Clinical observations have stimulated pathophysiologic research in the past, and the present state of knowledge about the splanchnic circulation is likely to gain some direction from observations by clinicians, who during their daily evaluation of patients, including their endoscopies, make observations which could lead to clarification of the role of the circulation in gastrointestinal pathophysiology.

Even though there has been a relative lack of inquiry about the intestinal circulation in recent times, it has been studied by distinguished scientists of ancient times including Diogenes, Hippocrates, Aristotle, and their contemporaries. Their belief in the vascular communication between the veins of the forearm and the splanchnic circulation probably accounts for the previous common practice of phlebotomy for the treatment of abdominal ailments. More modern scientists who dealt directly with the splanchnic circulation include William Harvey, Leeuwenhoek, Steven Hales, and Poiseuille.

The three editors of these volumes are pioneers and contributors to the understanding of the intestinal circulation and, therefore, have produced the most advanced work in this field, which often presents contradictory data. One of the explanations for the contradictory data and the lack of current clinical application of this data, is that methods for measurement of gastrointestinal blood flow have been more difficult to develop than comparable methods in other vascular beds. This led to conflicting results based on methodological differences.

Scientific inquiry answers some questions but usually stimulates further inquiry. This monograph is no exception. It answers some questions about the role of the circulation in normal physiologic and disease states but also gives direction for further work in these fields.

Richard L. Wechsler
Department of Medicine
University of Pittsburgh Medical School

THE EDITORS

Dr. Peter R. Kvietys is an Associate Professor in the Department of Physiology and Biophysics at Louisiana State University Medical Center, Shreveport. He received his Ph.D. degree from Michigan State University. He is currently serving on the editorial board of the *American Journal of Physiology: Gastrointestinal and Liver Section.* Dr. Kvietys has published more than 80 research papers in the scientific literature.

Dr. James A. Barrowman is Professor of Gastroenterology and Gastrointestinal Physiology, as well as Assistant Dean of Research and Graduate Studies at Memorial University of Newfoundland. He received his M.B. from Edinburgh University and Ph.D. from London University. Dr. Barrowman has been Deputy Editor of *Drug and Therapeutics Bulletin* and is currently serving on the Editorial Board of the *American Journal of Physiology: Gastrointestinal and Liver Section.* He is or has been a consultant to various government agencies and pharmaceutical firms. He has authored a book on gastrointestinal lymphatics and has published over 110 research papers.

Dr. D. Neil Granger is Professor and Chairman, Department of Physiology and Biophysics at Louisiana State University Medical Center, Shreveport. He received his Ph.D. from the University of Mississippi School of Medicine. He is currently an Associate Editor of the *American Journal of Physiology: Gastrointestinal and Liver Section* and on the Editorial Board of *Microvascular Research.* Dr. Granger is or has been a consultant to various government agencies and pharmaceutical firms. He has coauthored or coedited four books on the gastrointestinal system, and has published more than 170 research papers.

CONTRIBUTORS

Jeffrey L. Ardell
Assistant Professor
Department of Physiology
College of Medicine
University of South Alabama
Mobile, Alabama

Stanley W. Ashley, M.D.
Research Fellow
Department of Surgery
Washington University
St. Louis, Missouri

Robert W. Bailey, M.D.
Research Fellow
Department of Surgery
Johns Hopkins University
Baltimore, Maryland

James A. Barrowman, M.D., F.R.C.P.
Professor
Department of Medicine (Gastroenterology)
Faculty of Medicine
Memorial University of Newfoundland
St. John's, Newfoundland, Canada

Ivan T. Beck, M.D., Ph.D., F.R.C.P. (C), F.A.C.P.
Professor of Medicine and Physiology
Departments of Medicine and Physiology
Director, Gastrointestinal Diseases Research Unit
Queen's University
Chairman
Division of Gastroenterology
Hotel Dieu Hospital
Kingston, Ontario, Canada

Joseph N. Benoit, Ph.D.
Assistant Professor
Department of Physiology and Biophysics
Louisiana State University Medical Center
Shreveport, Louisiana

Gregory B. Bulkley, M.D., F.A.C.S.
Associate Professor
Director of Surgical Research
Department of Surgery
The Johns Hopkins University School of Medicine
Baltimore, Maryland

Laurence Y. Cheung, M.D.
Professor
Department of Surgery
Washington University Medical School
St. Louis, Missouri

Lorris G. Cockerham, Ph.D.
Air Force Office of Scientific Research
Bolling AFB, D.C.
Adjunct Assistant Professor
Department of Physiology
Uniformed Services University of the Health Sciences
Bethesda, Maryland

D. Neil Granger, Ph.D.
Professor and Head
Department of Physiology and Biophysics
Louisiana State University Medical Center
Shreveport, Louisiana

Robert N. Hawkins, Ph.D.
Principal Investigator
Department of Physiology
Armed Forces Radiobiology Research Institute
Bethesda, Maryland
Professorial Lecturer
Department of Biology
The American University
Washington, D.C.

Eugene D. Jacobson, M.D.
Dean
School of Medicine
The University of Kansas Medical Center
Kansas City, Kansas

Ronald J. Korthuis, Ph.D.
Assistant Professor
Department of Physiology and Biophysics
Louisiana State University Medical Center
Shreveport, Louisiana

Peter R. Kvietys, Ph.D.
Associate Professor
Department of Physiology and Biophysics
Louisiana State University Medical Center
Shreveport, Louisiana

David Mailman, Ph.D.
Professor
Department of Biology
University of Houston
Houston, Texas

Miklós Papp, M.D., Sc.D.
Division Chief
Scientific Advisor
Institute of Experimental Medicine
Hungarian Academy of Sciences
Budapest, Hungary

Dale A. Parks, Ph.D.
Assistant Professor
Departments of Anesthesiology and Physiology
University of Alabama
Birmingham, Alabama

Michael A. Perry, Ph.D.
Senior Lecturer
School of Physiology and Pharmacology
University of New South Wales
Kensington, New South Wales, Australia

TABLE OF CONTENTS

Volume I

Volume II

Chapter 6

THE ROLE OF SPLANCHNIC CIRCULATORY AND MUCOSAL MICROVASCULAR CHANGES IN ETHANOL-INDUCED ACUTE SMALL BOWEL INJURY

Ivan T. Beck

TABLE OF CONTENTS

I. INTRODUCTION

It is now well-accepted that acute exposure of the small intestine to ethanol, in concentrations which occur intraluminally in the course of moderate drinking, may result in compromised intestinal function and altered morphology. The principal manifestation of impaired function is a capacity for absorption of glucose,[1-6] other hexoses,[6,7] and amino acids;[1,7-12] inhibition of membrane digestion of disaccharides[13] and peptides;[14] and depression of intracellular enzyme function[15] and cellular metabolism of the enterocytes.[7,9,16] Permeability of the gut to macromolecules is increased[17-20] and fluid secretion,[4,5,21,22] without equivalent changes in electrolyte secretion,[4,5] has also been reported. In addition to this functional impairment, ethanol causes morphological alterations of the small intestinal mucosa.[5,23-27] These consist of subepithelial bleb formation and, if these blebs rupture, denudation of the villi.[5,21,22,26-29] Although many of these physiological[1-3,7,12,13,30,31] and some of the morphological changes also have been demonstrated in vitro (in the absence of circulation),[2] recent evidence indicates that alterations in splanchnic circulation, and especially in the microcirculation of the mucosa, may play an important role in some of these events.[21,22,29,32]

In order to provide an understanding of a possible role of the microcirculation in ethanol-induced small bowel injury, it is necessary first to review the pathophysiological and morphological effects of ethanol on the small bowel. Different ethanol concentrations may have dissimilar effects on various organs. Therefore, to allow for a realistic correlation of physiological and morphological changes in the mucosa with alterations in the general and local circulation caused by the ingestion of moderate amounts of alcohol, it is necessary to consider the ethanol concentrations which occur in the gut lumen, the gut wall, and the blood after moderate drinking.

II. ETHANOL CONCENTRATIONS AFTER MODERATE DRINKING

The effect of a toxin, including ethanol, on any organ depends on its concentration in the organ, duration of contact, and sensitivity of the tissue to its effect. For instance, 0.3 to 0.5% ethanol in the serum and the CNS causes coma and death,[33] but the same concentration of ethanol does not affect glucose absorption across the gut mucosa.

Table 1 shows the relative sensitivities of the CNS, the cardiovascular system, and the gut to different concentrations of ethanol. The section which follows will deal with the relationship of the various organ sensitivities to actual ethanol concentrations in the circulation and different organs after moderate alcohol ingestion.

A. Intraluminal Ethanol Concentrations

There are few studies in man which deal with the intraluminal ethanol concentration after ingestion of moderate amounts of alcohol. Israel et al.[10] gave 40 g of ethanol as a 10 or 20%* solution, and observed that the ethanol concentration in the jejunum reached maximum values of 2.5 to 3%. Halsted and co-workers[34] found that, after oral administration of ethanol in a dose of 0.8 g/kg body weight, the ethanol concentrations in the duodenum and proximal jejunum peaked between 1 and 5% during the first 45 min. Presumably as a result of rapid absorption of ethanol, the intraluminal concentration of this substance declined distally, and within 60 min the concentration of alcohol in the lumen of the ileum was 0.2%. After 120 min the concentrations of ethanol in the serum and in all GI sites were similar (0.02 to 0.05%). Ethanol diffuses freely from lumen to mucosa,[4,21,35-38] and from there through the extra- and intracellular spaces to the blood.[36] It passes with similar ease from the serosal side of the gut to the mucosa.[3] Therefore, it is not astonishing that 120 min after ingestion its concentrations become similar in the blood and all GI sites. In our own experience,[28] when alcohol was administered into the stomach of healthy human volunteers in a dose of 45 to 60 g of ethanol (either in pure form or as whiskey, both diluted to an ethanol concentration of 20%), the mean peak intraluminal ethanol concentrations varied between 6.46 and 9.37% in the duodenum and between 5.69 and 6.35% in the jejunum. With these doses of alcohol none of the subjects were drunk, and the mean peak serum concentrations (0.05 and 0.14%) were approximately 100 to 150 times lower than in the lumen of the duodenum. On the basis of the above, in human or animal studies designed to investigate the effect of ethanol on small intestinal function, the concentration of ethanol in the lumen and serum should not exceed 6 to 8 and 0.15%, respectively.

B. Comparison of Ethanol Concentrations in the Portal Vein, Splanchnic Arteries, and Splanchnic Tissues

Although data are available on the intraluminal ethanol concentrations which occur after alcohol intake, very little is known about the comparative ethanol concentrations in the intestinal lumen, the mucosa, the nonmucosal gut wall, the portal and hepatic vein, and the peripheral and splanchnic arteries. To investigate this problem, in a series of experiments we administered 0.4 g ethanol per kilogram (given as a 25% v/v solution) into the stomach of dogs.[39] This amount of ethanol was equivalent to approximately 4 oz of 100-proof whiskey for a 70-kg man. The findings of these experiments indicated that under steady-state conditions the mean ethanol concentration in the portal blood was 30m*M* (0.14%). This was 35 to 65 times lower than the expected duodenal intraluminal concentration of 5 to 9%, but significantly higher (2 times) than the simultaneously obtained concentration in the bile (0.1%); and the latter was significantly higher than that in the peripheral arterial blood (0.07%). Interestingly, the ethanol concentration in pancreatic secretion was similar to that in the peripheral arteries (Figure 1).[39] These differences in concentrations can easily be explained by the physical properties of alcohol, its route of absorption, its metabolic degradation, and its route of recirculation (Figure 2). Because ethanol passes through membranes as

* All percentages (unless otherwise stated) are given as w/v.

Table 1
EFFECT OF DIFFERENT CONCENTRATIONS OF ETHANOL ON CENTRAL NERVOUS SYSTEM (CNS), SMALL BOWEL ABSORPTION (SBA), SMALL BOWEL MORPHOLOGY (SBM), AND BLOOD VESSELS AND/OR BLOOD FLOW (BV)

Ethanol conc. (%)	Organ	Effect	Ref.
0.05	CNS	Sedation	33
	SBA	No effect	1—4, 6, 7
	SBM	No effect	51
	BV	Dilates terminal arterioles	100
		No effect on muscular venules	100
		No effect on large vessels	76, 97
		Fall in systolic blood pressure	22
0.1	CNS	Incoordination	33
	SBA	No effect	1, 3, 4, 6, 7
	SBM	No effect	26
	BV	Dilates terminal arterioles and venules	100
		Inhibits spontaneous activity of aortic strips and portal vein	76, 97
		Fall in systolic blood pressure	22
0.2	CNS	Intoxication	33
	SBA	No effect	1—4, 6, 7
	SBM	No effect	26
	BV	Dilates terminal arterioles and venules	100
		Inhibits spontaneous activity of aortic strips and portal vein	76, 97
0.3	CNS	Coma	33
	SBA	No effect	1, 3, 4, 6, 7
	SBM	No effect	2
	BV	Dilates terminal arterioles and venules	100
		Inhibits spontaneous activity of aortic strips and portal vein	76, 97
		Elevation in systemic blood pressure	90
0.5	CNS	Death	33
	SBA	No effect	1, 3, 4, 6, 7
	SBM	No effect	2
	BV	Dilates terminal arterioles and venules	100
		Inhibits spontaneous activity of arotic strips and portal vein	76, 97
2.0	CNS	Death	33
	SBA	Inhibition of amino acid and glucose absorption in vitro and in vivo	1—4, 6, 7
	SBM	Minimal changes	2
	BV	Dilates terminal arterioles and venules	100
		Inhibits spontaneous activity of aortic strips and portal vein	76, 97
		Contraction of aortic strip and veins in vitro	76, 97
5.0	CNS	Death	33
	SBA	Inhibition of amino acid and glucose absorption in vitro and in vivo	1—4, 6, 7
	SBM	Severe morphological damage	16
	BV	Dilates terminal arterioles and venules	100
		Contraction of large vessels in vitro	76, 97

Note: "No effect" denotes either that there was a proven absence of effect at that given concentration or that evidence of effect could be obtained only at higher concentrations.

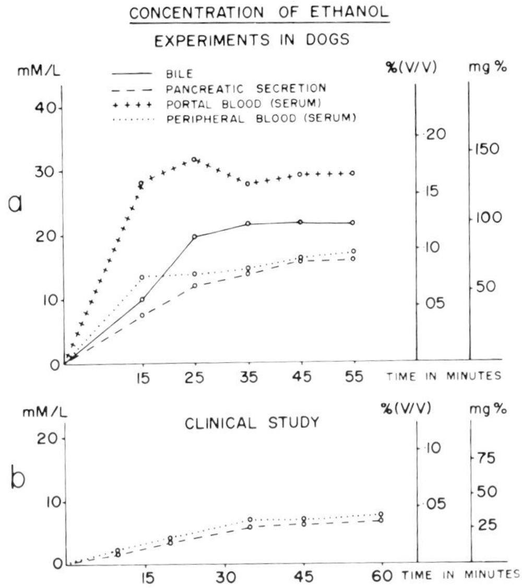

FIGURE 1. (a) Mean ethanol concentration in bile, pancreatic secretion, and portal and arterial serum (seven dogs). (b) Ethanol concentration in venous serum and in pancreatic secretion (human subject with a pancreatic fistula). Ordinate = ethanol concentration in millimolars per liter, percentage, and milligrams per 100 m*l*. Abscissa = time in minutes. (Reprinted from Beck, I. T., Paloschi, G. B., Dinda, P. K., and Beck, M., *Gastroenterology,* 67, 484, 1974. With permission.)

easily as tritiated water,[40] and because after ingestion its intraluminal concentration in the upper GI tract is high, it penetrates the wall of the stomach and upper small bowel rapidly and immediately enters the portal system. In view of the fact that the intraluminal ethanol concentration in the distal small bowel and colon is low, the ethanol concentration of the mesenteric blood draining the upper small bowel is diluted by mesenteric venous blood derived from the more distal parts of the gut. Accordingly, the concentration of ethanol in the portal serum is expected to be lower than in the gut lumen, but higher than in the peripheral circulation.[36] Because of this, the liver is the organ which is perfused with blood carrying the highest concentration of ethanol. However, due to an admixture of hepatic arterial blood, which (like the blood in other arteries) has a lower alcohol concentration, the ethanol derived from the portal vein is further diluted in the sinusoids. Since the liver cells contain alcohol-metabolizing systems,[41] a substantial portion of the ethanol reaching the liver is metabolized on first passage. Hence, at steady-state the alcohol concentration of the liver cell should be considerably lower than that in the portal, and higher than in the peripheral arterial blood. Theoretically, the intracellular alcohol diffuses with ease into the bile canaliculi and thus, under steady-state conditions, the concentration of ethanol in the bile should reflect that in the hepatocytes. This is in keeping with the observation that the biliary ethanol concentration is lower than that determined in the portal blood.* Ethanol is further diluted as hepatic venous blood mixes with that of the vena cava, and its con-

* The biliary system receives its blood supply from the hepatic artery, without admixture of portal blood. Therefore the hepatocellular ethanol concentration may be slightly higher than the concentration of ethanol in the bile duct.

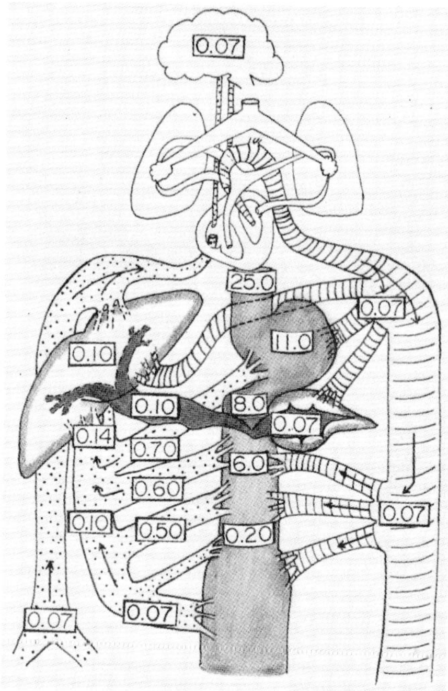

FIGURE 2. Schematic representation of relative ethanol concentration in different organs, ducts, and blood vessels. The example depicts a theoretical situation where ethanol was orally ingested in such amounts that the peripheral blood concentration reached 0.07% (w/v). (Legal upper limit for driving in Canada is 0.08%.)

centration becomes even lower as some of the alcohol is lost in the lungs.[42] It is for this reason that the concentrations of ethanol in peripheral blood are lower than those in the gut, portal vein, and liver. Because ethanol diffuses so easily from blood to extra- and intracellular tissues, the ethanol concentration of all splanchnic organs and their secretions (except for the gut wall and the liver) is similar to the ethanol concentration in the peripheral arteries. This is supported by the observation that the concentration of ethanol in pancreatic secretions is similar to that in peripheral blood (Figure 1).

Unfortunately, there are no data on the ethanol concentrations which occur after alcohol intake in the duodenal or jejunal villi or in the subepithelial capillaries. Theoretically, the concentration of ethanol in epithelial cells should be similar to (or only slightly lower than) that in the lumen. This is because transport across the epithelium is iso-osmotic,*[43,44] and a prerequisite for iso-osmotic transport is that the epithelial cell becomes iso-osmotic with the intraluminal content.[45] In the case of easily-diffusing substances, lumen-to-cell iso-osmolality is achieved by diffusion of the solute into the epithelial cells until its concentration in the cells is similar to that in the luminal fluid.[46] Since the capillaries of the villi are very close to the epithelial layer, it is likely that the ethanol concentration entering the capillaries approaches the intraluminal concentration. Theoretically, rapid dilution of ethanol should occur from this point on but, in view of the existence of a countercurrent multiplication of solutes in the intestinal villi

* Iso-osmotic fluid transport refers to a phenomenon where the osmolality of the transported fluid is similar to that of the mucosal solution whether the latter is hypo-, iso, or hypertonic.

of some species,[47] the ethanol concentration in the capillaries at the tip of the villi (and capillaries) may be equal to that in the lumen.

In view of the fact that different ethanol concentrations may have different effects on the vasculature,[48] it would be of considerable importance to obtain some data on the arteriolar, capillary, and venous concentration of ethanol at the tips (absorptive portion) of the intestinal villi.

III. EFFECT OF ETHANOL ON INTESTINAL TRANSPORT

A. Effect of Ethanol on Permeability of the Gut

The information available on ethanol-induced changes in permeability of the gut is controversial. We found that exposure in our laboratory of hamster intestine in vitro to 4.8% ethanol did not increase the permeability of the hamster jejunum to polyethylene glycol (4000) and meglumine diatrizoate (Renografin).[4] Since this concentration of ethanol does not produce discontinuity of the hamster epithelium,[26] these findings indicate that under acute conditions, if there is no major morphological damage to the epithelium, there is no alteration of permeability of the gut to these large molecules. Other investigators found that perfusion of rat small intestine with solutions of 0.5, 1.0, or 2.0% ethanol in vivo or in vitro did not increase the permeability of the gut wall to barbiturates and salicylates.[49-51] On the other hand, some evidence suggests that 5.4% v/v (4.1% w/v) ethanol increases the passive permeation of the gut to sodium, chloride, 3-*O*-methylglucose, and alanine,[7] but that this increased permeability is the result of increased diffusion through the brush border membrane and not necessarily the intercellular spaces.[30,52] Furthermore, recent evidence indicates that ethanol also increases the permeability of the rat small bowel to macromolecules such as horseradish peroxidase[19,20] and polyethylene glycol,[18] and that intraluminal ethanol in the dog causes an increased loss of serum albumin[29] and lactoglobulin[32] from gut wall to the lumen. The data of Worthington and colleagues[17] indicate that, at least in chronic alcoholic rats, the macromolecules pass through the epithelium via the paracellular pathway; and the studies of Talbot and co-workers[20] suggest that morphological damage is not a prerequisite for increased permeation of macromolecules.

B. Effect of Ethanol on Sugar, Amino Acid, Electrolyte, and Water Transport

Ethanol interferes with the absorption of many nutrients.[1,2,4,5,8-12,21,22,25,53-56] Reports on the effect of ethanol on fat absorption are inconsistent: according to some, ethanol stimulates[57,58] and according to others, it inhibits[59,60] lipid transport. The present discussion, however, is not intended to provide a full review on the effect of ethanol on the absorption of all nutrients investigated. Since the morphological and microcirculatory changes caused by ethanol were correlated only with the effect of ethanol on the transport of sugars, amino acids, sodium, and water, this review will be restricted to the effect of ethanol on the transport of these substances. Most data indicate that the inhibitory effect of ethanol on sugar and amino acid transport is concentration-dependent.[30] Spencer et al.[31] found that in everted sacs of hamster jejunum, 10 m*M* (0.046%) or 100 m*M* (0.46%) ethanol had no effect on the transport of L-proline and L-glycine, but that 1000 m*M* (4.6%) completely inhibited their absorption. A similar concentration-dependent depression of glucose transport was demonstrated by us,[2] where 150 m*M* (0.69%) ethanol in vitro decreased glucose uptake by 20%, 300 m*M* (1.38%) by 27%, and 450 m*M* (2.07%) by 41%. Simultaneous concentration-dependent depression occurred in the intracellular glucose concentration of the gut, the rate of intracellular glucose metabolism, and the glucose-dependent electrical potential difference. The inhibition of steady-state glucose transport was also concentration-de-

DIAMOND'S THEORY OF WATER TRANSPORT

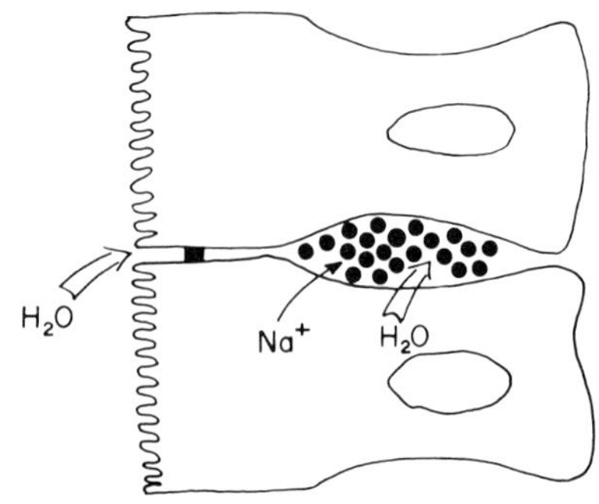

FIGURE 3. Sodium is transported across the basolateral membrane into the narrow LIS. As a result the osmolality of the LIS increases. This then "draws" water into these areas from the cell and across the tight junctions.

pendent (from 2.0 to 4.8% ethanol) in vivo,[4] where 450 m*M* (2.0%) ethanol in the lumen did not significantly influence glucose absorption, but 4.8% caused a 54% depression of this process. Ethanol also inhibits water transport both in vitro and in vivo.[2,4,5] and the magnitude of the depression depends on the concentration of ethanol used.[4]

Although ethanol increases the permeability of the brush border membrane to sodium,[52] very little information is available on the acute effect of ethanol on sodium absorption. The active (electrogenic) transport of glucose across the brush border is linked to sodium,[61] and water absorption is linked to sodium transport across the basolateral membrane.[62] According to the standing osmotic gradient theory of Diamond,[62] sodium is actively transported from the cell into the lateral intercellular spaces (LIS). Because of the closeness of the epithelial cells to each other the LIS are narrow, and continuous translocation of sodium into these spaces creates a localized area of high osmolality between the enterocytes. Hyperosmolality of the LIS draws water into these areas, and this is considered to be the driving force for water transport. Indeed the dilation of the LIS (due to accumulation of fluid) is considered to be the morphological expression of water absorption[63] (Figure 3). Under normal conditions 1 μmol of glucose is co-transported with 2 μmol of sodium and 17.5 $\mu\ell$ of water[64] (Figure 4). However, the ethanol-induced depression of water transport greatly exceeds that expected from the magnitude of the inhibition of glucose transport;[2,4,22] thus, ethanol disrupts this physiological relationship. In some species (hamster, rabbit, and dog) ethanol not only inhibits water absorption but actually induces fluid secretion.[5,21,22] The effect of ethanol on sodium transport is controversial. Kuo and Shabour[7] found that in rabbit jejunal mucosa 3.0 or 5.4% ethanol significantly depressed the short circuit current and transmural potential difference, but the unidirectional fluxes of sodium from mucosa to serosa or from serosa to mucosa increased. However, the difference between the two fluxes (the net mucosal-to-serosal flux) decreased. This observation is contrary to the findings of Mekhjian and May,[65] who reported that ethanol in 3, 4, or 10% solutions in the jejunum or ileum of healthy human subjects did not cause any significant alteration in net sodium transport. Similarly, Himal and Greenberg[66] found no change in sodium absorption by the duodenum. Our own observation also indicates that ethanol (while it depresses glucose transport and transmural PD, and inhibits or actually reverses water absorption[2-5,21,22]) does not influence sodium absorption.[2,3,22] All these findings indicate that ethanol causes a disturbance of

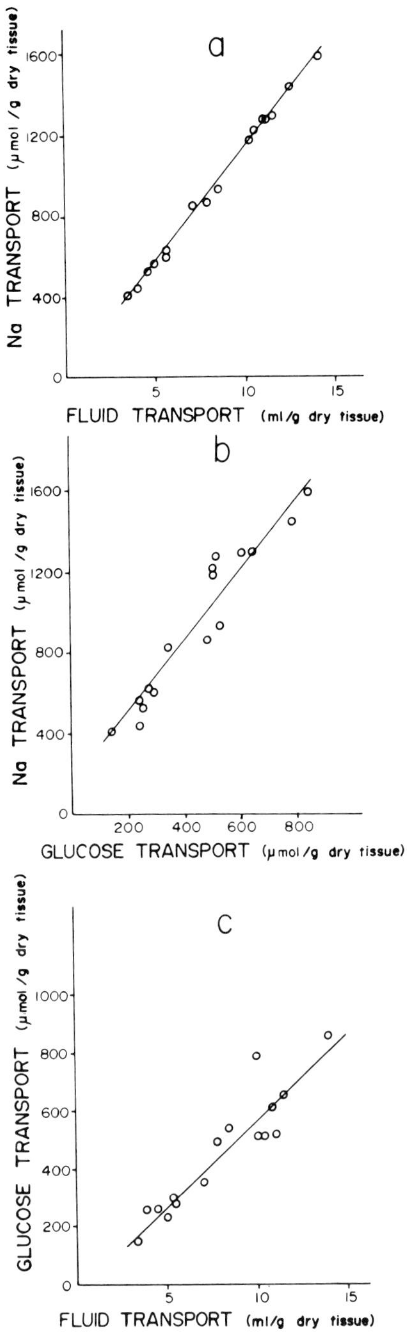

FIGURE 4. Relationship between net fluid, sodium, and glucose transport in hamster jejunum. (a) Fluid (X) and sodium (Y) transport ($r = 0.998$, $p < 0.001$; $Y = -5.75 + 115.12X$, $p < 0.001$). (b) Glucose transport to the serosal side (X) and sodium transport (Y) ($r = 0.951$, $p < 0.001$; $Y = 137.93 + 1.78X$, $p < 0.001$). (c) Fluid transport (X) and the transport of glucose to the serosal side (Y) ($r = 0.962$, $p < 0.001$; $Y = -35.92 + 59.01X$, $p < 0.001$). (Reprinted from Dinda, P. K., Beck, I. T, and Beck, M., *Can. J. Physiol. Pharmacol.*, 51, 130, 1973. With permission.)

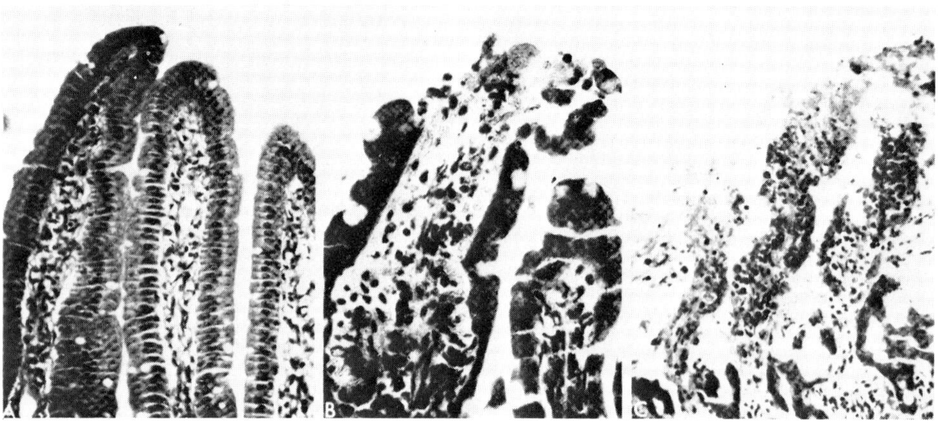

A B C

FIGURE 5. Microscopic appearance of rat jejunal villi 1 hr after intragastric administration of saline or ethanol solutions. (A) Normal appearance from a control rat after intubation with saline (H & E, magnification × 80). (B) Typical changes seen after ethanol administration with epithelial cell loss mainly affecting the villus tips and with hemorrhage in the corium (H & E, magnification × 160). (C) Gross damage of villi in an area on confluent hemorrhage after ethanol administration (H & E, magnification × 80). (Reprinted from Baraona, E., Pirola, R. C., and Lieber, C. S., *Gastroenterology*, 66, 226, 1974. With permission.)

the normal relationship of sodium-linked glucose and water transport, and suggest that fluid secretion is not related to electrolyte secretion but rather to secretory filtration. This is supported by the observation that in the presence of intraluminal ethanol the secreted fluid contains protein lost from the mucosal tissues and blood.[21]

IV. EFFECT OF ETHANOL ON SMALL INTESTINAL MORPHOLOGY

The morphological alterations caused by ethanol are dependent on the intraluminal concentration and the resistance of the mucosa to injury. Hayton[51] observed that in vivo perfusion of rat jejunum with 0.05% ethyl alcohol produced no structural changes of the epithelium. Gillespie and Lucas[23] found that intragastric administration of ethanol (12 to 76%) produced no small intestinal lesions in well-nourished rats, but induced hemorrhage in malnourished ones. Baraona et al.[16] also observed concentration-dependent morphological changes in the duodenum and jejunum of rats following intragastric administration of ethanol in concentrations ranging from 5 to 49% (given in doses equivalent to 1.0, 3.0, or 7.5 g ethanol per kilogram body weight). According to these authors the epithelial damage was most pronounced at the tips of the villi, where a great number of cells were lost. Inflammatory cell infiltration and hemorrhage in the lamina propria accompanied these changes (Figure 5). Similar concentration-dependent morphological alterations were observed by Broitman et al.[24] in rat small intestine following perfusion of this organ with solutions containing 50 to 400 m*M* ethanol (i.e., 0.23 to 1.84%). Hoyumpa et al.[25] reported that administration of ethanol (7.5 g/kg) to rats caused mild to moderately severe congestion of the lamina propria of the intestinal villi, where fragmentation of red blood cells and the presence of polymorphonuclear leukocytes was also detectable. The upper 20% of the villi was denuded of epithelial cells.

We have investigated the effects of ethanol on small intestinal morphology of the hamster,[2,26] rat,[26] rabbit,[21] dog,[21] and man.[28] The ethanol-induced morphological alterations we observed in the hamster were somewhat different from those described by the above investigators[16,24,25] in the rat. We found that perfusion of the hamster jejunum in vivo with solutions containing 2.1 to 4.8% ethanol caused a subepithelial

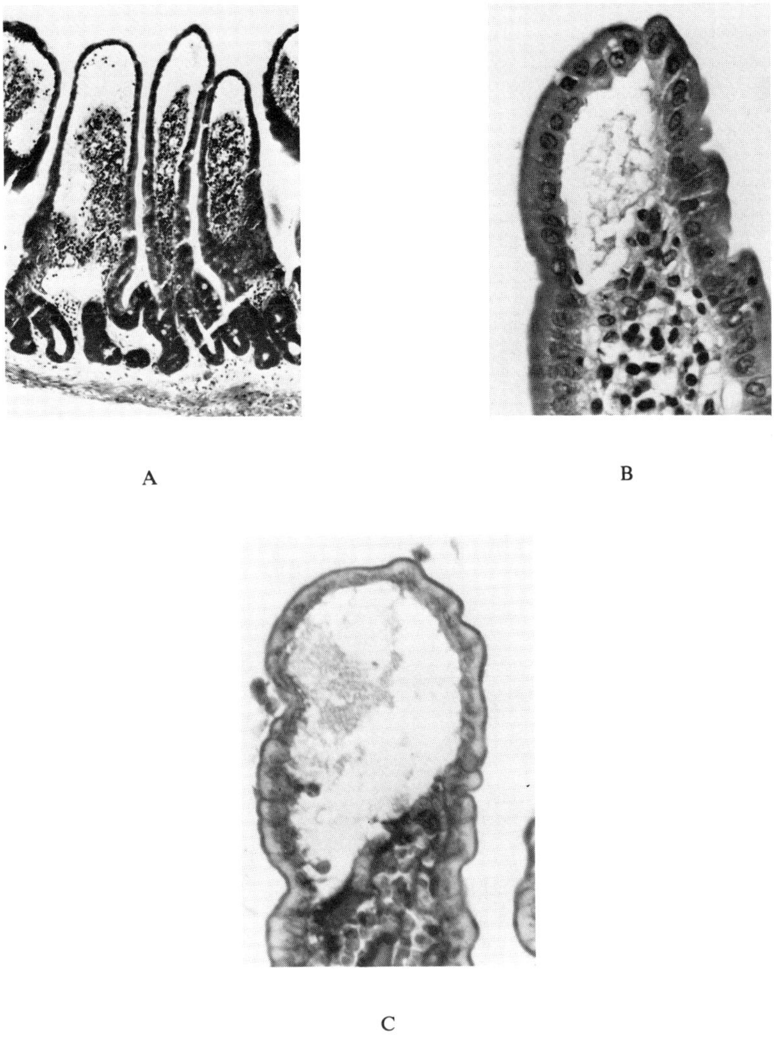

FIGURE 6. Photomicrographs of hamster jejunum which was perfused in vivo with Krebs-Ringer bicarbonate solution (KRBS) for 45 min, KRBS with 10 m*M* glucose (KRBSG) for 45 min, and KRBSG with alcohol (KRBSGE) for 45 min. (A) Perfused with KRBSGE (1050 m*M* ethanol) (magnification × 50). Four adjacent villi showing bleb formation. Note that the epithelial layer convering the blebs is intact and that the underlying stroma is compressed. The lacteals are not dilated. (B) Tip of villus of segment perfused with KRBSGE (450 m*M* ethanol) showing a bleb at higher magnification (× 200). (C) Tip of villus perfused with KRBSGE (1050 m*M* ethanol) (magnification × 200). Note that in (B) and (C) the blebs contain proteinaceous material and are devoid of RBC. Only a few stroma cells remain attached to the epithelial layer, which is intact and appears stretched. The stretched cells over the bleb have become cuboidal, and no LIS are visible. The cells forming the bleb have a normal brush border, and their nuclei are aligned regularly in a single layer. (Reprinted from Fox, J. E., McElligott, T. F., and Beck, I. T., *Am. J. Dig. Dis.,* 23, 201, 1978. With permission.)

accumulation of fluid.[26] This resulted in blisters (or blebs) at the tips of the villi. The blebs appeared within 5 min after the beginning of ethanol perfusion and could be seen on an occasional villus, or in some areas on every villus (Figure 6). Occasionally, there were adjacent areas in the epithelium where none of the villi had blebs, and in these areas the morphology was indistinguishable from that in the control animals. The ratio of villi with blebs to normal villi was concentration-dependent, and the higher the ethanol concentration the more villi were involved.[26] In the hamster, unlike the rat, the epithelial layer over the blebs was not disrupted, and as a result there was no denudation of the villus. On light microscopy the epithelial cells over the blebs appeared to have normal brush borders but, probably due to increased fluid pressure under the epithelial cell layers, the enterocytes were stretched to such an extent that their shape had become cuboidal and the LIS were unrecognizable (Figure 6C). Many of the blebs appeared to contain some proteinaceous material.

Transmission and scanning electron microscopic studies indicated that ultrastructural changes were restricted to the areas of the villus where blebs had formed.[27] There was a diminution in the density and thickness of the glycocalyx of the epithelial cells which covered the blebs (Figure 7). As a result, on scanning electron microscopy, unlike in the unaffected areas, the microvilli and the polygonal cell boundaries were clearly visible (Figure 8). It appeared that the epithelium forming the bleb detached gradually from the basal lamina (basement membrane), which remained in contact with the underlying villus core. At first the LIS became swollen, and in some instances we could observe that the basolateral membrane of the cell was attached only tenuously to the basal lamina of the villus core (Figure 9). Thus, the blebs were formed between the basal lamina of the villus and the basolateral membrane of the epithelial cells. Due to the detachment of the basolateral membrane of the enterocyte from the basal lamina of the villus core, the LIS between epithelial cells (which were held together only by their tight junctions) were fully opened, and consequently the narrow intercellular channels disappeared (Figure 10). In the epithelial cells over the bleb, the granular endoplasmic reticulum was swollen, and except for this no other cellular abnormality was seen in these cells. Epithelial cells in areas where there were no blebs remained normal and were indistinguishable by transmission electron microscopy from those in the control tissue. These findings indicate that any morphological alterations in the epithelial cells are not related to a morphologically detectable direct cytotoxic effect of ethanol, but are secondary to the mechanical distortion due to bleb formation.

The villus core (lamina propria) of villi with blebs appeared compacted. There was congestion of the capillaries, which appeared to have lost some proteinaceous material into the pericapillary areas and into the blebs. Lacteals were not dilated in this species (hamster); on the contrary, they appeared compressed.

The morphological changes described by others[16,24,25] in the rat jejunum, indicating complete denudation of villus tip, were different from those described above for the hamster. To assess whether these differences in morphology were due to a difference in species, technique, or ethanol concentration, we perfused rat jejunum with ethanol under conditions similar to those in the hamster experiments.[26] Although, in agreement with the observations of the above investigators, we also found denudation of villus tip in the ethanol-treated rat jejunum, a close examination of the slides revealed the existence of many remnants of ruptured blebs, and an occasional unruptured bleb (Figure 11). Therefore, it seems that ethanol induces bleb formation at the tips of the villi not only in the jejunum of the hamster, but also in the rat small intestine. However, while in the hamster the blebs remained intact, in the rat the majority of the blebs subsequently ruptured, resulting in the denudation of the villus tip. Although the reason for this difference is not known, it is likely due to the fact that the rat jejunum is less resistant to injury than that of the hamster. This suggestion is supported by the observation that under in vitro conditions the rat jejunum degenerates more rapidly than the jejunum of the hamster.[54,67] It is therefore likely that the difference in morphological response of rat and hamster jejunum to alcohol is one of degree rather than of basic character.

In fact, we have found that bleb formation in the small intestine is the common morphological response to alcohol in all species we examined. The species differences

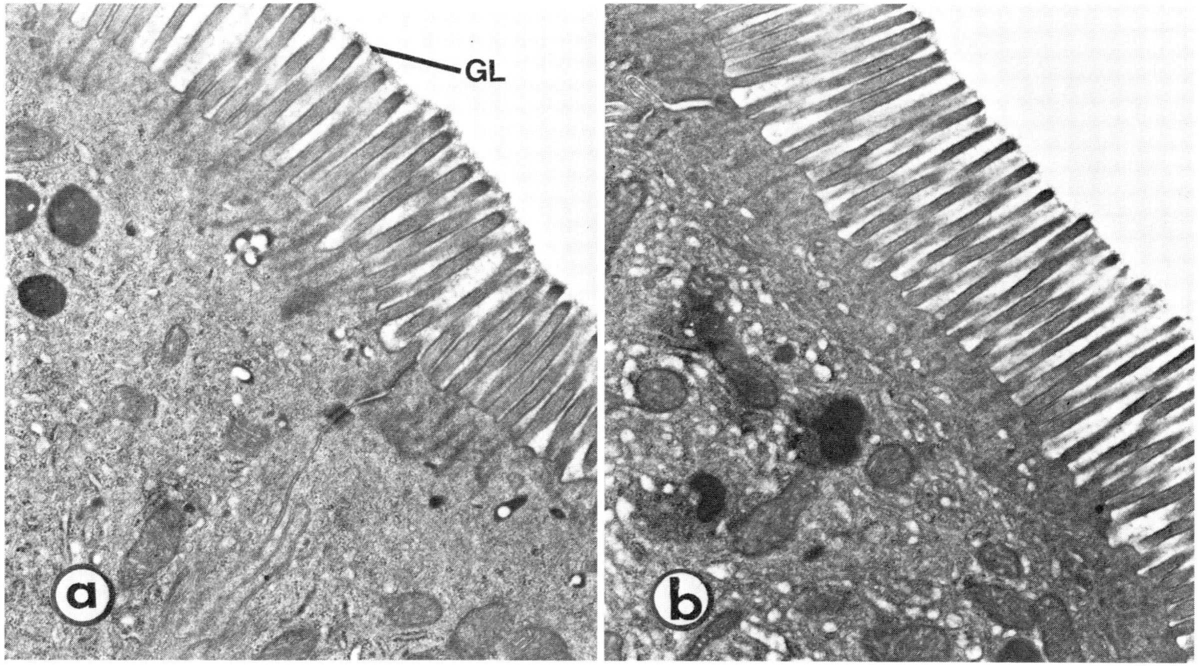

FIGURE 7. Transmission electron micrographs. (a) Apical cytoplasm and microvilli of epithelial cells from upper one third of villus of hamster jejunal segment perfused with 4.8% (1050 m*M*) ethanol for 45 min. Perfusion with ethanol produces no visible damage. Note the obvious glycocalyx (GL). (Magnification × 13,700.) (b) Apical cytoplasm and microvilli of epithelial cells covering a bleb. Note diminished glycocalyx and swelling of endoplasmic reticulum. This cell was on the same villus as the one shown in (a). (Magnification × 14,000.) (Reprinted from Fox, J. E., Morris, G. P., Beck, I. T., and McElligott, T. F., *Can. J. Physiol. Pharmacol.*, 57, 305, 1979. With permission.)

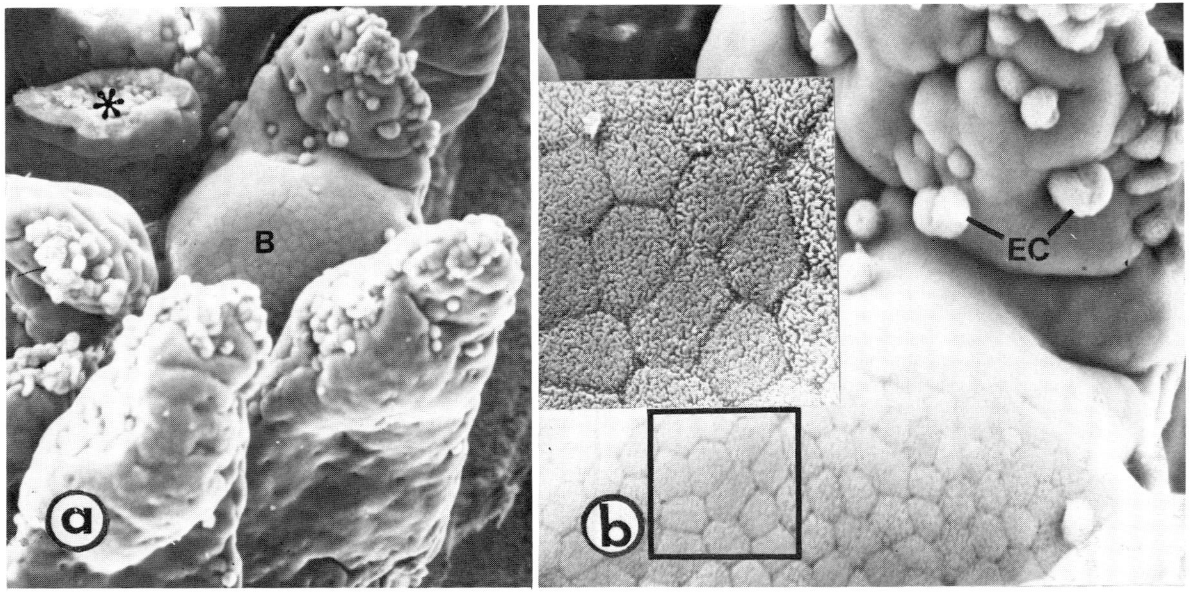

FIGURE 8. Scanning electron micrograph of ethanol-perfused hamster jejunum. (a) Bleb (B) can be seen on the lateral surface of a villus. The asterisk indicates a villus broken during specimen preparation. (Magnification × 184.) (b) Detail of bleb shown in (a). Cell boundaries are clearly visible over bleb epithelium. EC, extruding cells. (Magnification × 530.) Inset shows area contained within square at higher magnification (× 1100). (Reprinted from Fox, J. E., Morris, G. P., Beck, I. T., and McElligott, T. F., *Can. J. Physiol. Pharmacol.*, 57, 305, 1979. With permission.)

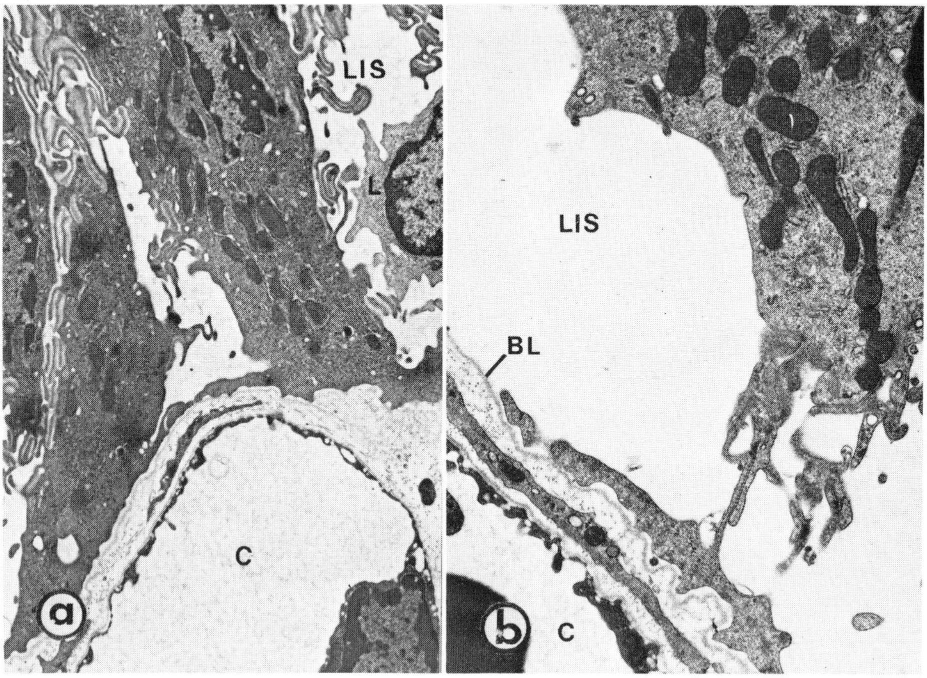

FIGURE 9. Transmission electron micrograph of ethanol-perfused segment of hamster jejunum. (a) Epithelial cells at tip of villus which did not show a bleb. Note LIS and lymphocyte (L). C, capillary. (Magnification × 5360.) (b) Base of an epithelial cell near a bleb. Note the swollen LIS. Only tenuous connections remain between the cell base and the basal lamina (BL). C, capillary. (Magnification × 8800.) (Reprinted from Fox, J. E., Morris, G. P., Beck, I. T., and McElligott, T. F., *Can. J. Physiol. Pharmacol.*, 5, 305, 1979. With permission.)

observed appear to be only in degree, and are manifested by different ratios of intact to broken blebs. In the rabbit, ethanol-induced morphological alterations were intermediate to those seen in the hamster and rat. Both intact and ruptured blebs were observed, and the proportion of the ruptured blebs depended on the concentration of ethanol perfused (Table 2). In this species, as in the hamster, there was vascular congestion in the villus core but, contrary to our observations on the hamster, the lacteals were frequently dilated. Furthermore, small macro- and light microscopic hemorrhagic lesions were occasionally observed in the ethanol-treated segments.[21] In the dog, ethanol caused both intact and ruptured blebs, but the proportion of intact blebs was much higher than in the rabbit (Table 3). There was also congestion of blood vessels in the villus core, and morphometric studies demonstrated that in villi with damaged epithelium (irrespective of whether this damage consisted of intact or ruptured blebs) the villus cores were approximately 20% shorter than those with normal, intact epithelium (Figure 12). Finally, in a biopsy study in man, where we infused 45 or 60 g of ethanol (equivalent to 4.8 or 6.4 oz of 80-proof whiskey diluted to 20%) into the stomachs of 20 normal volunteers, we found that in suction biopsies obtained during the control period (before ethanol administration) 7.5% of villi had blebs and 10.3% had ruptured blebs. On the other hand, biopsies taken 5 min after peak ethanol concentration (Figure 13) exhibied a significantly higher percentage of damaged villi (26% with blebs and 19% with broken blebs). For reasons to be discussed later, it is likely that the 18% of villi with blebs or broken blebs observed in the control biopsies was due to microvascular stasis caused by the suction applied to obtain the biopsy. The additional damage (over and above that caused by suction biopsy) which occurred during peak

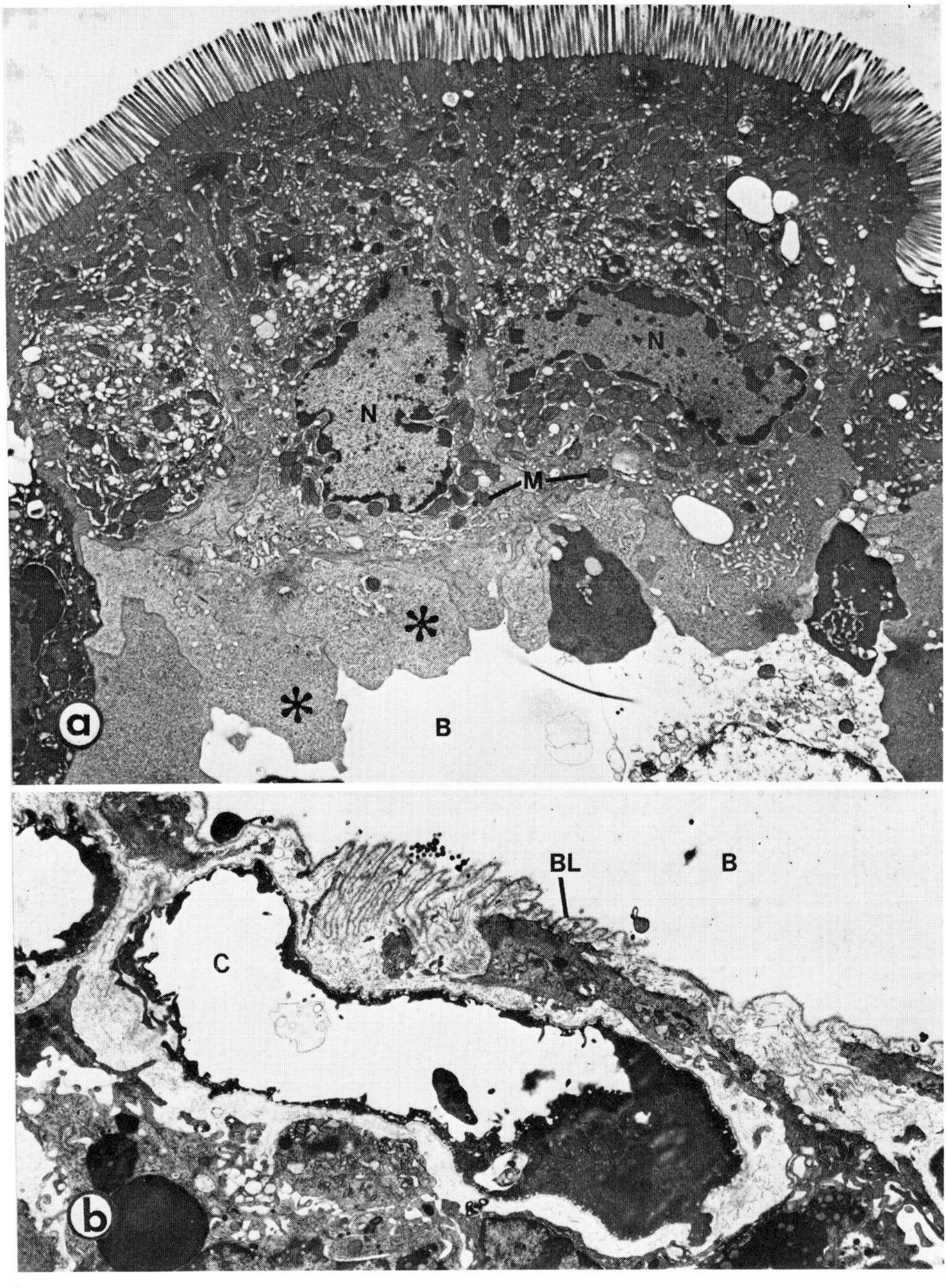

FIGURE 10. Ethanol-perfused hamster jejunal segment. (a) Epithelium covering bleb (B). Note extensive swelling of endoplasmic reticulum and pseudopod-like extensions of basal cytoplasm (indicated by asterisks). Also note absence of LIS between epithelial cells. Mitochondria (M) display normal morphology. N, nucleus. (Magnification × 4160.) (b) Ethanol-perfused hamster jejunal segment. Base of large bleb (B). The basal lamina (BL) remains adherent to the underlying lamina propria. C, capillary. (Magnification × 5360.) (Reprinted from Fox, J. E., Morris, G. P., Beck, I. T., and McElligott, T. F., *Can. J. Physiol. Pharmacol.*, 57, 305, 1979. With permission.)

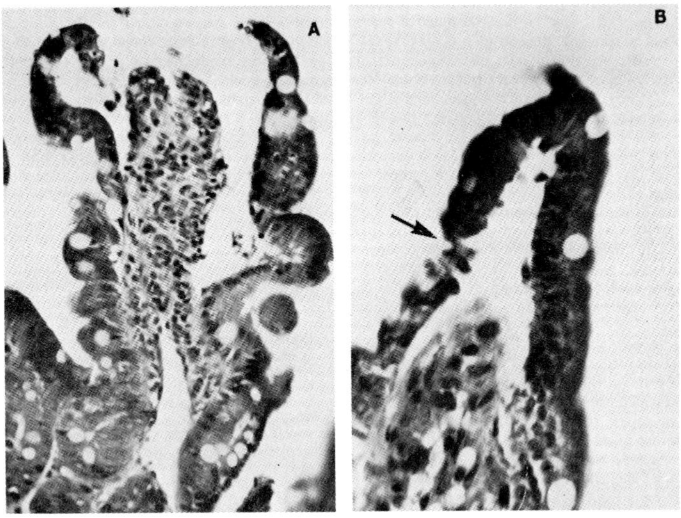

FIGURE 11. Photomicrographs of rat jejunum after perfusion for 45 min with KRBSG and 1050 m*M* (4.8%) ethanol (magnification × 240). (A) This villus shows the typical extensive damage seen in the rat. The epithelial layer is broken and appears to be stripping away from the underlying stroma. Open LIS are not obvious. There are necrotic cells at the edge of the break. (B) This shows an unbroken bleb with an epithelial layer which appears to be disintegrating (arrow). (Reprinted from Fox, J. E., McElligott, T. F., and Beck, I. T., *Am. J. Dig. Dis.*, 23, 201, 1978. With permission.)

Table 2
EFFECT OF ETHANOL PERFUSION ON RABBIT JEJUNAL MORPHOLOGY — MORPHOMETRIC STUDY[a]

Jejunal segment	n	% villi with normal epithelium	% villi with intact blebs (A)	% villi with ruptured blebs or exfoliation (B)	% villi with epithelial damage (A + B)
Unperfused	3	97.2 ± 1.0	1.9 ± 0.6	0.9 ± 0.4	2.8 ± 0.9
Control	4	99.6 ± 0.1	0.4 ± 0.1	0.0 ± 0.0	0.4 ± 0.2
3% ethanol	4	82.0 ± 8.9	12.2 ± 5.1	7.2 ± 4.6	19.0 ± 9.8
6% ethanol	4	60.2 ± 12.0[b]	8.8 ± 3.3	32.0 ± 11.2	40.8 ± 12.0[b]

[a] Control segments were perfused with Krebs-Ringer bicarbonate solution containing 10 m*M* glucose (KRBSG), 3% ethanol segments with KRBSG containing 3% w/v ethanol, and 6% ethanol segments with KRBSG containing 6% w/v ethanol. n denotes the number of segments examined. All values shown are mean ± SEM.

[b] Values that were significantly different from control at $p < 0.05$.

From Buell, M. G. and Beck, I. T., *Gastroenterology*, 84, 81, 1983. With permission.

ethanol period indicates that ethanol can produce morphological changes (blebs and broken blebs) in man similar to those observed in other species.

V. MORPHOLOGICAL RECOVERY AFTER ETHANOL-INDUCED ACUTE INJURY

In the hamster (where during ethanol perfusion the continuity of the elevated epithelial cell layer over the blebs remained uninterrupted), 45 min after discontinuation of

Table 3
EFFECT OF ETHANOL PERFUSION ON CANINE JEJUNAL MORPHOLOGY — MORPHOMETRIC STUDY[a]

Jejunal segment	*n*	% villi with normal epithelium	% villi with intact blebs (A)	% villi with ruptured blebs or exfoliation (B)	% villi with epithelial damage (A + B)
Control	4	95 ± 3	3 ± 2	2 ± 1	5 ± 3
3% ethanol	4	69 ± 3[b]	31 ± 5[b]	10 ± 2	41 ± 3[b]
6% ethanol	4	62 ± 8[b]	28 ± 6[b]	10 ± 3	38 ± 8[b]

[a] Control segments were perfused with KRBSG, 3% ethanol segments with KRBSG containing 3% w/v ethanol, and 6% ethanol segments with KRBSG containing 6% w/v ethanol. *n* denotes the number of segments examined. All values shown are mean ± SEM.
[b] Values that were significantly different from control at $p < 0.05$.

From Buell, M. G., Dinda, P. K., and Beck, I. T., *Dig. Dis. Sci.*, 28, 1005, 1983. With permission.

the ethanol perfusion all morphological abnormalities had disappeared. The epithelial layer was again approximated to the stroma, the enterocytes had regained their normal columnar shape, and the LIS were again easily recognizable. The stroma was no longer compact and the lacteals were again open.[5] Acute alcohol damage is also reversible in man (Figure 13), where jejunal biopsies returned to preethanol morphology once the ethanol concentration in the lumen fell to near 0 (approximately 1.5 to 2 hr after the peak ethanol concentration).[28] Since normal proliferation and replacement of villus tip cells, depending on species, takes between 2 and 5 days,[68-70] the rapid repair could not be explained by this mechanism. It is more likely that, similar to the rapid repair of the ethanol-induced injury in the stomach, reattachment of the bleb epithelium and replacement of damaged cells occur by epithelial cell migration along the basal lamina.[71,72]

VI. CORRELATION OF ETHANOL-INDUCED FUNCTIONAL AND MORPHOLOGICAL ALTERATIONS

It is generally accepted that morphological alteration results in abnormal function. If, for instance, as the result of any type of injury the villi would lose all their epithelial cell coverage, active transepithelial transport would cease. Even villus atrophy (not complete denudation), as seen in celiac disease, leads to malabsorption. On the other hand, functional abnormality (e.g., primary lactase deficiency in man) may be present without detectable morphological damage. In the case of acute alcohol-induced injury, both situations can occur* (functional abnormality without obvious morphological damage, and functional damage secondary to morphological changes).

Evidence that solute (glucose, amino acid, etc.) transport, as well as other biochemical functions, can be altered without obvious morphological damage is provided by the following observations:

1. Depression of hexose[30,52] and amino acid[12] transport by ethanol can be demonstrated in morphologically normal isolated brush border membrane preparations.

* This statement holds only for ethanol concentrations normally found in the human jejunum (up to 7%) after moderate drinking. Severe damage (complete denudation) due to abnormally high concentrations of ethanol, of course, will affect both morphology and absorption in parallel.

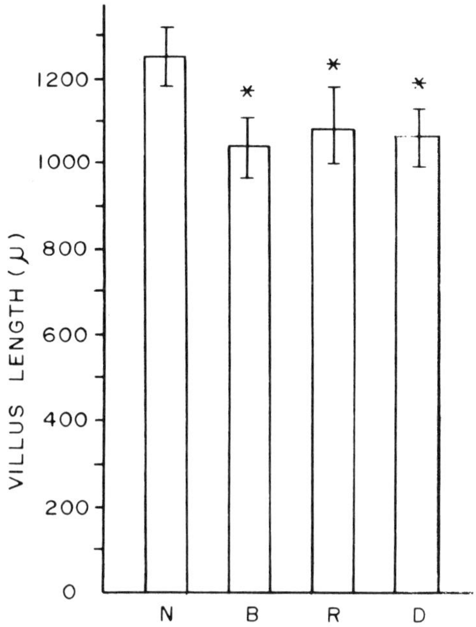

FIGURE 12. Relationship between jejunal villus length and epithelial damage. The vertical axis represents the length of villi in micrometers, measured from the base of longitudinally sectioned villi to the apical tip of the lamina propria. The horizontal axis indicates the condition of the villus epithelium: N = villi with undamaged, normal epithelium (n = 409); B = villi with intact subepithelial blebs (n = 119); R = villi with ruptured blebs or exfoliation (n = 37); D = villi with epithelial damage (B + R). All values show mean ± SEM. n represents the number of villi measured. An asterisk above the bars indicates a significant ($p < 0.05$) difference in villus length from undamaged, normal (N) villi. (Reprinted from Buell, M. G., Dinda, P. K., and Beck, I. T., *Dig. Dis. Sci.*, 28, 1005, 1983. With permission.)

2. Jejunal brush border enzymes are affected by ethanol in isolated brush border membrane vesicles.[13,14]
3. Cytosol peptidases extracted from homogenized enterocytes are inhibited by ethanol in vitro.[15]
4. Concentrations of ethanol, which do not affect the morphology of small bowel, depress glucose transport across the jejunum in vitro.[2,3]

Correlation of ethanol-induced morphological changes with glucose and water transport indicates that the mechanism of action of ethanol on intestinal biochemical function is separate from that on water transport and morphology.[5] The data shown in Figure 14 are based on the results of this study and provide a composite overview of the findings. As shown in the figure, glucose and water transport were both depressed during perfusion with 4.8% ethanol. However, the magnitude of inhibition of glucose absorption (28%) was much smaller than that expected from the 156% depression of water absorption (where secretion actually occurred). Ethanol perfusion also caused the appearance of fluid-filled blebs at the tips of the villi. The epithelial cells over the

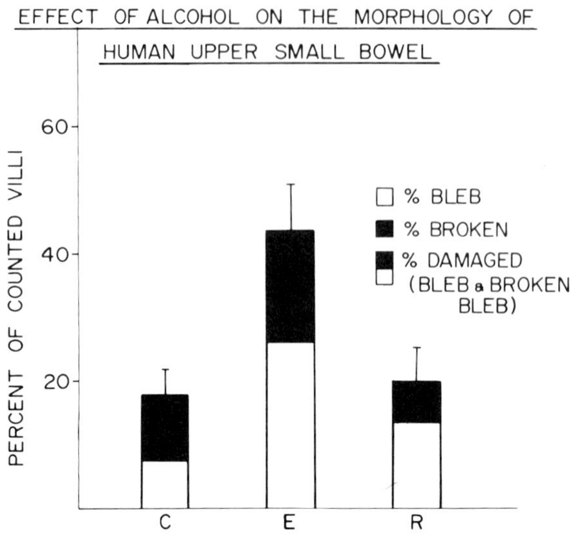

FIGURE 13. Effect of alcohol on mucosal damage in 13 human volunteers. The abscissa represents the percentage of damaged villi in relation to all counted villi for each individual. The unshaded portion of the bar represents the percentage of villi with blebs. The shaded portion of the bar represents the percentage of villi with broken blebs. The total height of the bar indicates the total percentage of damaged villi irrespective of whether the damage was due to blebs or broken blebs. Villi with mechanical damage were excluded from the calculations. Values represent mean ± SEM of the data individually obtained in the 13 subjects. The letters C, E, and R on the ordinate represent the period when the biopsies were obtained: C = control period; E = biopsies obtained 5 min after peak ethanol concentration; R = biopsies obtained during the recovery period (approximately 90 to 120 min after peak ethanol concentration), when the ethanol concentration returned to 0. (Reprinted from Millan, M. S., Morris, G. P., Beck, I. T., and Henson, J. T., *Dig. Dis. Sci.,* 25, 513, 1980. With permission.)

blebs lost their LIS (there were 27.5 ± 5.3 open intercellular spaces over the upper third of villi during the control period, and only 0.5 ± 0.2 over the tips of blebbed villi during ethanol perfusion). The lacteals were closed during ethanol perfusion. Water transport returned to normal 45 min after discontinuation of ethanol perfusion, simultaneously with the reversal of the morphological changes and the reappearance of the LIS (24.9 ± 1.2 over the upper third of villi). However, glucose transport (which remained depressed by 29%) did not return to normal simultaneously with the morphological recovery. Accordingly, the depression in water transport correlates with the morphological alterations of the gut, but the depression in glucose transport does not.

When alcohol was present in the jejunal lumen, the depression of water transport, the appearance of subepithelial blebs, the disappearance of LIS, the compaction of the lamina propria, and the closure of the lacteals occurred at the same time. Since water transport depends on the standing osmotic gradient across the basolateral membrane of the epithelial cells,[62] and the dilation of the LIS is believed to represent the morphological manifestation of water absorption,[63] the disappearance of the LIS between the epithelial cells over the blebs during ethanol perfusion may be one of the morphological expressions (or cause ?) of the ethanol-induced depression of water transport. Similarly, since increased flow into the lacteals is the result of absorption of water, the

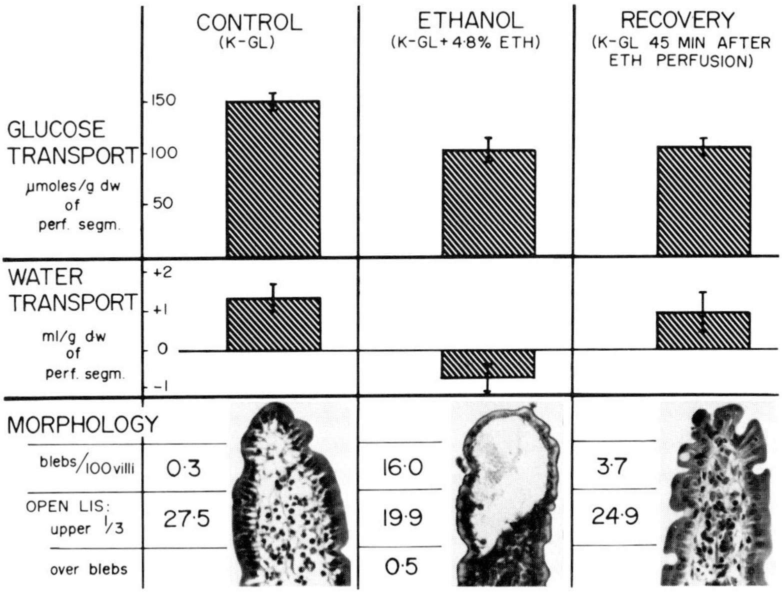

FIGURE 14. Correlation of glucose and water transport with morphometric measurements in the hamster jejunum. Top: glucose transport in micromoles per gram dry weight of perfused segment. Middle: water transport in milliliters per gram dry weight of perfused segment. Lower: morphological appearance and morphometric measurements — blebs per 100 villi; open LIS between the cells of the upper one third of villi without blebs (100 villi counted) and over blebs. Control: perfused with Krebs-Ringer bicarbonate solution containing 10 m*M* glucose (K-GL). Ethanol: perfused with K-GL containing 1050 m*M* (4.8%) ethanol (K-GL + 4.8% ETH). Recovery: perfused for 45 min with K-GL, started at the end of a 45-min perfusion with K-GL + 4.8% ETH. (Redrawn from data by Fox, J. E., McElligott, T. F., and Beck, I. T., *Can. J. Physiol. Pharmacol.*, 56, 123, 1978. with permission.)

compaction of the stroma of the villus core and the closure of the lacteals during ethanol perfusion may also be a morphological expression (or cause) of the diminished water absorption. The fact that both water transport and morphology returned to normal 45 min after discontinuation of ethanol perfusion further supports the relationship between morphological changes and water absorption.

All the above evidence seems to indicate that, while the ethanol-induced modification of water transport is related to morphological changes, the alterations in brush border digestion and transport are unrelated to morphological damage detectable on light and electron microscopy. This purely biochemical damage can be demonstrated in purified membrane preparations, and evidence exists that these changes are related to modification of membrane fluidity,[73] conformational changes of enzymes,[13] and probably transport proteins, as well as leakiness of the membranes.[30,52]

VII. HYPOTHESIS FOR THE MECHANISM OF ETHANOL-INDUCED MORPHOLOGICAL DAMAGE IN RELATION TO INTESTINAL SOLUTE AND WATER TRANSPORT

Several investigators have suggested that the adverse effect of ethanol on intestinal morphology (and absorption) could be related to the high osmolality of the intraluminal solution.[16,24] There are, however, several reasons why this simple explanation cannot be correct. Ethanol is a solute of small molecular weight, and even when it produces an azeotrope containing 4% water, its molecular radius is only 2.6 Å[74] and its partition coefficient between lipids and water is high (0.032).[37,38] Because of these physical properties, ethyl alcohol penetrates membranes very rapidly, and therefore is unlikely to exert any effective osmotic pressure on the mucosa. The addition of any solute to a solvent causes an increase in the osmolality of the resulting solution, and this can be measured by freezing point depression. This method of determining osmolality provides a measure of the "theoretic osmotic pressure" which the solute may exert on a true semipermeable membrane (i.e., on a membrane which is fully permeable to the solvent but not to the solute). Since biological membranes are not perfectly semipermeable (because they are permeable not only to solvents, but also to certain solutes), the "effective osmotic pressure" produced by permeant solutes is always less than the theoretic osmotic pressure. Accordingly, the effective osmotic pressure produced by a solute depends not only on its molecular concentration in the solvent, but also on the permeation of the solute through the membrane. The ratio of the effective to the theoretic osmotic pressure of a solute was defined by Staverman[75] as its reflection coefficient (σ) for a certain membrane. This coefficient is not an arbitrary "correction factor", but relates by thermodynamic equations to other rate constants such as the filtration, sieving, and permeability coefficients.[37,38] Depending on the molecular radius, molecular configuration, and lipid-water partition coefficient of the solute on the one hand, and the permeability of the membrane to the solute on the other, σ may have any value between 1 and 0. When σ for a solute is 1, it implies that the membrane is completely impermeable to the solute (i.e., the membrane is perfectly semipermeable), and the effective osmotic pressure exerted by the solute is equal to the theoretic osmotic pressure determined by freezing point depression. A σ of 0 for a solute, on the other hand, indicates that the solute is so highly permeant that the membrane is unable to discriminate between the solvent and solute. We have determined the Staverman σ of ethanol in hamster and rabbit jejunum and found that in both species it approximates 0,[4,21] indicating that ethanol in concentrations usually found in the intestinal lumen exerts no osmotic pressure on the mucosal membrane. (Figure 15 shows that, unlike mannitol, ethanol in concentrations used does not dehydrate the rabbit jejunum.) Accordingly, the small intestinal mucosa cannot discriminate between the solute (ethanol) and the solvent (water); this is consistent with the observation that ethanol passes through the walls of the cerebral ventricles at least as rapidly as tritiated water.[40] In other words, ethanol in concentrations found in the intestinal lumen does not exert an effective osmotic pressure and therefore cannot produce its effect on intestinal function or morphology as a result of its high theoretical osmotic pressure. Interestingly, by comparing the effects of ethanol and mannitol in rat aortic strips in vitro, Altura and co-workers[76] also concluded that the effect of ethanol on arterial smooth muscle is not related to the high osmolality of the solution. Therefore, some other explanation had to be found to explain the effect of ethanol in intestinal function and morphology.

Subepithelial bleb formation in intestinal villi is not uniquely related to ethanol. It occurs in any situation where the villus drainage is disturbed. Lee[77] has observed the development of subepithelial blebs in dog villi following spontaneous or drug-induced vigorous contractions of the villus core. The injection of fluid into the central lacteal, a procedure which increases lymphatic pressure and interferes with normal drainage, also induces blister formation.[77] Subepithelial blebs of intestinal villi have been demonstrated by Granger and co-workers[78] following occlusion of the portal circulation in the dog. The same result was obtained in patients with advanced cirrhosis, where portal hypertension may have been the causative factor.[79] Villus tip blebs were also seen in patients with diabetes,[80] another disease which affects the microcirculation. Subepithe-

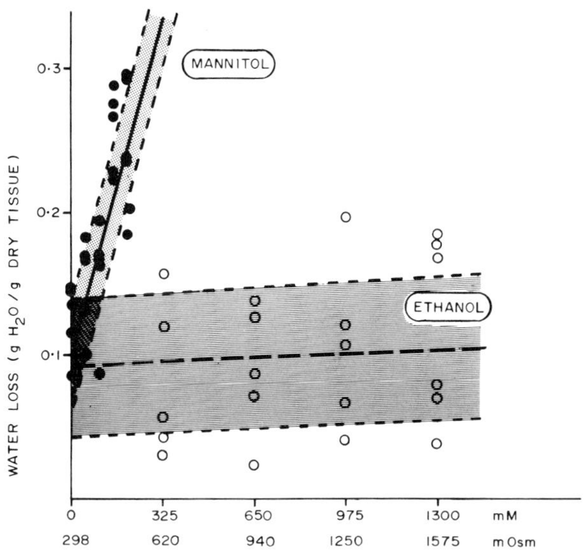

FIGURE 15. Effect of ethanol (Y = 0.00001X + 0.0928; r = 0.1111; p = NS) and mannitol (Y = 0.0007X + 0.1071; r = 0.7836; $p < 0.001$) on water content of rabbit jejunal sacs after a 30-sec immersion in vitro. The abscissa represents the changes in water content of the tissue (in grams of H_2O per gram dry tissue). The ordinate represents the millimolars of solute (mannitol or ethanol) added to the Krebs-Ringer becarbonate solution containing 10 m*M* glucose and the respective osmolalities of the solution. Immersion in ethanol (O); immersion in mannitol (•). Shaded areas indicate standard error estimate of the regression lines. n = 28 for ethanol and for mannitol. (Reprinted from Buell, M. G. and Beck, I. T., *Gastroenterology,* 84, 81, 1983. With permission.)

lial fluid accumulation was also observed during the early stages of mucosal destruction in patients with shock or with occlusive vascular disease of the small intestine.[81] We have observed blebs and broken blebs in small intestinal suction biopsies of normal subjects.[28] In this situation the suction of the mucosa into the instrument may have interfered with villus circulation. Recently Malo and Morin,[188] as well as Perdue and co-workers,[82] observed similar subepithelial blebs in rat small intestine in the course of another condition where microvascular abnormalities occur, i.e., ovalbumin-induced acute allergic injury. Therefore, it is not unlikely that ethanol-induced bleb formation may also be the result of impaired villus drainage and/or stasis in the microcirculation. The mechanism by which ethanol could affect primarily the villus core and/or the capillaries may be related to the rapid permeation of the solute across the epithelial cell. It is now well-established that alcohol does not produce epithelial cell damage in areas where blebs do not form.[27] Therefore, it could pass through the epithelium without affecting enterocyte morphology, and thus exert its initial action on the stroma of the villus core. Here ethanol could disrupt the normal villus drainage, either by inducing contraction of the villus core[22] as is the case with some other toxins,[77] and/or by a direct action on the microcirculation. Impaired drainage (due to villus core contraction and compression of lymphatic channels in vitro, and a combination of villus contraction and microcirculatory stasis in vivo) in the presence of normal sodium and water transport across the basolateral membrane could result in the accumulation of transported fluid between the basal lamina of the villus core and the basolateral membranes

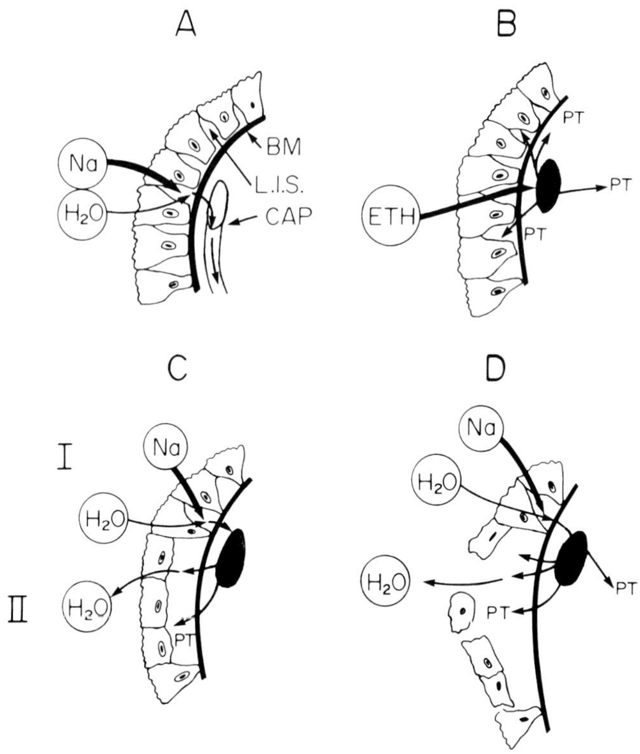

FIGURE 16. Possible mechanism of ethanol-induced morphological alteration in relation to water transport in vivo. (A) Demonstrates normal Na and water transport. Na is transported into the narrow LIS, resulting in local hypertonicity. This causes a flow of water into the LIS. The water subsequently diffuses across the basement membrane (BM) into the capillary (CAP) and is carried away into the circulation. (B) The freely permeable ethanol traverses the epithelium without directly affecting the epithelial cell morphology. It causes capillary stasis either by affecting the microcirculation directly or by inducing contraction of the villus core. This leads to plasma transudation (PT) into the pericapillary spaces and the LIS.(C.I) Water is not removed from the capillary, but Na transport continues and water accumulates in the LIS, which dilate. (C.II) Once sufficient fluid has accumulated, the abnormal swelling of the LIS leads to detachment of the epithelium from the basement membrane. As a result, the anchoring of the epithelium is lost, cells become cuboidal, the LIS disappear, and the bleb is formed. In the absence of LIS and consequently in the absence of hypertonicity within the LIS, water influx ceases and, due to the increased hydrostatic pressure in the bleb, fluid efflux may occur. (D) If the fluid accumulation is excessive or if the epithelium is not sufficiently resilient, the bleb breaks, leading to denudation of the villus. In vitro, the interference with villus drainage of fluid is probably due to vigorous contraction of the villus core alone. Except for the plasma exudation, the mechanism of bleb formation is similar to that in vivo. (Reprinted from Beck, I. T. and Dinda, P. K., *Dig. Dis. Sci.*, 26, 817, 1981. With permission.)

of the epithelial cells. The retention of water in this area would lead to distention of the LIS. Once sufficient fluid has accumulated, the exaggerated swelling of the LIS may lead to detachment of epithelium from the basal lamina (see Figure 16). As a result, the anchoring of the epithelium would be lost. The epithelium then would detach from the basal lamina of the villus core and thus the bleb would be formed. Because in normal epithelium the intercellular spaces are surrounded by the lateral membranes of the attached cells, detachment would lead to disappearance of the LIS. Since the existence of a narrow channel between the epithelial cells (i.e., the LIS) is an essential requirement for the establishment of an osmotic gradient (which is the driving force of epithelial water transport[62]), the disappearnce of LIS would cause the influx of water to cease, resulting in impaired water absorption.

In the presence of microvascular stasis in vivo (due either to obstruction of venous outflow by the contraction of the villus core, or to direct ethanol effect on villus capillaries and veins), transudation of plasma may occur. This would lead to a further increase in the hydrostatic pressure inside the blebs. The increased intravesicular pressure would cause a pressure gradient from the blebs toward the lumen, and this in turn would result in water efflux (secretion due to secretory filtration). At this stage some blebs may rupture, and whether the majority of blebs remain intact or break may depend on the resilience of the epithelium and the severity of the microvascular stasis. Recovery subsequent to disappearance of ethanol from the lumen presumably occurs by the resolution of the stasis in the villus core. Fluid could then be removed from the villus tip and severely damaged cells would exfoliate, while less-damaged cells would readhere to the basal lamina. Once the LIS were reestablished, solute-linked fluid transport would resume. To assess the validity of this hypothesis, subsequent sections of this chapter will deal with a review of the action of ethanol on blood vessels in general, and its action on the microcirculation of the mucosa in particular.

VIII. EFFECT OF ETHANOL ON THE SYSTEMIC CIRCULATION

A. Ethanol Effect on the Heart, Large Arteries, and Veins

Before reviewing the local effects of alcohol on the microcirculation of the villus, it is necessary to summarize its action on the circulation in general. However, while considering the effects of ethanol on cardiac function and on the behavior of large vessels, it is important to keep in mind that the alcohol concentrations which reach these structures in vivo are much lower (and, as shown in Table 1, are limited by the depressing effect of ethanol on the CNS) than those encountered in the subepithelial capillaries and venules of the villi of the upper small bowel (Figure 2). Furthermore, depending on the route of administration, the dose, and the local concentration of acutely administered ethanol, its effect on the circulation may vary both quantitatively and qualitatively.[83] The overall effect on the heart was recently reviewed by Bing[84] and Rubin,[85] and both concluded that the contractile function of this organ is inhibited, and that the mechanism underlying this diminished contractility is multifactorial. Depression of mitochondrial function by inhibition of ATP production, inhibition of the malate-aspartate shuttle, interference with the calcium-dependent contractile mechanism, change in fluidity of the plasma membrane, and interference with the sarcolemmal sodium pump and with the sarcoplasmic reticulum calcium transport all play a role.[84-86]

The data in the literature on the effect of alcohol on peripheral blood vessels are controversial. Ethanol administration has been reported to cause vasoconstriction, vasodilation, or a biphasic response.[87-91] Fewings and co-workers[88] reported that intra-arterial administration of ethanol produced a direct constrictor action on the blood vessels of the forearm of man. Nakano and Kessinger[90] showed that ethanol levels up to 3 mg/mℓ (0.3%) caused an increase in systemic arterial blood pressure in anesthetized dogs, while higher concentrations resulted in a fall in blood pressure. These authors have suggested that the rise in blood pressure may be related to ethanol-induced reflex action mediated by catecholamines and serotonin.[92-95] In order to resolve these questions and to better understand these contradictory results on the general circulation, Kalsner[96] and subsequently Altura and co-workers[76] performed in vitro studies on rat aortic strips. Indeed, the latter investigators[76] found that even in this simple preparation ethanol had a concentration-dependent, biphasic effect. Concentrations of less than 5 m*M* (0.024%) did not influence spontaneous mechanical activity, while concentrations of 17 m*M* (0.08%) ethanol attenuated the spontaneous mechanical activity of these aortic strips. Increasing the ethanol concentrations to levels which can-

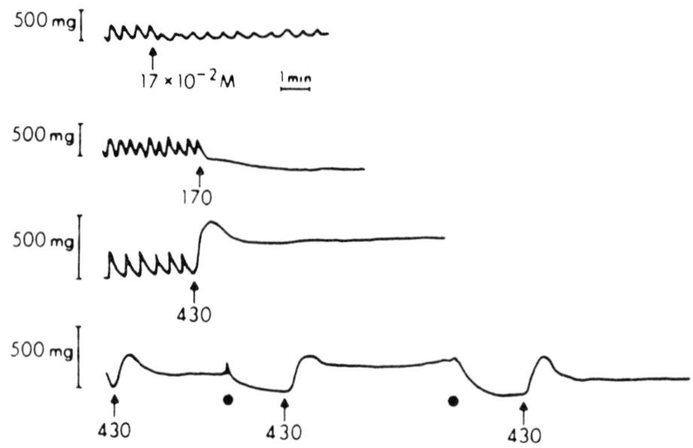

FIGURE 17. Influence of various concentrations of ethanol on the development of spontaneous mechanical activity and base line tension in isolated rat aortic strips. The arrows indicate the point at which the tissues were exposed to ethanol (millimolar concentrations). The bars on the left represent tension. Filled circles (•) indicate point at which strips were washed (and relaxed) in normal Krebs-Ringer bicarbonate. (Reprinted from Altura, B. M., Edgarian, H., and Altura, B. T., *J. Pharmacol. Exp. Ther.*, 197, 352, 1976. With permission.)

not be reached in vivo in the general circulation (170 m*M*, 0.8%) not only inhibited the spontaneous mechanical activity of the rat aorta, but also reduced the base line tension of the preparation. Raising the ethanol concentration to 430 m*M* (approximately 2%) resulted in depressed spontaneous contractile activity and the development of an additional contractile force (see Figure 17). It is also of interest that low doses (17 m*M*) of ethanol potentiated the contractions induced by epinephrine, while larger doses (430 m*M*) inhibited contraction caused by KCl, vasopressin, and epinephrine. Ethanol also inhibited the calcium-induced contractions of KCl-depolarized rat aortic strips.

The effect of ethanol on the vena cava was also investigated in vitro.[97] The findings were only partially similar to those in the aorta. Ethanol in a concentration of 17 m*M* (0.08%) inhibited the spontaneous mechanical activity of isolated rat portal veins, but potentiated the contractions induced by epinephrine. It did not, however, influence the contraction caused by KCl and angiotensin. Higher concentrations of ethanol (100 to 170 m*M*) completely suppressed the spontaneous contractile functions of the vein and attenuated the contractions induced by epinephrine, angiotensin, and KCl. The calcium-induced contraction of KCl-depolarized portal veins was also attenuated, and ethanol antagonized drug- and calcium-induced venous contractions. Further work by the same group indicated that ethanol reduced calcium uptake and concentration in arterial and venous smooth muscle.[98] In view of this observation and those of their previous studies which indicated that (1) alcohol consistently depressed the calcium-dependent spontaneous contractions of vascular smooth muscle, and (2) the inhibitory response of very low doses of ethyl alcohol was not mediated by the release or action of prostaglandin,[99] angiotensin, vasopressin, and KCl, Turlapaty and co-workers[98] postulated that the direct (decrease of spontaneous contractions) as well as indirect (counteraction of vasoconstriction) peripheral vasodilator effects of higher concentrations of ethanol are mediated through its influence on calcium ion movement (or translocation) in the smooth muscle cells.

B. Ethanol Effect on the Microcirculation

In a series of experiments using an image-splitting television microscope recording system, Altura and co-workers[100] found that ethanol, whether applied topically or by intra-arterial or i.v. infusion, dilated in a dose-dependent manner both the terminal arterioles and the muscular venules of the terminal vascular bed of the mesentery of rats. The arterial vessels observed were 15 to 23 μm (I.D.), and the venules, 28 to 39 μm (I.D.). The mean increase in arteriolar lumen size was 7.3 ± 1.5% upon application of 0.05% ethanol. Venules did not dilate significantly at this low concentration. From 0.1 to 10% ethanol, there was a striking similarity between the relative increases in lumen sizes of the terminal arterioles and muscular venules. However, beyond 10% ethanol the increase in lumen sizes of the terminal arterioles became significantly greater than those of the venules (Figure 18). Vasodilation was also observed when ethanol was injected intra-arterially, and the sensitivity of the vessels was greater than with topical administration. The ethanol-induced dilator responses were not modified by the anticholinergic agent atropine, the antihistaminics diphenhydramine (blockade of H_1 receptors) and burimamide and metiamide (blockade of H_2 receptors). Nor was the ethanol-induced vasodilation influenced by methysergide (serotonergic antagonist) or the prostaglandin synthetase antagonist, indomethacin. However, β-adrenergic blockade with propranolol significantly enhanced the vasodilatory effect of alcohol. Furthermore, ethanol dose dependently inhibited the constrictor effects of epinephrine and norepinephrine, angiotensin, vasopressin, and barium chloride. These findings seem to indicate that ethanol exerts a direct vasodilator effect on the microvascular smooth muscle, attenuates microvascular constrictor responses, and possibly interferes with smooth muscle cell inactivation or disposition of catecholamines and the direct smooth muscle stimulant barium.[100]

IX. EFFECT OF ETHANOL ON THE BLOOD FLOW OF SPLANCHNIC ORGANS OTHER THAN THE SMALL BOWEL

A. Hepatic

Studies on the effect of ethanol on hepatic blood flow have provided many controversial data. Using the sulfobromophthalein (BSP) extraction method, Smythe and co-workers[101] found the ethanol (50 mℓ of a 50% solution) administered into the stomach had no significant effect on hepatic blood flow and vascular resistance. Interestingly, these authors also found that this dose did not affect cardiac output, renal blood flow, or mean systemic arterial blood pressure. Using the same method in human subjects, Castenfors and co-workers[102] also observed that the i.v. infusion of ethanol had no effect on hepatic blood flow. In a similar study on human subjects, Mendeloff,[103] using the BSP extraction technique, showed that ethanol infusion in doses which caused blood levels of 0.025 to 0.08% led to an increase in estimated hepatic blood flow without a generalized increase in cardiac output. Therefore, he concluded that the increased hepatic blood flow was the result of decreased peripheral resistance in the splanchnic vascular bed. On the other hand, Stein et al.[104] found that blood ethanol concentrations of 0.033 to 0.103% caused an increase in hepatic blood flow. The increase in cardiac output, however, was comparable to that in hepatic blood flow. Therefore, contrary to Mendeloff,[103] Stein and co-workers[104] concluded that the increase in hepatic flow was a direct result of the increased cardiac output. Using the same technique in baboons, Shaw and colleagues[105] found that the i.v. administration of ethanol increased the estimated hepatic blood flow without a change in cardiac output. Carrying out experiments on conscious conditioned dogs, Friedman and co-workers[106] observed that the i.v. infusion of ethanol (leading to blood levels of 0.06 to 0.15%) caused an increase in hepatic blood flow, while arterial and aortic pressure remained unchanged and pancreatic flow decreased.

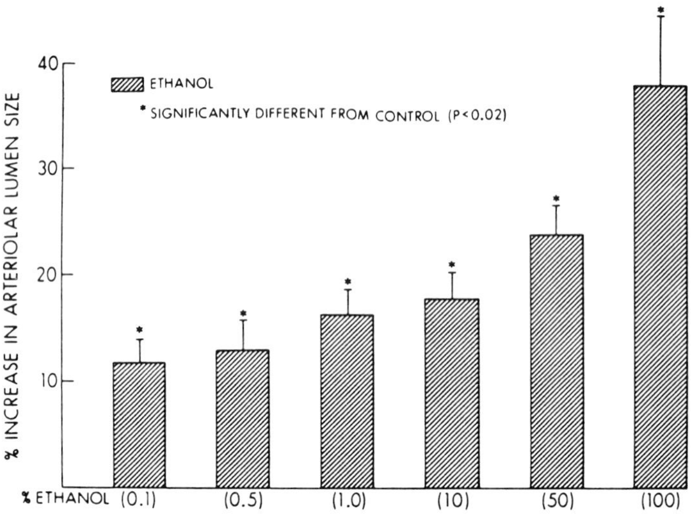

A

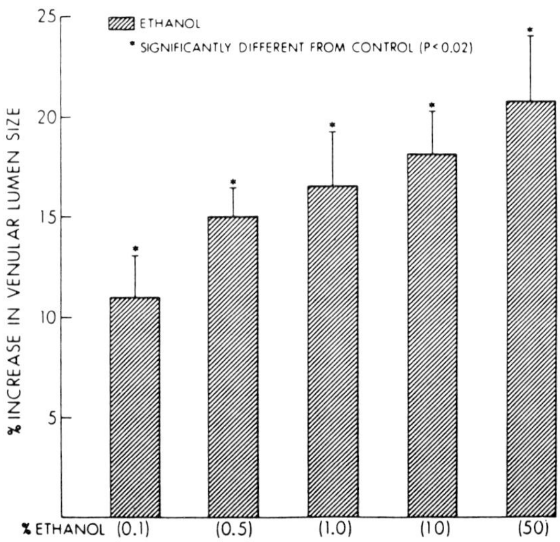

B

FIGURE 18. Microcirculatory effects of ethanol. (A) Influence of topically applied ethanol on rat mesenteric terminal arterioles. n = 39 different rat mesenteries. Small bars: +1 SEM. The control lumen sizes were 15 to 23 μm. Each large bar represents the mean percentage change in lumen size obtained from measurements on vessels of different rats. (B) Influence of topically applied ethanol on rat mesenteric muscular venules. n = 39 different rat mesenteries. The control lumen sizes were 28 to 39 μm. (Reprinted from Altura, B. M., Ogunkoya, A., Gebrewold, A., and Altura, B. T., *J. Cardiovasc. Pharmacol.*, 1, 97, 1979. With permission.)

Contrary to the results of all studies where alcohol was administered intravenously, Bravo and co-workers[107] have shown that when alcohol was infused into the portal vein at a dose of 0.01 g/kg body weight (leading to an estimated hepatic ethanol concentration of 0.075 mg/100 mℓ) hepatic arterial and portal blood flow decreased. In these experiments ethanol increased the release of norepinephrine into the hepatic venous blood, and the effects of ethanol on hepatic blood flow were inhibited by the α-adrenergic antagonist yohimbine. Therefore, these investigators concluded that the decreased hepatic blood flow was the result of a norepinephrine-induced increase in hepatic vascular resistance. Using a microsphere technique, Israel et al.[108] showed that the oral administration to rats of 4 g/kg ethanol (in a 20% solution) increased hepatic blood flow through the portal vein by 50% without increasing cardiac output and hepatic arterial flow. The increase in portal vein flow was the result of increased arterial inflow into the stomach and small intestine. Comparing the results of this study to those obtained by some other investigators may indicate that the contradictory findings on hepatic blood flow among experiments using i.v., intraportal, or intraluminal administration of ethanol may be explained by the occurrence of hyperemia in the splanchnic organs (which results in increased portal vein flow) when ethanol is administered orally, and the absence of increased splanchnic arterial inflow with i.v. administration of ethanol. Furthermore, intraluminal administration of ethanol leads to higher intrahepatic ethanol concentrations than does i.v. infusion.[39]

B. Pancreatic

The effect of ethanol on pancreatic blood flow has been investigated recently by Horwitz and Myers[109] and Friedman and co-workers.[106] Both groups of investigators found that ethanol caused a fall in pancreatic blood flow. Horwitz and Myers gave alcohol by the i.v. route at doses of 0.5 and 1.5 g/kg body weight. These authors concluded that the fall in pancreatic blood flow was the result of an increased local vascular resistance. Since the effect could not be influenced by α- and β-adrenergic blockers, the experiments of these investigators suggest that the fall in blood flow was not mediated through adrenergic neurotransmitters.[109] Friedman and co-workers[106] studied the effect of intragastric ethanol in awake and barbiturate-anesthetized animals. They also found that, in contrast to the effect of ethanol on most other areas of the splanchnic circulation, ethanol diminished pancreatic flow in unanesthetized dogs. This, however, was not the case in anesthetized animals, where pancreatic flow remained unchanged.

C. Gastric

Ethanol also increases gastric blood flow. Since the observation of Wolf and Wolff,[110] who found that following the introduction of 30 mℓ of 90-proof whiskey into the gastrostomy of their human subject the mucosa became hyperemic, turgid, and engorged, many investigators suggested that ethanol-induced gastric injury may be related to alterations in mucosal blood flow. Using the aminopyrine clearance method, Auger[111] demonstrated that 9% ethanol increases gastric mucosal blood flow in the dog. This observation was confirmed by Cheung and co-workers[112] with a microsphere technique. However, the studies of Puurunen[113] have indicated that gastric mucosal blood flow increases only in the presence of a low pH, and that in a less acid stomach the mucosal blood flow actually decreases. Therefore, this author theorized that the increased blood flow was secondary to the mucosal injury caused by hydrogen ion back-diffusion. Using an in vivo video microscopic system (based on the method described by Guth and Smith[114]), Hakkinen and Oates[115] demonstrated that intragastric administration of ethanol to urethane-anesthetized rats caused gross mucosal hyperemia. The 70- to 15-μm-diameter submucosal venules constricted 10 sec after intragastric ethanol, causing blood to back up into the basal mucosal venule network. Within the next few seconds many of the 10- to 150-μm-diameter arterioles began to dilate, often reaching more than twice their original size. This was accompanied by progressive reddening of the overlying mucosal tissue, severe congestion, and hyperemia. There was also increased mucosal edema, probably due to elevation of the hydrostatic pressure within the mucosal capillaries and venules.

X. EFFECT OF INTRALUMINAL ETHANOL ON SMALL INTESTINAL BLOOD FLOW

There are very few studies which deal with the effects of intraluminal ethanol on small intestinal blood flow. Siregar and Chou[116] studied the effects of 4.5% intraluminal ethanol (pure ethanol or gin, diluted to 4.5% alcohol) on the venous outflow and arteriovenous oxygen difference of dog jejunum. These workers found that intraluminal ethanol decreased the arteriovenous oxygen gradient, but increased jejunal total gut wall blood flow,* and thus concluded that intestinal oxygen consumption remained unchanged. Israel and co-workers[108] found that after intragastric administration of 4.0% g/kg ethanol (small intestinal intraluminal concentration was not given) the total arterial inflow into the small intestine increased by 43%.

Using microsphere techniques we investigated the ethanol-induced changes in regional blood flow** in the jejunum. In the rabbit the intestine was separated into mucosa plus submucosa (luminal layer) and muscularis plus serosa (external layer), using the method of Powell et al.[117] We found that 3 and 6% intraluminal ethanol perfusion of the jejunum increased blood flow through the total jejunal wall and the mucosal plus submucosal layer, but the blood flow did not change in the layer consisting of the muscularis plus serosa (Figure 19). Because the increase in the mucosa (plus submucosa) was proportional to the increase in total blood flow and was not accompanied by a decrease in the flow to the muscularis and serosa, we concluded that the mucosal hyperemia could not be explained by shunting of blood from the external to the internal layer of the gut wall. Thus, it appears that intraluminal ethanol administration causes a localized mucosal (and/or submucosal) hyperemia in the rabbit jejunum.[21] While this study (in which only 15-μm microspheres were used) established that the mucosal (plus submucosal) arteriolar inflow increased during ethanol perfusion, it did not provide data as to whether this ethanol-induced increase in arteriolar flow caused a proportional increase in nutritive (capillary) blood flow or whether some of the blood entering the mucosa (plus submucosa) was shunted through noncapillary (nonnutritive) arteriovenous connections (smaller than arterioles but larger than capillaries). Furthermore, because of the difficulties in separating the rabbit gut into more than two layers, this study could not provide a clear-cut answer as to whether the hyperemia was restricted to the mucosa, the submucosa, or both.

To provide experimental support for a possible role of microcirculatory changes in the pathogenesis of ethanol-induced morphological injury and secretory filtration, it is necessary to (1) localize the blood flow changes to the mucosa and (2) provide physiological evidence for stasis in the microvessels of this layer. Therefore, we decided (1) to reinvestigate the ethanol-induced local vascular changes in the dog (the jejunum of

* "Total gut wall blood flow" or "whole gut tissue blood flow" in this chapter refers to the blood flow through the full thickness of the gut wall consisting of the three major anatomical layers — the mucosa, submucosa, and muscularis.

** "Regional blood flow" refers to the separately measured blood flow of the different layers of the gut wall (mucosa, submucosa, and muscularis) of an intestinal segment.

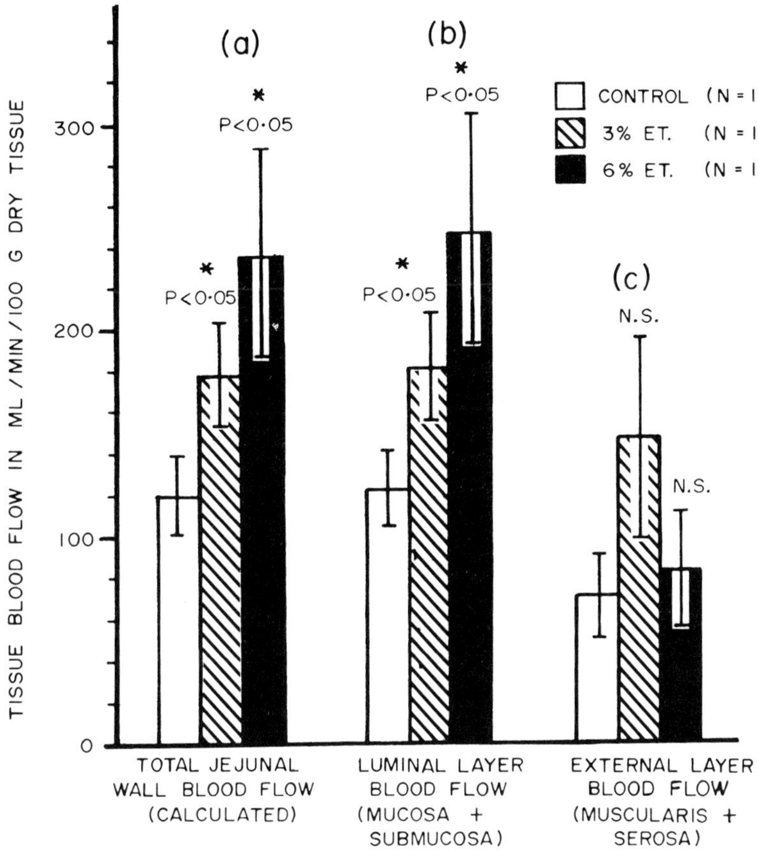

FIGURE 19. Effect of 3 and 6% w/v ethanol on rabbit total and regional jejunal blood flow. (a) Total jejunal wall (luminal plus external layer); (b) luminal layer (mucosal plus submucosal tissue); (c) external layer (muscularis plus serosa). The abscissa indicates tissue blood flow in milliliters per minute per 100 g dry tissue. Shading of the bars indicates treatment of the segments; unshaded bars = control, KRBSG-perfused segments; striped bars = segments perfused with KRBSG containing 3% w/v ethanol; solid bars = segments perfused with KRBSG containing 6% w/v ethanol. All values show mean ± SEM. Significant differences from control (at $p < 0.05$), determined using the paired *t*-test, are shown by an asterisk above the bars. NS = not significatnly different from control. (Reprinted from Buell, M. G. and Beck, I. T., *Gastroenterology*, 84, 81, 1983. With permission.)

which can easily be separated into its three layers) and (2) to develop a method in which arteriolar, capillary, and shunt flow through nonnutritive vessels could be measured separately. To examine the feasibility of concurrently estimating total arteriolar, capillary, and shunted blood flows in the different layers of the small intestine, we injected simultaneously into the left ventricle 9-μm microspheres (to study capillary flow) and 15-μm microspheres (to assess arteriolar flow).[118] The results of this feasibility study indicated that 15-μm microspheres were totally entrapped in the jejunal wall, but a significant proportion of 9-μm microspheres was shunted into the portal blood.* On the other hand, once entrapped during vasoconstriction (vasopressin infusion), none

* Since 15-μm microspheres are known to fully entrap in arterioles[119-121] and 9-μm microspheres in the precapillary sphincters,[122,123] the difference in entrapment of these two sizes of spheres represents shunt (nonnutritive) flow through vessels which are larger than nutritive capillaries and smaller than arterioles.

of the microspheres (neither 9 nor 15 μm) was redistributed among the mucosa, submucosa, and muscularis during subsequent vasodilation induced by isoproterenol. Thus it was concluded that the simultaneous injection of 9 ± 1.5-μm (labeled with ^{45}Sc) and 15 ± 2.5-μm microspheres (labeled with ^{141}Ce) allowed for the estimation of arteriolar, capillary, and shunt blood flow separately in the mucosa, submucosa, and muscularis. In contrast to the observation that 15-μm microspheres did not migrate in significant numbers from submucosa to mucosa, vasodilation did cause a significant movement of these spheres from the crypt to the villus. This shift was likely the result of an upward movement of prematurely impacted (due to Pitressin-induced vasoconstriction) 15-μm microspheres, and indicated that arterioles supplying the villus via the crypt contained a significant series-coupled component. Thus, 9-μm microspheres provide a potentially valid estimate of capillary or nutrient blood flow in the villus, the crypt, the mucosa (villus plus crypt), the submucosa, and the muscularis, whereas 15-μm microspheres can be used to estimate total arteriolar inflow into the mucosa (but not for the independent estimation of inflow into the villus and crypt).[124] Accordingly, when 9- and 15-μm microspheres are injected simultaneously, it is possible to calculate shunting through vessels which are bigger than normal nutritive capillaries, but smaller than the arterioles (15 μm). However, accurate estimate of flow through these shunts can only be obtained in layers where reliable measurement of arteriolar blood flow is possible (where the impaction of 15-μm spheres is not influenced by vasoconstriction or vasodilation). Therefore, shunt flow (similarly to arteriolar inflow) can be separately calculated in the mucosa (villus plus crypt layer), the submucosa, and the muscularis, but not in the villus and the crypt separately.

Having established the validity of the double-sized microsphere technique,[118,124] we investigated the effect of 3 and 6% intraluminal ethanol on total arteriolar, capillary, and shunt blood flow of the three main anatomical layers of the dog jejunum.[22] One segment of the dog jejunum was perfused with Krebs-Ringer bicarbonate solution containing 10 m*M* glucose (KRBSG), another segment with 3% ethanol in KRBSG, and the third with 6% ethanol in KRBSG. Both 3 and 6% ethanol increased arteriolar blood flow into the whole gut wall as well as the mucosa, but had no appreciable effect on the arteriolar inflow of the submucosa and muscularis (Figure 20). Furthermore, 3 and 6% ethanol also increased the capillary flow in the total gut wall, the villus, and the mucosa (villus plus crypt), but did not influence the capillary flow in the crypt layer, the submucosa, and the muscularis (Figure 21). However, the relative increase in mucosal capillary flow was smaller than that of the arterial flow, so that the ethanol-induced percentage increase in jejunal mucosal shunt flow was 20 times greater than the increase in capillary blood flow (Table 4). Thus it appears that a high proportion of the ethanol-induced increase in arterial flow was diverted through nonnutritive shunt pathways. This then would explain the observation of Siregar and Chou[116] that the ethanol-induced increased intestinal blood flow was not accompanied by an increase in oxygen utilization. More importantly, the disproportional increase in mucosal nonnutritive shunt flow provides experimental support for the hypothesis that ethanol induces capillary stasis in this tissue layer. Although it is possible that the disproportional increase in shunt flow occurs because alcohol preferentially dilates nonnutritive shunt channels, it is more likely that the increase in shunting occurs as a compensatory pressure relief mechanism to an increased capillary resistance caused by capillary stasis.[22] If the latter is the correct explanation, one would expect that capillary pressure would also be increased; in accordance with Starling's principles, this would lead to increased capillary filtration. Indeed, in a recent study Kvietys and colleagues[32] reported that perfusion with 5% v/v (4.0% w/v) intraluminal ethanol in the jejunum (as well as in the ileum) raises capillary pressure and capillary filtration coefficient (Figure

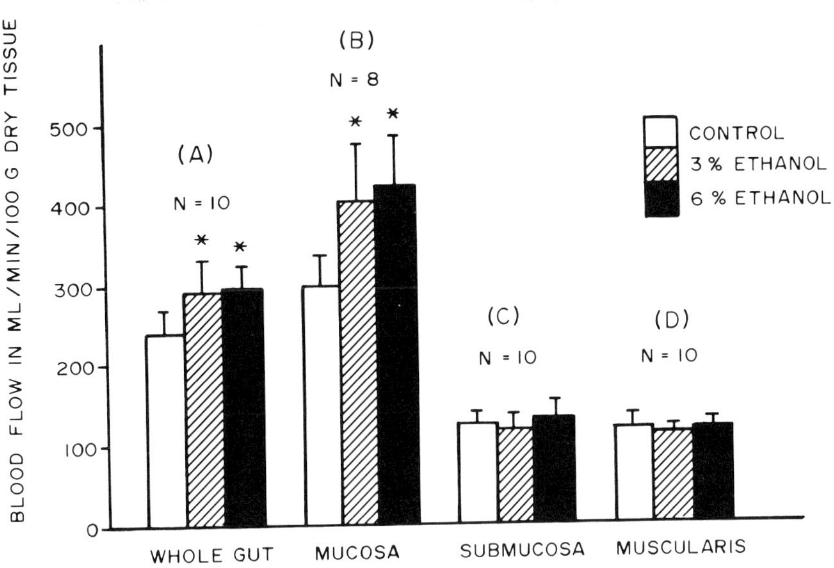

FIGURE 20. Effect of 3 and 6% w/v ethanol on arteriolar blood flow into jejunal tissue regions (A) Jejunal wall, (B) mucosal, (C) submucosal, (D) muscularis blood flow. All values were estimated using 15-μm microspheres. The vertical axis indicates tissue blood flow in milliliters per minute per 100 g dry tissue weight. Shading of the bars indicates treatment of the segments: unshaded bars = KRBSG-perfused control segments; striped bars = segments perfused with KRBSG containing 3% w/v ethanol; solid bars = segments perfused with KRBSG containing 6% w/v ethanol. All values show mean ± SEM. Significant differences from control (at $p < 0.05$) are shown by an asterisk above the bars. (Reprinted from Buell, M. G., Dinda, P. K., and Beck, I. T., *Dig. Dis. Sci.*, 28, 1005, 1983. With permission.)

22) as well as lymph flow and transcapillary oncotic pressure (Figure 23), and increases total blood flow. This is accompanied by a decrease in precapillary and total vascular resistance (Table 5).

If capillary stasis occurs, this should result in hemoconcentration in the subepithelial capillaries and should lead to increased protein loss into the interstitium and from there to the gut lumen. In order to assess whether this occurs, further experiments were carried out in our laboratory[29] in which the effect of ethanol on mucosal RBC volume (determined by ^{51}Cr-labeled autologous RBC), mucosal plasma (albumin) volume (determined by ^{125}I-labeled bovine serum albumin), and mucosal arteriolar blood flow (measured by ^{46}Sc-labeled 15-μm microspheres) was simultaneously studied. These experiments indicated that the intraluminal ethanol-induced increase in mucosal arterial blood flow was accompanied by an increased mucosal RBC volume without equivalent changes in the mucosal plasma volume (as reflected by total mucosal albumin volume). This mucosal hemoconcentration (Figure 24) was accompanied by a loss of plasma (assessed by the loss of bovine serum albumin) from the mucosal microvasculature into the lumen. This plasma protein loss, although significantly increased with 3% ethanol perfusion, was considerably (and disproportionately) greater with 6% ethanol (Figure 25).[29] Thus, the results of these experiments provide further evidence for capillary stasis and secretory filtration in the mucosa of ethanol-perfused segments.

Because in many other conditions increased protein exudation is the result of increased permeability of the microvasculature, we set out to resolve whether the ethanol-induced loss of protein into the lumen resulted from changes in the Starling equilibrium (increased capillary pressure) alone, or whether it was accompanied by an

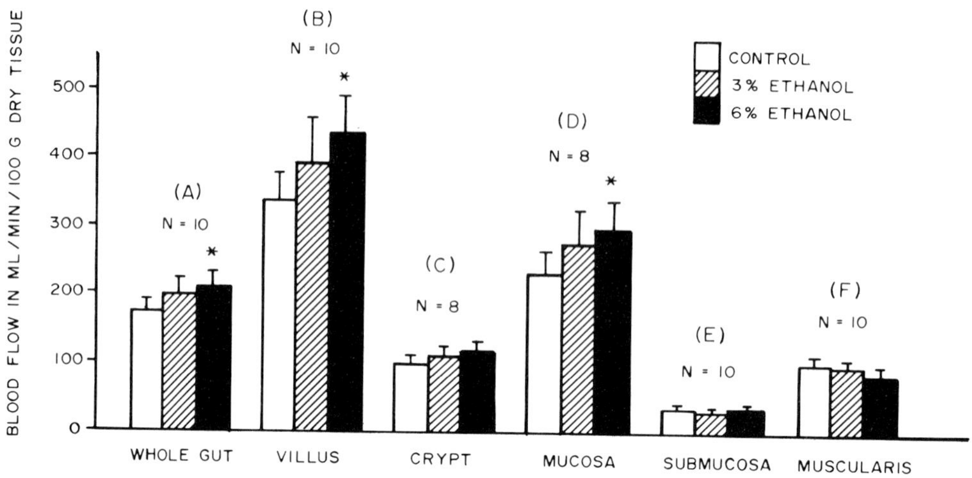

FIGURE 21. Effect of 3 and 6% w/v ethanol on canine jejunal capillary blood flow (A) Whole gut wall, (B) villus, (C) crypt, (D) mucosal, (E) submucosal, (F) muscularis blood flow. All values were estimated using 9-μm microspheres. The vertical axis indicates tissue capillary blood flow in milliliters per minute per 100 g dry tissue weight. Shading of the bars indicates treatment of the segment: unshaded bars = KRBSG-perfused control segments; striped bars = segments perfused with KRBSG containing 3% w/v ethanol; solid bars = segments perfused with KRBSG containing 6% w/v ethanol. All values show mean ± SEM. Significant differences from control (at $p < 0.05$) are shown by an asterisk above the bars. (Reprinted from Buell, M. G., Dinda, P. K., and Beck, I. T., *Dig. Dis. Sci.*, 28, 1005, 1983. With permission.)

Table 4
EFFECT OF ETHANOL ON JEJUNAL MUCOSAL BLOOD FLOWS — PERCENT CHANGE FROM CONTROL[a]

	Total arteriolar inflow	Capillary blood flow	Blood flow shunted
3% ethanol	36.1 ± 16.9	19.6 ± 13.6	402.3 ± 196.6
6% ethanol	42.2 ± 9.8	26.5 ± 8.5	510.9 ± 243.7

[a] Total arteriolar inflow represents blood flow estimated using 15-μm microspheres; capillary blood flow represents blood flow estimated using 9-μm microspheres; shunted blood flow represents the difference in blood flow estimates between 15- and 9-μm microspheres (blood flow perfusing a tissue region but bypassing the capillaries). All values shown are mean ± SEM of the percent change from control. $n = 8$. 3% ethanol indicates segments perfused with 3% w/v ethanol in KRBSG. 6% ethanol indicates segments perfused with 6% w/v ethanol in KRBSG.

From Buell, M. G., Dinda, P. K., and Beck, I. T., *Dig. Dis. Sci.*, 28, 1005, 1983. With permission.

increase in capillary (and postcapillary venular) permeability. To provide an answer to this question, we carried out a series of experiments[125] in which we examined capillary permeation utilizing a modification of the colloidal carbon labeling technique developed by Majno and Palade[126] and Majno and colleagues.[127] This method has been employed by many investigators to study the effect of inflammation and its mediators

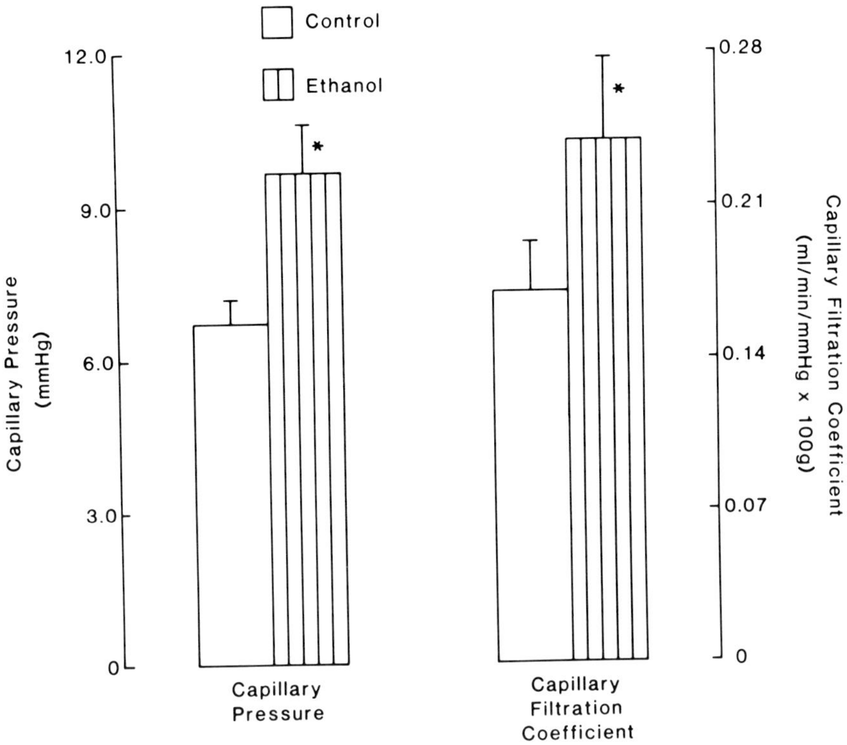

FIGURE 22. Effects of 5% v/v (4% w/v) ethanol on ileal capillary pressure (n = 17) and the capillary filtration coefficient (n = 18). Significant differences from control are indicated by asterisks. (Reprinted from Kvietys, P. R., Patterson, W. G., Russell, J. M., Barrowman, J. A., and Granger, D. N., *Gastroenterology,* 87, 562, 1984. With permission.)

on microvascular permeability.[128-135] The technique is based upon the observation that in capillaries (or immediate postcapillary venules) where permeability is increased, the endothelial cells temporarily retract with a resultant gap between the cells. Colloidal carbon then passes through these gaps and becomes entrapped between the endothelial cells and the basal lamina of the microvessels. The rest of the circulating colloidal material is cleared by the reticuloendothelial system and thus, after a clearing time of 1 hr, carbon particles outside the tight junctions between endothelial cells and the basal lamina can be seen only at sites where permeability was increased at the time of the injection of the carbon colloid.* Intraluminal collection of carbon can be seen only in areas of stasis, where at the time of injection the carbon particles became entrapped among the cellular elements of blood contained in the microvessels.**

The experiments to investigate the effect of ethanol on capillary permeability were carried out in dogs. Three adjacent jejunal segments were perfused, the first (control) with KRBSG, the second with 3% w/v ethanol in KRBSG, and the third with 6% ethanol in KRBSG. Colloidal carbon was injected intravenously during the perfusion. The animals were killed 1 hr after the injection of the carbon, and the tissues of the three segments were examined by light and electron microscopy. The light microscopic examination was carried out on thick (0.5 to 1.0 mm) sections of fixed tissue mounted

* "Increased permeability" assessed by this method refers to transient contraction of endothelial cells at the time of injury and does not reflect change in permeation through fenestrations of endothelial cells.

** The words microvessels and microvasculature refer to capillaries and immediate postcapillary venules. The latter can be distinguished from capillaries by the presence of pericytes.

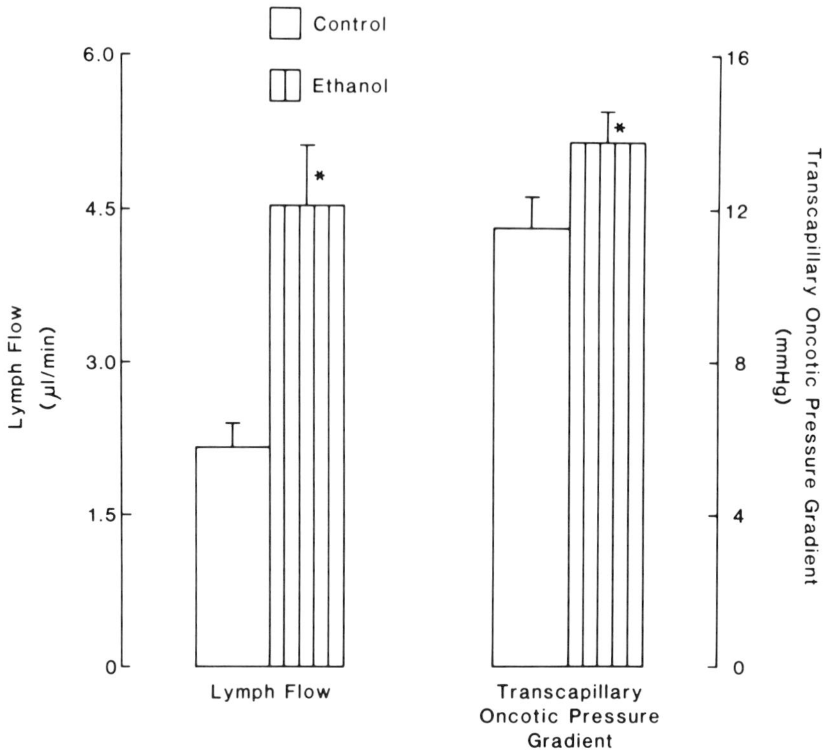

FIGURE 23. Effects of 5% v/v (4% w/v) ethanol on ileal lymph flow and the transcapillary oncotic pressure gradient ($n = 18$). Significant differences from control are indicated by asterisks. (Reprinted from Kvietys, P. R., Patterson, W. G., Russell, J. M., Barrowman, J. A., and Granger, D. N., *Gastroenterology,* 87, 562, 1984. With permission.)

Table 5
EFFECTS OF ALCOHOL ON JEJUNAL HEMODYNAMICS

	Control	Alcohol	n
Arterial pressure (mmHg)	125.6 ± 5.8	128.3 ± 5.3	18
Venous pressure (mmHg)	0.6 ± 0.2	0.8 ± 0.2	18
Blood flow (mℓ/min/100 g)	44.8 ± 3.9	52.3[a] ± 4.3	15
Vascular resistance (mmHg/mℓ · min/100 g)	2.99 ± 0.24	2.57[a] ± 0.21	15
Precapillary resistance (mmHg/mℓ · min/100g)	2.86 ± 0.24	2.43[a] ± 0.21	15
Postcapillary resistance (mmHg/mℓ · min/100 g)	0.13 ± 0.02	0.14 ± 0.02	15

[a] Value significantly different from control at $p < 0.005$.

From Kvietys, P. R., Patterson, W. G., Russell, J. M., Barrowman, J. A., and Granger, D. N., *Gastroenterology,* 87, 562, 1984. With permission.

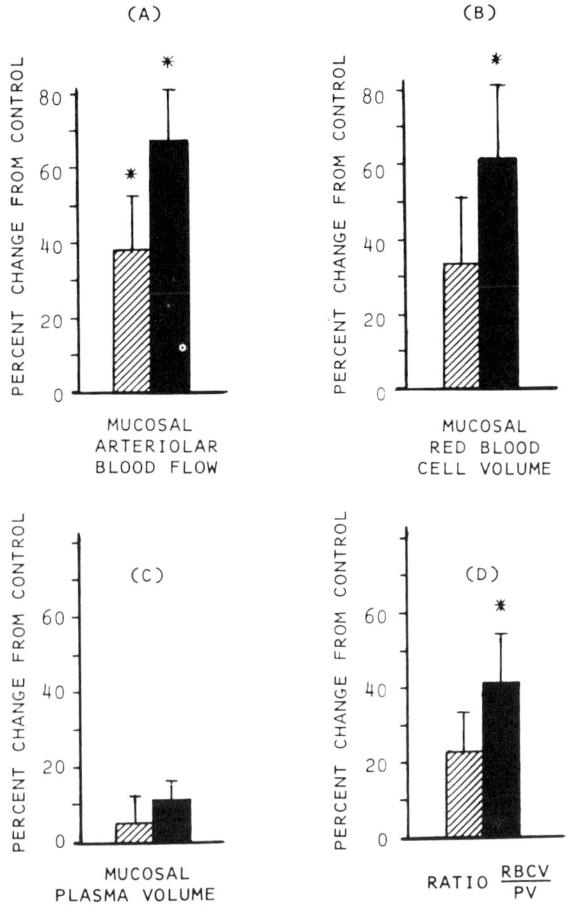

FIGURE 24. Effects of intraluminal perfusion with 3 and 6% w/v (3.75 and 7.5% v/v, respectively) ethanol on canine jejunal mucosal arteriolar blood flow, RBC volume, and "plasma volume" (as reflected by mucosal total albumin volume). (A) Mucosal arteriolar blood flow, (B) mucosal RBC volume, (C) mucosal plasma volume, and (D) ratio of mucosal RBC volume to plasma volume. The vertical axis represents the percentage change in these parameters from control. Control segments were perfused with KRBSG. Shading of the bars indicates treatment of the segments: striped bars = segments perfused with KRBSG containing 3% w/v ethanol; solid bars = segments perfused with KRBSG containing 6% w/v ethanol. All values show mean ± SEM. $n = 9$. Significant differences from control (at $p < 0.05$) are shown by an asterisk above the bars. (Reprinted from Buell, M. G. and Beck, I. T., *Gastroenterology,* 86, 413, 1984. With permission.)

in glycerine. Morphometric assessment of these thick sections indicated that less than 1 and 10% of villi of the control and the 3% ethanol-perfused segments, respectively, had visible carbon, while approximately 50% of the villi of segments perfused with 6% ethanol had clearly visible carbon (Figure 26). On electron microscopy very few of the villi from the control or from the 3% ethanol-perfused segments contained entrapped carbon particles between the endothelial cells and the basal lamina of capillaries or immediate postcapillary venules. Furthermore, none of the microvessels of the control

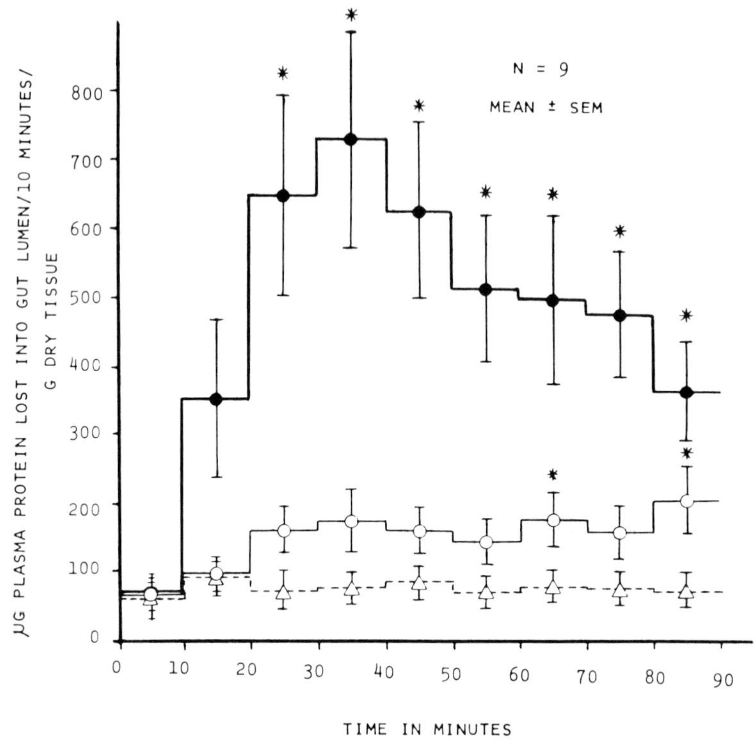

FIGURE 25. Effect of intraluminal ethanol perfusion (3 and 6% w/v) on canine jejunal plasma protein loss. The vertical axis represents the rate of plasma protein loss into the gut lumen in micrograms of protein lost per 10 min/g dry intestinal tissue. The horizontal axis represents the time (in minutes) during the 90-min experimental perfusion period. Time 0 = start of the experimental perfusion period. (Δ) Control segments perfused with KRBSG; (O) segments perfused with 3% w/v ethanol in KRBSG; (•) segments perfused with 6% w/v ethanol in KRBSG. All values show mean ± SEM. $n = 9$. Asterisk indicates values significantly different from control (at $p < 0.05$) estimated during the same timed collection period. (Reprinted from Buell, M. G. and Beck, I. T., *Gastroenterology,* 86, 413, 1984. With permission.)

or 3% perfused preparations had intraluminal carbon. With 6% ethanol perfusion, more than 75% of villi contained microvessels with subendothelial carbon and 20% of villi had carbon particles in the lumina of obviously congested capillaries and postcapillary venules (Figure 27). These findings indicate that capillary permeability (as assessed by this method) was not appreciably increased with 3% ethanol perfusion, but that there was considerable stasis and increase in permeability with 6% intraluminal ethanol. Interestingly, intraluminal entrapment of carbon particles in the congested capillaries (in addition to entrapment between endothelial cells or basal lamina) was always associated with broken (rather than intact) subepithelial blebs. This seems to indicate that the severe microvascular congestion caused by 6% ethanol is usually associated with more extensive epithelial damage. It appears, therefore, that increased permeability and severe stasis of the microvasculature occur only in association with more severe damage caused by higher concentrations of ethanol. These findings are in accordance with the observations of Kvietys et al.,[32] who did not observe increased capillary permeability with 5% v/v (equivalent to 4.0% w/v) ethanol. The data also support our previous observation that although 3% ethanol slightly increased serum protein loss into the lumen, the protein exudation caused by 6% is disproportionately

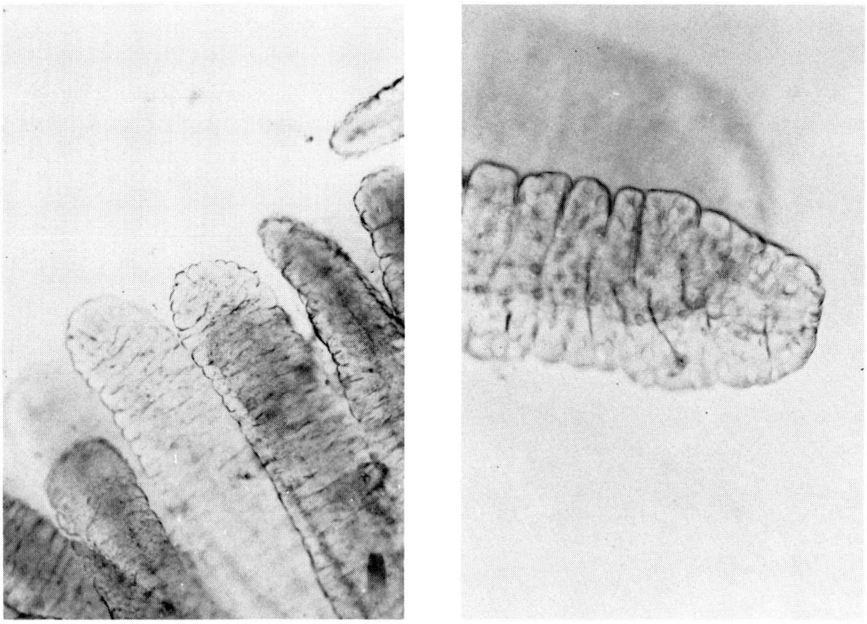

FIGURE 26. Photomicrographs of glycerol-cleared thick sections of dog jejunum resected 1 hr after injection of colloidal carbon. (A) Control segment perfused with KRBSG for 45 min (magnification × 10). Note that the villi have normal structures and no flocculent material is seen. There is no obvious vascular labeling. (B) Villus from a similarly treated control segment at a higher magnification (× 80). (C) Segment perfused with KRBSG containing 6% ethanol. Note the heavy vascular labeling. The labeling was always restricted to the upper third of the villus. Also note the presence of the flocculent material suggestive of cellular debris trapped in proteinaceous material (magnification × 30). (D) Villu from segment treated similarly to the one in (C), but shown at higher magnification (× 80).

higher. Accordingly, some protein loss into the lumen can be explained by alteration of the Starling equilibrium (e.g., with 3% ethanol), while the more severe protein loss caused by 6% ethanol is associated with increased capillary and venular permeability.

XI. COULD THE EFFECT OF ETHANOL ON THE SMALL BOWEL BE MEDIATED BY ITS METABOLITES, ACETALDEHYDE, AND/OR ACETATE?

Ethanol is metabolized to acetaldehyde and acetate, and it has been suggested that the vasodilator and some other effects of alcohol may be mediated by these metabolic products.[136,137] There are, however, several arguments against this possibility.

1. Even though both acetaldehyde and acetate are able to exert vasoactive activity on isolated arterial and venous smooth muscle,[138] the effects of acetate and acetaldehyde on the microvasculature are very different from those of ethanol.[139] While the mesenteric arterioles and muscular venules dilate with ethanol (Figure 18), acetaldehyde and acetate cause vasoconstriction.
2. The relative concentrations of acetaldehyde and acetate required to exert any vascular action are higher than one would expect in the blood, even if all the ethanol in the intestinal tissue would be converted to these metabolites.[140]

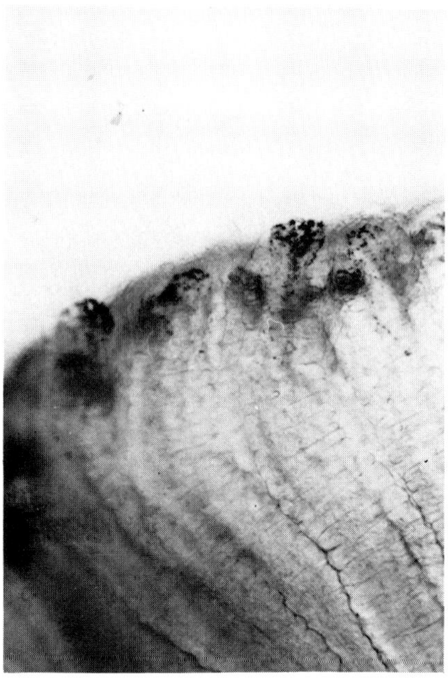

FIGURE 26C

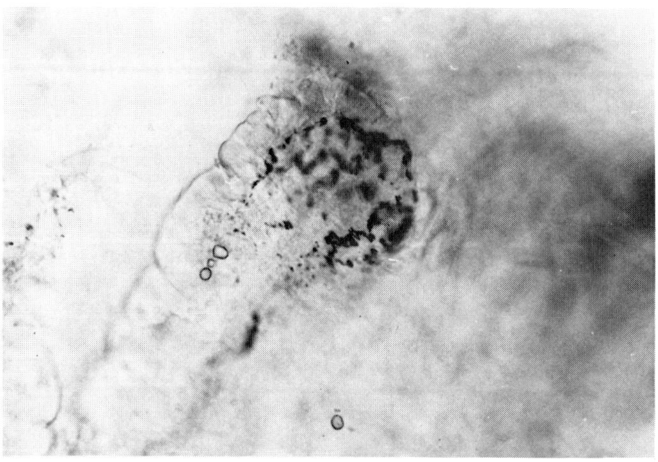

FIGURE 26D

3. Although there is species-related variation in intestinal alcohol dehydrogenase activity, with the exception of the rat small bowel, the activity of this enzyme is very low in the small intestine of most other species. For instance, in the hamster where ethanol induces morphological changes and vascular congestion in the villus stroma,[5,26] the activity of this enzyme is less than 0.1 U/mg protein.[31]
4. Unpublished data in our laboratory indicate that in the dog no acetaldehyde can be detected on gas chromatography in the effluent of the intestinal perfusate containing 3 and 6% ethanol. Furthermore, mucosal villus scrapings obtained in the course of these experiments were devoid of detectable quantities of acetaldehyde.

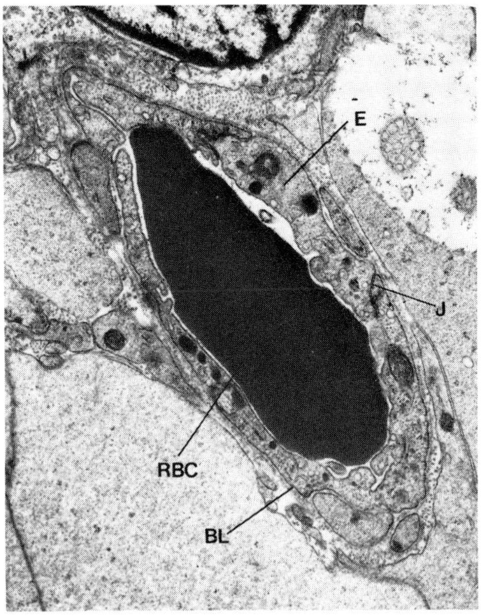

A

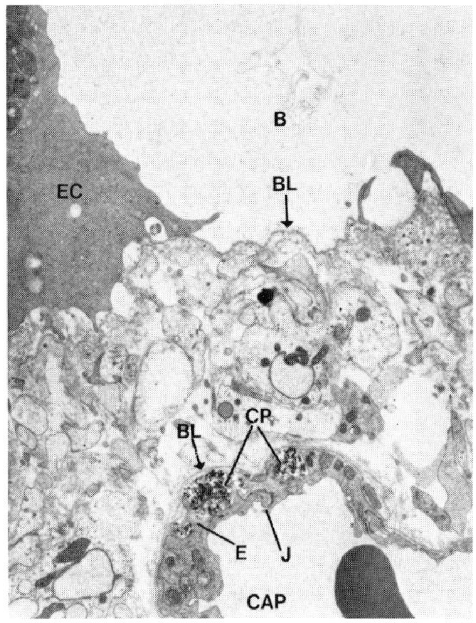

B

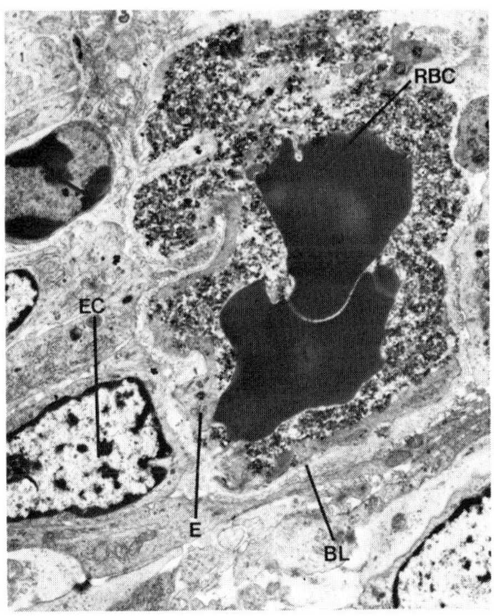

C

FIGURE 27. Electron micrographs of dog jejunal villus tip subepithelial capillaries and venules. Segments were removed 1 hr after injection of colloidal carbon. (A) Control segment perfused with KRBSG for 45 min (magnification × 11,000). Note the normal structure of the capillaries, red blood cell (RBC), endothelial cell(E), intercellular tight junction (J), basal lamina (BL), and absence of carbon labeling. (B) Capillary from segment perfused with 6% ethanol in KRBSG. Carbon particles (CP) are located close to the endothelial cell (E) junction (J) between the endothelium (E) and basal lamina (BL). A small bleb (B) is present in the adjacent epithelium. EC = epithelial cell. (Magnification × 4800.) (C) Congested capillary from segment treated similarly to (B). Here the capillary is more congested and, as a result of occlusion, in addition to subendothelial entrapment there is also intraluminal entrapment of carbon. (Magnification × 4200.)

XII. CORRELATION OF ETHANOL-INDUCED FUNCTIONAL AND MORPHOLOGICAL DAMAGE WITH ALTERATIONS IN THE MICROCIRCULATION OF THE SMALL INTESTINAL MUCOSA

The relationship of ethanol-induced functional and morphological injury was described in Section VI and it was concluded that the modification in water transport correlates well with the morphological changes, while the alterations in membrane digestion and transport of nutrients do not. A hypothesis for the mechanisms involved in these relationships was discussed in Section VII. It was suggested that the basic mechanism which causes the alterations in water transport and the resultant morphological damage is an interference with drainage from the subepithelial region of the villus tip. According to the original hypothesis, the interruption of fluid drainage was either due to villus core contraction or stasis in the microcirculation. Since bleb formation can occur in vitro (where mucosal circulatory changes cannot play a role), it now appears that the primary event which interferes with drainage may be the contraction and compaction of the villus core. Indeed, evidence was presented by us that the cores of the villi which have blebs or broken blebs on their tips are shorter than the cores of unaffected villi (Figure 12). What then is the role of the circulatory changes in the functional and morphological damage caused by ethanol? To answer this question, it is necessary to distinguish between the effect of the absorbed circulating (low concentration: 0.05 to 0.15%) ethanol from that of the high concentrations encountered locally at the luminal side of the villus tip. As shown in Table 1, blood concentrations of ethanol which occur during inebriation (0.05 to 0.2%) do not affect intestinal blood flow significantly, nor do they have an effect on absorption or morphology. Even blood concentrations which can cause coma or death have no direct effect on these parameters of gut function. Thus, one could safely conclude that splanchnic circulatory changes related to ethanol concentrations reached from the absorbed alcohol do not cause significant bowel injury. The situation, however, is different with the local high concentrations of ethanol. Even though the initial morphological injury and changes in water transport may occur in the absence of a microcirculation (in vitro), the more severe changes appear to be related to the grossly disturbed drainage caused by the local capillary congestion. For instance, while in the hamster ethanol causes only diminished water absorption in vitro,[2,3] in the same species ethanol induces fluid secretion in vivo.[5] Similarly, in the absence of microcirculation (in vitro), permeability to macromolecules is not increased;[4] but in the presence of microvascular stasis (in vivo), permeation is not only increased from blood to lumen,[21,32] but also from the luminal content into the circulation.[18-20] The association of intraluminal entrapment of carbon particles with breakage of subepithelial blebs and the higher prevalence of subendothelial entrapment of carbon in segments perfused with 6% ethanol than in those perfused with 3% seem to indicate that the degree of the morphological damage also depends on the severity of the microvascular stasis and the presence of increased permeability. Thus, although the first event in ethanol-induced damage may be the contraction of the villus core, it appears that the more severe morphologic injury and the secretory filtration are the result of abnormalities in the microcirculation at the villus tip. The explanation for this additional damage may be that the microvascular stasis at the villus tip provides additional interference with the drainage of fluid from the intercellular spaces of the epithelial cells. Thus, fluid would accumulate in a greater number of intercellular spaces, and the size of the subepithelial blebs would increase. In addition, the exudation of plasma proteins from congested microvessels into the interstitium, and from there into the blebs, would increase the hydrostatic pressure in these spaces, and thus (depending on the resistance of the epithelium) the blebs would rupture.

XIII. AREAS OF FUTURE CONCERN

There remain, however, many unresolved problems. For instance, entrapment of colloidal carbon between the tight junctions of the endothelial cells and the basal lamina of the capillaries and postcapillary venules only indicates that at the time of injection of the carbon the endothelial cells were sufficiently separated to allow the passage of this colloidal material. Whether this finding truly implies increased permeability is not proven, but this is likely to be the case because observations by many other investigators have shown that similar carbon deposition occurs in the leaky microvessels involved in the early phases of inflammation caused by turpentine,[128] mustard,[129] serotonin, and histamine.[126,127] Whether ethanol also increases permeability through fenestrations of the endothelial cells is not known, and merits further investigation. There is also a lack of knowledge concerning the effect of ethanol on tissue channels, and the findings regarding lymphatic flow are controversial. In some of the morphological studies the lymphatics of contracted villi appeared compressed,[5,27] while in others these channels were dilated[22] and lymph flow was increased.[32] Clearly this issue is not resolved, but to allow for a better understanding of the ethanol-induced interference with fluid drainage and secretory filtration it needs to be further studied.

There is a strong possibility that endogenous chemical mediators may be involved in the ethanol-induced intestinal microvascular events. The initial local inflammatory reaction of the microcirculation to any type of injury involves a transient contraction, followed by a sustained arteriolar and precapillary sphincter dilation. At this stage the arterioles dilate to a greater extent than do the capillaries and the collecting venules. Concomitantly there is increased vascular permeability due to opening of the endothelial intercellular junctions of the capillaries and postcapillary venules.[141] These changes cause a loss of protein-containing plasma fluid from the vascular bed into the surrounding interstitium.[142-144] In view of this, the ethanol-induced blood-flow changes, capillary congestion, and the loss of plasma fluid into the interstitium and into the intestinal lumen are reminiscent of the initial vascular phase of inflammation. Therefore, one could wonder whether the chemical mediators implicated in the inflammatory process also play a role in the genesis of the ethanol-induced microvascular (and secondarily morphological and secretory) changes. The most important mediators of the early vascular events of inflammation are histamine, serotonin, kinins, and prostaglandins.

A. Histamine

The effect of histamine on the microcirculation consists of the dilation of arterioles, capillaries, and venules followed by leakage of plasma constituents (mainly from postcapillary venules) into the surrounding interstitium.[135] Stimulation of both types of histamine receptors seems to play a role in these reactions. While the initial vasodilator response of the intestinal vasculature is thought to be mediated via H_1 receptors, the sustained vasodilator response is dependent upon the stimulation of H_2 receptors.[145,146] On the other hand, the direct action of histamine on venular endothelial cells (resulting in increased permeability) appears to be mediated solely via H_1 receptors.[147] The release of histamine from mast cells can occur not only due to the binding of antigen-IgE complexes or components to the mast cells, but also due to physical stimuli, such as trauma, cold, or heat,[148] as well as hypoxia.[149] The degranulation of mast cells in response to stimuli is brought about by a series of intracellular events mediated by cyclic nucleotides[150,151] which are affected, or modulated, by various endogenous transmitter substances such as epinephrine, norepinephrine, prostaglandins, and acetylcholine.[152] Ethanol alters the release, action, and metabolism of several of these endogenous neurotransmitters, including norepinephrine and acetylcholine.[153] Another factor which plays a role in the degranulation of mast cells is calcium,[154,155] the availability of which also has been shown to be influenced by ethanol.[98] Therefore, ethanol may indeed alter the release of endogenous histamine from mast cells, and thus histamine may play a role in microvascular (and therefore morphologic) changes produced by ethanol.

B. Serotonin

In non-GI tissues the role of serotonin (5-hydroxytryptamine — 5-HT) in inflammation appears to be less important than that of histamine.[156] However, due to its high concentration in the intestinal mucosa, the role of 5-HT in the mediation of vascular events during intestinal injury may be greater than its role in other vascular beds. 5-HT causes vasodilation in the intestine, but its effectiveness varies according to dose, species, and method of administration.[157] 5-HT has also been shown to increase vascular permeability and cause loss of plasma fluid into the interstitium,[158] although again there are species-related differences in responsiveness. As well, 5-HT has been implicated as a mediator of the vasodilator response to mucosal irritation in the small intestine.[159] The responsiveness of the intestinal vascular beds to 5-HT has been reported to depend on the prevailing sympathetic[160-163] and vagal[164] tone in the vascular bed. Since ethanol has been demonstrated to stimulate the release of 5-HT from the intestinal mucosa,[165] and since it has also been reported that it stimulates the release of catecholamines[153] (hence altering the sympathetic tone of the intestinal vascular beds), it is possible that the role of 5-HT in ethanol-induced microvascular changes may be of some significance.

C. Kinins

Vasoactive plasma kinins are also present in areas of inflammation and cause vasodilation,[157] increased vascular permeability,[166] and exudation of plasma fluid into the surrounding interstitium.[167] These polypeptides do not exist as freely circulating kinins, but are produced *de novo* when tissue injury occurs. Injury, by activating factor XII, initiates a cascade process involving the activation of prekallikrein to kallikrein, plasminogen to plasmin, and kininogen to kinin. The tissue kinin is short-lived, because it is rapidly inactivated by the ubiquitous kininase.[168] Although it is unlikely that the primary event in ethanol-induced microvascular changes is the activation of this cascade, once (due to the action of other factors) exudation of plasma proteins has occurred, activation of the cascade may play an important secondary role. At this time, plasma may be exposed to connective tissue components (i.e., elastin, collagen, basement membrane) of the microvascular beds. These connective tissue components have been considered as possible initiators for the contact activation of factor XII,[168] and it has been reported that ethanol may enhance the local release and depress the metabolism of endogenous catecholamines which have been shown to lead to the activation of the kinin cascade system.[169]

D. Prostaglandins

Several recent reviews dealt with the biochemistry and physiologic functions of prostaglandins and the derivatives of the arachidonic acid cascade,[170,171] and Pennington[172] surveyed the literature on the interactions of these compounds with ethanol. The effect of these substances (prostaglandins, thromboxanes, prostacyclin, and leukotrienes) on vascular smooth muscle, the microcirculation, capillary permeability, and intravascular thrombosis is complex. There are, however, some data which suggest that these substances may play a role in ethanol-induced microvascular alterations. Prostaglandins (PGs), particularly PGE_2 and I_2, have been reported to cause vasodilation in the mesenteric blood vessels, while $PGF_{2\alpha}$ tends to cause vasoconstriction.[173] Furthermore,

PGs may sensitize blood vessels to other vasoactive compounds,[174] which in turn may exert their effect on the vasculature indirectly by altering the synthesis and release of endogenous PGs.[175-177] PGs also have been shown to increase vascular permeability and, concomitantly, extravasation of plasma fluid.[178,179] Although the effect of PGs on small intestinal morphology is not known, there is evidence to indicate that, similarly to ethanol, the 16,16-dimethyl analogue of PGE_2 causes damage to the gastric mucosal barrier,[180] and at high doses can produce acute hemorrhage and erosion of the gastric mucosa.[189]

There are, however, some apparent dissimilarities between the action of PGs and ethanol. These are (1) the mechanism by which PGE_2 induces secretion and (2) the cytoprotective action of PGE_2 and its derivatives. The literature indicates that PGs play a dual role in the secretory process. They can produce secretion not only by secretory filtration of plasma fluid (due to increased blood flow and vascular permeability[178,179]), but also by the physiological route of electrolyte-linked net secretion (through stimulation of adenyl cyclase[181-183] coupled with inhibition of Na^+ absorption[184]). To further complicate the issue, PGs have been shown to have cytoprotective action in the GI tract.[185] In the gastric mucosa this can be demonstrated either by administration of exogenous PGs or by the administration of mild irritants (including low concentrations of ethanol) prior to challenge with the more severe irritants or higher concentrations of ethanol.[72,186] Since cytoprotection produced by the latter method could be inhibited by pretreatment with indomethacin, it was concluded that the cytoprotection afforded by pretreatment with mild irritants was due to the production of endogenous local PGs.[185] Recently cytoprotection, in its true sense of protecting cells from acute necrosis, has been seriously challenged, and it has been suggested that prevention of damage is related to the vasodilation caused by the PGs.[187] It is therefore not unlikely that the production of PGs may be enhanced in the intestinal mucosa exposed to ethanol, and hence PGs may exert (depending on the ethanol concentration and amount of PG released) a "beneficial" or "harmful" effect in the production of ethanol-induced morphological lesions in the small intestine.

E. Criteria to Establish Involvement of Mediators and Preliminary Results with Histamine

To establish whether any of the above-mentioned mediators of inflammation plays a role in ethanol-induced functional or morphological damage or in microvascular abnormalities, four criteria will have to be met:

1. The administration of the putative mediator will have to reproduce the ethanol-induced response.
2. Substances which inhibit the synthesis or the release, or which antagonize the action of the putative mediator in vivo, should diminish the intensity of one or more of the components of the expected pathological response (i.e., stasis, bleb formation, vascular changes, and/or protein loss).
3. Adminsitration of substances which diminish the destruction or uptake by tissue of the putative mediator should enhance the response.
4. The chemical proposed to mediate the pathological response should be released or generated in the small intestine in the presence of ethanol in the lumen.

Some evidence for prerequisites (1) and (2) has already been obtained for histamine in ethanol-induced damage: (1) our experiments have shown that carbon colloid labeling of microvessels after ethanol administration is indistinguishable from that described for histamine by Majno et al.[127] and Majno and Palade,[126] and (2) in preliminary experiments we also found that a combination of H_1 and H_2 antagonists (promethazine

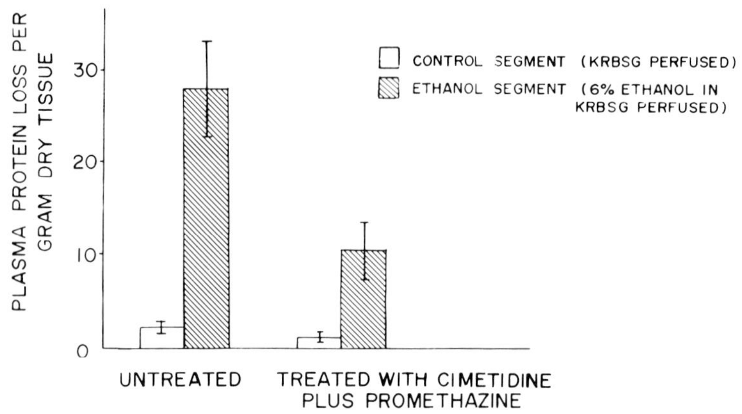

FIGURE 28. The effect of H_1 and H_2 inhibition on ethanol-induced plasma protein loss. Two groups of rabbits were studied. The day before the experiment ^{51}Cr-labeled rabbit albumin was injected intravenously. Group 1 (untreated) served as control and the experimental group was treated with i.v. cimetidine (47 mg/kg) and promethazine (2.0 mg/kg). Two jejunal segments were perfused in each rabbit: one (control segment) with KRBSG and the second (ethanol segment) with KRBSG which contained 6% w/v ethanol. Perfusion rate was 1.9 mℓ/min and the effluent was analyzed for ^{51}Cr content for each 10-min perfusion period. The data presented in the figure were obtained at steady state (on the effluent collected in the 10-min period between 30- and 40-min perfusion). The protein loss from the control segments (empty bars) was not different from that of the H_1- and H_2-blocked animals. Ethanol (hatched bars) significantly ($p < 0.001$) increased protein loss in both groups, but the protein loss from the ethanol-perfused segments was significantly ($p < 0.05$) lower in the H_1 and H_2-blocked animals than in the ethanol-perfused segments of the untreated (control) group.

and cimetidine) significantly reduced the ethanol-induced intraluminal protein loss in rabbits. In these experiments (as yet unpublished), two groups of rabbits were studied: group 1 served as control and group 2 was treated with a combination of cimetidine (47 mg/kg) and promethazine (2.0 mg/kg). In the course of these experiments, two jejunal segments were perfused in each rabbit of both groups: one with KRBSG and one with 6% ethanol in KRBSG. Measurement of protein loss was carried out in similar fashion as described previously in our experiments on dogs,[29] except that ^{51}Cr-tagged albumin was used. Figure 28 shows that the intraluminal protein loss produced by ethanol was significantly reduced in the animals which were treated with H_1 plus H_2 antagonists.

XIV. CONCLUSION

Intraluminal ethanol depresses transport of nutrients and enterocyte enzyme function. This effect of ethanol appears to be independent of changes in the microcirculation. Morphological damage and secretory filtration caused by ethanol are probably initiated by contraction of the villus core, but are aggravated by microvascular stasis at the villus tip. The possibility that chemical mediators of acute inflammation (e.g., histamine) play a role in the initiation of the microvascular stasis and in the increase in the microvascular permeability (and possibly the contraction of the villus core) has been raised.

ACKNOWLEDGMENTS

The author is indebted to his co-workers, friends, and students who, with their intellectual contributions and hard work in the laboratory, made it possible to obtain the results of our experimental studies, many of which are quoted in this chapter. Special acknowledgments are due to my colleague Dr. P. K. Dinda and my previous Ph.D. students, Dr. J. E. T. Fox and Dr. M. G. Buell. My sincere thanks must be recorded to Mrs. Hope Williams who sat faithfully by her word processor and who did not rebel each time I changed the text and the order of references. The experiments originating from our laboratory, quoted in this chapter, were supported by the Medical Research Council of Canada (MT 4257).

REFERENCES

1. Chang, T., Lewis, J., and Glazko, A. J., Effect of ethanol and other alcohols on the transport of amino acids and glucose by everted sacs of rat small intestine, *Biochim. Biophys. Acta,* 135, 1000, 1967.
2. Dinda, P. K., Beck, I. T., Beck, M., and McElligott, T. F., Effect of ethanol on sodium-dependent glucose transport in the small intestine of the hamster, *Gastroenterology,* 68, 1517, 1975.
3. Dinda, P. K. and Beck, I. T., On the mechanism of the inhibitory effect of ethanol on intestinal glucose and water absorption, *Am. J. Dig. Dis.,* 22, 529, 1977.
4. Fox, J. E., Bourdages, R., and Beck, I. T., Effect of ethanol on glucose and water absorption in hamster jejunum *in vivo.* Methodological problems: anesthesia, nonabsorbable markers, and osmotic effect, *Am. J. Dig. Dis.,* 23, 193, 1978a.
5. Fox, J. E., McElligott, T. F., and Beck, I. T., The correlation of ethanol-induced depression of glucose and water transport with morphological changes in the hamster jejunum in vivo, *Can. J. Physiol. Pharmacol.,* 56, 123, 1978b.
6. Thomson, A. B. R., Acute exposure of rabbit jejunum to ethanol. In vitro uptake of hexoses, *Dig. Dis. Sci.,* 29, 267, 1984a.
7. Kuo, Y. J. and Shanbour, L. L., Effects of ethanol on sodium, 3-*O*-methyl glucose, and L-alanine transport in the jejunum, *Am. J. Dig. Dis.,* 23, 51, 1978.
8. Panowicz, H., The influence of ethyl alcohol on glucose absorption in the isolated segment of the small intestine of the rat, *Rocz. Pomor. Akad. Med. Swierczewski,* 13, 385, 1967.
9. Israel, Y., Salazar, I., and Rosenmann, E., Inhibitory effects of alcohol on intestinal amino acid transport *in vivo* and *in vitro, J. Nutr.,* 96, 499, 1968.
10. Israel, Y., Valenzuela, J. E., Salazar, I., and Ugarte, G., Alcohol and amino acid transport in the human small intestine, *J. Nutr.,* 98, 222, 1969.
11. Jacobs, F. A., Crandall, J. C., and Fabel, C. B., An effect of ethanol on the bidirectional intestinal flux of amino acids, *Nutr. Rep. Int.,* 21, 397, 1980.
12. Beck, I. T. and Dinda, P. K., Effect of ethanol on $Na^{+}K^{+}$-ATPase and active transport of sugars and amino acids, in *Alcohol and the Gastrointestinal Tract,* Vol. 95, Stock, C. and Sarles, H., Eds., INSERM, Amsterdam, 1980, 423.
13. Dinda, P. K., Hurst, R. O., and Beck, I. T., Effect of ethanol on disaccharidases of hamster jejunal brush border membrane, *Am. J. Physiol.,* 237, E68, 1979.
14. Dinda, P. K. and Beck, I. T., Effect of ethanol on peptidases of hamster jejunal brush-border membrane, *Am. J. Physiol.,* 242, G442, 1982.
15. Dinda, P. K. and Beck, I. T., Effects of ethanol on cytoplasmic peptidases of the jejunal epithelial cell of the hamster, *Dig. Dis. Sci.,* 29, 46, 1984.
16. Baraona, E., Pirola, R. C., and Lieber, C. S., Small intestinal damage and changes in cell population produced by ethanol ingestion in the rat, *Gastroenterology,* 66, 226, 1974.
17. Worthington, B. S., Meserole, L., and Syrotuck, J. A., Effect of daily ethanol ingestion on intestinal permeability to macromolecules, *Am. J. Dig. Dis.,* 23, 23, 1978.
18. Robinson, G. M., Orrego, H., Israel, Y., Devenyi, P., and Kapur, B. M., Low-molecular-weight polyethylene glycol as a probe of gastrointestinal permeability after alcohol ingestion, *Dig. Dis. Sci.,* 26, 971, 1981.

19. Draper, L. R., Gyure, L. A., Hall, J. G., and Robertson, D., Effect of alcohol on the integrity of the intestinal epithelium, *Gut*, 24, 399, 1983.
20. Talbot, R. W., Foster, J. R., Hermon-Taylor, J., and Grant, D. A., Induced mucosal penetration and transfer to portal blood of luminal horseradish peroxidase after exposure of mucosa of guinea pig intestine to ethanol and lysolecithin, *Dig. Dis. Sci.*, 29, 1015, 1984.
21. Buell, M. G. and Beck, I. T., Effect of ethanol on jejunal regional blood flow in the rabbit, *Gastroenterology*, 84, 81, 1983.
22. Buell, M. G., Dinda, P. K., and Beck, I. T., Effect of ethanol on morphology and total, capillary, and shunted blood flow of different anatomical layers of dog jejunum, *Dig. Dis. Sci.*, 28, 1005, 1983.
23. Gillespie, R. J. G. and Lucas, C. C., Effect of single intoxicating doses of ethanol on the gastric and intestinal mucosa of rats, *Can. J. Biochem. Physiol.*, 39, 237, 1961.
24. Broitman, S. A., Gottlieb, L. S., and Vitale, J. J., Augmentation of ethanol absorption by mono- and disaccharides, *Gastroenterology*, 70, 1101, 1976.
25. Hoyumpa, A. M., Breen, K. J., Schenker, S., and Wilson, F. A., Thiamine transport across the rat intestine. II. Effect of ethanol, *J. Lab. Clin. Med.*, 86, 803, 1975.
26. Fox, J. E., McElligott, T. F., and Beck, I. T., Effect of ethanol on the morphology of hamster jejunum, *Am. J. Dig. Dis.*, 23, 201, 1978c.
27. Fox, J. E., Morris, G. P., Beck, I. T., and McElligott, T. F., The ultrastructure of blebs induced in the hamster jejunum by ethanol, *Can. J. Physiol. Pharmacol.*, 57, 305, 1979.
28. Millan, M. S., Morris, G. P., Beck, I. T., and Henson, J. T., Villous damage induced by suction biopsy and by acute ethanol intake in normal human small intestine, *Dig. Dis. Sci.*, 25, 513, 1980.
29. Buell, M. G. and Beck, I. T., Ethanol-induced mucosal microvascular stasis and enhanced plasma protein loss in the dog jejunum, *Gastroenterology*, 86, 413, 1984.
30. Dinda, P. K. and Beck, I. T., Ethanol-induced inhibition of glucose transport across the isolated brush-border membrane of hamster jejunum, *Dig. Dis. Sci.*, 26, 23, 1981.
31. Spencer, R. P., Brody, K. R., and Lutters, B. M., Some effects of ethanol on the gastrointestinal tract, *Am. J. Dig. Dis.*, 9, 599, 1964.
32. Kvietys, P. R., Patterson, W. G., Russell, J. M., Barrowman, J. A., and Granger, D. N., Role of the microcirculation in ethanol-induced mucosal injury in the dog, *Gastroenterology*, 87, 562, 1984.
33. Kalant, H., Effects of ethanol on the nervous system, in *International Encyclopedia of Pharmacology and Therapeutics, Section 20*, Vol. 1, Tremolieres, J., Ed., Pergamon Press, Toronto, 1970, 189.
34. Halsted, C. H., Robles, E. A., and Mezey, E., Distribution of ethanol in the human gastrointestinal tract, *Am. J. Clin. Nutr.*, 26, 831, 1973.
35. Beck, I. T., Effets de l'alcool sur l'intestin grele, *La Vie Med. Can. Fr.*, 6, 1049, 1977.
36. Falconer, B. and Gladnikoff, H., Ueber den Alkoholgehalt des Blutes verschiedener Gefasse beim Kaninchen nach Alkoholzufuhr, *Scand. Arch. Physiol.*, 68, 245, 1934.
37. Wright, E. M. and Diamond, J. M., Patterns of non-electrolyte permeability, *Proc. R. Soc. London, Ser. B*, 172, 227, 1969a.
38. Wright, E. M. and Diamond, J. M., An electrical method of measuring non-electrolyte permeability, *Proc. R. Soc. London, Ser. B*, 172, 203, 1969b.
39. Beck, I. T., Paloschi, G. B., Dinda, P. K., and Beck, M., Effect of intragastric administration of alcohol on the ethanol concentrations and osmolality of pancreatic juice, bile, and portal and peripheral blood, *Gastroenterology*, 67, 484, 1974.
40. Pappenheimer, J. R. and Heisey, S. R., Exchange of material between cerebrospinal fluid and blood, in *Drugs and Membranes, Vol. 4, Proc. 1st Int. Pharmacol. Meet.*, Hogben, C. A. M. and Lindgren, P., Eds., Pergamon Press, Oxford, 1963, 95.
41. Lieber, C. S., Metabolism and metabolic effects of alcohol, *Med. Clin. N. Am.*, 68, 3, 1984.
42. Kalant, H., Absorption, diffusion, distribution, and elimination of ethanol: effects on biological membranes, in *The Biology of Alcoholism, Vol. 1*, Kissin, B. and Beigleiter, H., Eds., Plenum Press, New York, 1971, 1.
43. Lee, J. S., Isosmotic absorption of fluid from rat jejunum in vitro, *Gastroenterology*, 54, 366, 1968.
44. Dinda, P. K., Beck, M., and Beck, I. T., On the mechanism of isoosmotic transport across the small intestine. The composition of the absorbate transported from a mucosal solution made hypertonic by the addition of mannitol, *Can. J. Physiol. Pharmacol.*, 51, 130, 1973.
45. Dinda, P. K., Beck, M., and Beck, I. T., Effect of changes in the osmolality of the luminal fluid on intracellular concentration of solutes in the hamster jejunum, *Can. J. Physiol. Pharmacol.*, 50, 72, 1972.
46. Beck, I. T. and Dinda, P. K., On the mechanism of isoosmotic transport of fluid across the small intestine. The effect of the Staverman reflection coefficient of the solute used to increase the osmolality of the mucosal solution on the composition of the absorbate, *Can. J. Physiol. Pharmacol.*, 52, 96, 1974.

47. Haljamae, A. H., Jodal, M., and Lundgren, O., Countercurrent multiplication of sodium and intestinal villi during absorption of sodium chloride, *Acta Physiol. Scand.*, 89, 580, 1973.
48. Altura, B. M. and Altura, B. T., Microvascular and vascular smooth muscle actions of ethanol, acetaldehyde, and acetate, *Fed. Proc., Fed. Am. Soc. Exp. Biol.*, 41, 2447, 1982.
49. Magnussen, M. P., The influence of ethanol on the absorption of drugs from the rat small intestine, *Acta Pharmacol. Toxicol.*, 25 (Suppl. 4), 40, 1967.
50. Magnussen, M. P., The effect of ethanol on the gastrointestinal absorption of drugs in the rat, *Acta Pharmacol. Toxicol.*, 26, 130, 1968.
51. Hayton, W. L., Effects of normal alcohols on intestinal absorption of salicylic acid, sulfapyridine, and prednisolone in rats, *J. Pharm. Sci.*, 64, 1450, 1975.
52. Tillotson, L. G., Carter, E. A., Inui, K.-I., and Isselbacher, K. T., Inhibition of Na^+-stimulated glucose transport function and perturbation of intestinal microvillus membrane vesicles by ethanol and acetaldehyde, *Arch. Biochem. Biophys.*, 207, 360, 1981.
53. Baraona, E. and Lindenbaum, J., Metabolic effects of alcohol on the intestine, in *Metabolic Effects of Alcoholism*, Lieber, C. S., Ed., University Park Press, Baltimore, 1977, 81.
54. Levine, R. R., McNary, W. F., Kornguth, P. J., and LeBlanc, R., Histological re-evaluation of everted gut technique for studying intestinal absorption, *Eur. J. Pharmacol.*, 9, 211, 1970.
55. Althausen, T. L., Uyeyama, K., and Loran, M. R., Effects of alcohol on absorption of vitamin A in normal and gastrectomized subjects, *Gastorenterology*, 38, 942, 1960.
56. Adibi, S. A., Intestinal phase of protein assimilation in man, *Am. J. Clin. Nutr.*, 29, 205, 1976.
57. Tapper, E. J., Bushi, S., Ruppert, R. D., and Greenberger, N. J., Effect of acute and chronic ethanol treatment on the absorption of iron in rats, *Am. J. Med. Sci.*, 255, 46, 1968.
58. Charlton, R. W., Jacobs, R., Seftel, H., and Bothwell, T. H., Effect of alcohol on iron absorption, *Br. Med. J.*, 2, 1427, 1964.
59. Mansbach, C. M., II, Effect of ethanol on intestinal lipid absorption in the rat, *J. Lipid Res.*, 24, 1310, 1983.
60. Thomson, A. B. R., Effect of chronic ingestion of ethanol on in vitro uptake of lipids and glucose in the rabbit jejunum, *Am. J. Physiol.*, 246 *(Gastrointest. Liver Physiol.*, 9), G120, 1984b.
61. Crane, R. K., Absorption of sugars, in *Handbook of Physiology: Section 6: Alimentary Canal*, Vol. 3, Code, C. F. and Heidel, H., Eds., Williams & Wilkins, Baltimore, 1968, 1323.
62. Diamond, J. M. and Bossert, W. H., Standing-gradient osmotic flow. A mechanism for coupling of water and solute transport in epithelia, *J. Gen. Physiol.*, 50, 2061, 1967.
63. Tomasini, J. T. and Dobbins, W. O., Intestinal mucosal morphology during water and electrolyte absorption. A light and electron microscopic study, *Am. J. Dig. Dis.*, 15, 226, 1970.
64. Dinda, P. K., Beck, M., and Beck, I. T., Isoosmotic transport of fluid across the hamster small intestine in the presence of phlorizin induced inhibition of sugar transport, *Can. J. Physiol. Pharmacol.*, 53, 375, 1975.
65. Mekhjian, H. S. and May, E. S., Acute and chronic effects of ethanol on fluid transport in the human small intestine, *Gastroenterology*, 72, 1280, 1977.
66. Himal, H. S. and Greenberg, L., The effect of ethanol and bile on electrolyte movement across canine proximal duodenal mucosa, *Am. J. Gastroenterol.*, 68, 45, 1977.
67. Faelli, A., Esposito, G., Burlini, N., Tosco, M., and Capraro, V., The rat and hamster jejunum during transintestinal transport *in vitro*, *Arch. Int. Physiol. Biochim.*, 87, 73, 1979.
68. Leblond, C. P. and Walker, B. E., Renewal of cell populations, *Physiol. Rev.*, 36, 255, 1956.
69. Lipkin, M. and Deschner, E. E., Comparative analysis of cell proliferation in the gastrointestinal tract of newborn hamster, *Exp. Cell Res.*, 49, 1, 1968.
70. Fry, R. J. M., Lesher, S., and Kohn, H. I., Age effect on cell-transit time in mouse jejunal epithelium, *Am. J. Physiol.*, 201, 213, 1961.
71. Wallace, J. L., Morris, G. P., Krausse, E. J., and Greaves, S. E., Reduction by cytoprotective agents of ethanol-induced damage to the rat gastric mucosa: a correlated morphological and physiological study, *Can. J. Physiol. Pharmacol.*, 60, 1686, 1982.
72. Lacy, E. R. and Ito, S., Microscopic analysis of ethanol damage to rat gastric mucosa after treatment with a prostaglandin, *Gastroenterology*, 83, 619, 1982.
73. Wilson, F. A. and Hoyumpa, A. M., Ethanol and small intestinal transport, *Gastroenterology*, 76, 388, 1979.
74. Vyrodov, I. P., Bud'Ko, P. S., and Derkach, L. V., Use of kinetic concepts of the structure of a liquid to determine molecular dimensions, *Russ. J. Physiol. Chem.*, 38, 126, 1964.
75. Staverman, A. J., The theory of measurement of osmotic pressure, *Recl. Trav. Chim. Pays-Bas*, 70, 344, 1951.
76. Altura, B. M., Edgarian, H., and Altura, B. T., Differential effects of ethanol and mannitol on contraction of arterial smooth muscle, *J. Pharmacol. Exp. Ther.*, 197, 352, 1976.

77. Lee, J. S., Epithelial cell extrusion during fluid transport in canine small intestine, *Am. J. Physiol.*, 232, E408, 1977.
78. Granger, D. N., Cook, B. H., and Taylor, A. E., Structural locus of transmucosal albumin efflux in canine ileum, a fluorescent study, *Gastroenterology*, 71, 1023, 1976.
79. Astaldi, G. and Strosselli, E., Peroral biopsy of the intestinal mucosa in hepatic cirrhosis, *Am. J. Dig. Dis.*, 5, 603, 1960.
80. Adrich, Z., Boj, E., Kryszewski, A., and Rynkiewicz, H., Jejunal mucosa structure and small intestine function in diabetes, *Przegl. Lek.*, 32, 782, 1975.
81. Haglund, U., Hulten, L., Ahren, C., and Lundgren, O., Mucosal lesions in the human small intestine in shock, *Gut*, 16, 979, 1975.
82. Perdue, M., Roomi, N., Forstner, J., and Gall, D. G., Effect of IgE-mediated reactions on rat intestinal epithelium: goblet cell reaction and enterocyte damage, *Gastroenterology*, 86 (Abstr.), 1209, 1984.
83. Regan, T. J., Regional circulatory responses to alcohol and its congeners, *Fed. Proc., Fed. Am. Soc. Exp. Biol.*, 41, 2438, 1982.
84. Bing, R. J., Effect of ethanol on the heart and cardiac metabolism, *Fed. Proc., Fed. Am. Soc. Exp. Biol.*, 41, 2443, 1982.
85. Rubin, E., Alcohol and the heart: theoretical considerations, *Fed. Proc., Fed. Am. Soc. Exp. Biol.*, 41, 2460, 1982.
86. Katz, A. M., Effects of ethanol on ion transport in muscle membranes, *Fed. Proc., Fed. Am. Soc. Exp. Biol.*, 41, 2456, 1982.
87. Dickson, W. E., The action of alcohol on the circulation, *J. Physiol. (London)*, 35, 346, 1907.
88. Fewings, J. D., Hanna, M. J. D., Walsh, J. A., and Whelan, R. F., The effects of ethyl alcohol on the blood vessels of the hand and forearm in man, *Br. J. Pharmacol.*, 27, 93, 1966.
89. Horwitz, O., Montgomery, H., Longake, E. D., and Sayen, A., Effect of vasodilator drugs and other procedures on digital cutaneous blood flow; cardiac output, blood pressure, pulse rate, body temperature and metabolic rates, *Am. J. Med. Sci.*, 218, 669, 1949.
90. Nakano, J. and Kessinger, J. M., Cardiovascular effects of ethanol, its congeners and synthetic bourbon in dogs, *Eur. J. Pharmacol.*, 17, 195, 1972.
91. Webb, W. R. and Degerli, I. U., Ethyl alcohol and the cardiovascular system, *JAMA*, 191, 1055, 1965.
92. Wallgren, H. and Barry, H., III, *Actions of Alcohol*, Vol. 1, Elsevier, Amsterdam, 1970, 155.
93. Anton, A. H., Ethanol and urinary catecholamines in man, *Clin. Pharmacol. Ther.*, 6, 462, 1965.
94. Feldstein, A., Effect of ethanol on neurohumoral amine metabolism, in *The Biology of Alcoholism*, Vol. 1, Kissin, B. and Beigleiter, H., Eds., Plenum Press, New York, 1971, 127.
95. Pohorecky, L. A., Jaffe, L. S., and Berkeley, H. A., Effects of ethanol on serotonergic neurons in the rat brain, *Res. Commun. Chem. Pathol. Pharmacol.*, 8, 1, 1974.
96. Kalsner, S., The potentiating effects of ethanol on responses of aortic strips to stimulant drugs, *J. Pharm. Pharmacol.*, 22, 877, 1970.
97. Edgarian, H. and Altura, B. M., Ethanol and contraction of venous smooth muscle, *Anesthesiology*, 44, 311, 1976.
98. Turlapaty, P. D. M. V., Altura, B. T., and Altura, B. M., Ethanol reduces Ca^{2+} concentrations in arterial and venous smooth muscle, *Experientia*, 35, 639, 1979.
99. Altura, B. M. and Altura, B. T., Vascular smooth muscle and prostaglandins, *Fed. Proc., Fed. Am. Soc. Exp. Biol.*, 35, 2360, 1976.
100. Altura, B. M., Ogunkoya, A., Gebrewold, A., and Altura, B. T., Effects of ethanol on terminal arterioles and muscular venules: direct observations on the microcirculation, *J. Cardiovasc. Pharmacol.*, 1, 97, 1979.
101. Smythe, C. M., Heinemann, H. O., and Bradley, S. E., Estimated hepatic blood flow in the dog: effect of ethanol on it, renal flow, cardiac output and arterial pressure, *Am. J. Physiol.*, 172, 737, 1953.
102. Castenfors, H., Hultman, E., and Josephson, B., Effect of intravenous infusions of ethyl alcohol on estimated hepatic blood flow in man, *J. Clin. Invest.*, 39, 776, 1960.
103. Mendeloff, A. I., Effect of intravenous infusions of ethanol upon estimated hepatic blood flow in man, *J. Clin. Invest.*, 33, 1298, 1954.
104. Stein, S. W., Lieber, C. S., Leevy, C. M., Cherrick, G. R., and Abelmann, W. H., The effect of ethanol upon systemic and hepatic blood flow in man, *Am. J. Clin. Nutr.*, 13, 68, 1963.
105. Shaw, S., Heller, E. A., Friedman, H. S., Baraona, E., and Lieber, C. S., Increased hepatic oxygenation following ethanol administration in the baboon, *Proc. Soc. Exp. Biol. Med.*, 156, 509, 1977.
106. Friedman, H. S., Lowery, R., Shaughnessy, E., and Scorza, J., The effects of ethanol on pancreatic blood flow in awake and anesthetized dogs, *Proc. Soc. Exp. Biol. Med.*, 174, 377, 1983.

107. Bravo, I. R., Acevedo, C. G., and Gallardo, V., Acute effects of ethanol on liver blood circulation in anesthetized dog, *Alcoholism Clin. Exp. Res.*, 4, 248, 1980.
108. Israel, Y., MacDonald, A., and Orrego, H., Contribution of portal and arterial flow to the increase in liver blood flow induced by acute ethanol administration, *Gastroenterology*, 84, 1377, 1983.
109. Horwitz, L. D. and Myers, J. H., Ischaemia of the pancreas due to ethanol in conscious dogs, *Circulation*, 62 (Suppl. 3), 22, 1980.
110. Wolf, S. and Wolff, H. G., *Human Gastric Function*, Oxford University Press, New York, 1943.
111. Auger, N. A., Gastric mucosal blood flow following damage by ethanol, acetic acid, or aspirin, *Gastroenterology*, 58, 311, 1970.
112. Cheung, L. Y., Moody, F. G., and Reese, R. S., Effect of aspirin, bile salt and ethanol on canine gastric mucosal blood flow, *Surgery*, 77, 786, 1975.
113. Puurunen, J., Gastric mucosal blood flow in ethanol-induced mucosal damage in the rat, *Eur. J. Pharmacol.*, 63, 275, 1980.
114. Guth, P. H. and Smith, E., Neural control of gastric mucosa blood flow in the rat, *Gastroenterology*, 69, 935, 1975.
115. Hakkinen, J. P. and Oates, P. J., Microvascular responses to concentrated intragastric ethanol in rats, *Gastroenterology*, 86 (Abstr.), 1104, 1984.
116. Siregar, H. and Chou, C. C., Relative contribution of fat, protein, carbohydrate, and ethanol to intestinal hyperemia, *Am. J. Physiol.*, 242, G27, 1982.
117. Powell, D. W., Malawer, S. J., and Plotkin, G. R., Secretion of electrolytes and water by the guinea pig small intestine in vivo, *Am. J. Physiol.*, 215, 1226, 1968.
118. Dinda, P. K., Buell, M. G., DaCosta, L. R., and Beck, I. T., Simultaneous estimation of arteriolar, capillary and shunt blood flow of the gut mucosa, *Am. J. Physiol.*, 245, G29, 1983.
119. Delaney, J. P., Arteriovenous anastomotic blood flow in the mesenteric organs, *Am. J. Physiol.*, 216, 1556, 1969.
120. Fan, F. C., Schuessler, G. B., Chen, R. Y. Z., and Chien, S., Determinations of blood flow and shunting of 9- and 15-micrometer spheres in regional beds, *Am. J. Physiol.* 237 (*Heart Circ. Physiol.*, 6), H25, 1979.
121. Maxwell, L. C., Shepherd, A. P., Riedel, G. L., and Morris, M. D., Effect of microsphere size on apparent intramural distribution of intestinal blood flow, *Am. J. Physiol.*, 241 (*Heart Circ. Physiol.*, 10), H408, 1981.
122. Bond, J. H. and Levitt, M. D., Use of microspheres to measure small intestinal villus blood flow in the dog, *Am. J. Physiol.*, 236 (*Endocrinol. Metab. Gastrointest. Physiol.*, 5), E577, 1979.
123. Gelman, S., Granger, D. N., Fowler, K., and Smith, L. R., Clearance of 9-micron spheres and rubidium in the intestinal circulation, *Am. J. Physiol.*, 247 (*Gastrointest. Liver Physiol.*, 10), G13, 1984.
124. Dinda, P. K., DaCosta, L. R., and Beck, I. T., Microsphere fractionation of intestinal blood flow, *Am. J. Physiol.*, 246 (*Gastrointest. Liver Physiol.*, 5), G644, 1984.
125. Beck, I. T., Buell, M. G., and Morris, G. P., Ethanol-induced vascular permeability changes in the jejunal mucosa of the dog, *Gastroenterology*, 90, 1137, 1986.
126. Majno, G. and Palade, G. E., Studies in inflammation. I. The effect of histamine and serotonin on vascular permeability: an electron microscopic study, *J. Biophys. Biochem. Cytol.*, 11, 571, 1961.
127. Majno, G., Palade, G. E., and Schoefl, G. I., Studies in inflammation. II. The site of action of histamine and serotonin along the vascular tree: a topographic study, *J. Biophys. Biochem. Cytol.*, 11, 607, 1961.
128. Ham, K. N. and Hurley, J. V., Acute inflammation. An electron microscope study of turpentine-induced pleurisy in the rat, *J. Pathol. Bacteriol.*, 90, 365, 1965.
129. Hurley, J. V. and McQueen, A., The response of fenestrated vessels of the small intestine of rats to application of mustard oil, *J. Pathol.*, 105, 21, 1971.
130. Cotran, R. S. and Majno, G., The delayed and prolonged vascular leakage in inflammation. I. Topography of the leaking vessels after thermal injury, *Am. J. Pathol.*, 45, 261, 1964.
131. Wells, F. R. and Miles, A. A., Site of the vascular response to thermal injury, *Nature*, 200, 1015, 1963.
132. Hurley, J. V. and Spector, W. G., A topographical study of increased vascular permeability in acute turpentine-induced pleurisy, *J. Pathol. Bacteriol.*, 89, 245, 1965.
133. Wells, F. R., Standardization of biological ink for the study of vascular injury in inflammation, *Experientia*, 28, 371, 1971.
134. Hurley, J. V., The sequence of early events, in *Inflammation, (Handbook of Experimental Pharmacology*, Vol. 50 (Part 1), Vane, J. R. and Ferreira, S. H., Eds., Springer-Verlag, Basel, 1978, 26.
135. Majno, G., Gilmore, V., and Leventhal, M., On the mechanism of vascular leakage caused by histamine-type mediators. A microscopic study in vivo, *Circ. Res.*, 21, 833, 1967.

136. Gailis, L., Cardiovascular effects of acetaldehyde: evidence for the involvement of tissue SH groups, in *The Role of Acetaldehyde in the Actions of Ethanol,* Lindros, K. O. and Eriksson, C. J. P., Eds., Kautpakirjapaino, Helsinki, 1975, 135.
137. Rix, K. J. B., *Alcohol and Alcoholism,* Eden, Montreal, 1977.
138. Altura, B. M., Carella, A., and Altura, B. T., Acetaldehyde on vascular smooth muscle: possible role in vasodilator action of ethanol, *Eur. J. Pharmacol.,* 52, 73, 1978.
139. Altura, B. M. and Gebrewold, A., Failure of acetaldehyde or acetate to mimic the splanchnic arteriolar or venular dilator actions of ethanol: direct in situ studies on the microcirculation, *Br. J. Pharmacol.,* 73, 580, 1981.
140. Altura, B. M. and Altura, B. T., Microvascular and vascular smooth muscle actions of ethanol, acetaldehyde, and acetate, *Fed. Proc., Fed. Am. Soc. Exp. Biol.,* 41, 2447, 1982.
141. Casley-Smith, J. R., The response of the microcirculation to inflammation, in *The Cell Biology of Inflammation, (Handbook of Inflammation,* Vol. 2), Weissman, G., Ed., Elsevier/North-Holland, Amsterdam, 1980, 53.
142. Aschheim, E. and Zweifach, B. W., Quantitative studies of protein and water shifts during inflammation, *Am. J. Physiol.,* 202, 554, 1962.
143. Hauck, G. and Schroer, H., Vitalmikroskopische Untersuchungen zur Lokalization der Eiweibpermeabilitat und der Endstrombahn von Warmblutern, *Pfluegers Arch.,* 312, 32, 1969.
144. Beck, I. T., The inflammatory process: cellular response and tissue repair, in *Idiopathic Inflammatory Bowel Disease,* Thomson, A. B. R., Ed., Canadian Public Health Association, Ottawa, 1982, 70.
145. Pawlik, W., Tague, L. L., Tepperman, B. L., Miller, T. A., and Jacobson, E. D., Histamine H_1- and H_2-receptor vasodilation of canine intestinal circulation, *Am. J. Physiol.,* 233, E219, 1977.
146. Owen, D. A., Flynn, S. B., Harvey, C. A., et al., The evidence for histamine receptors in the gastromesenteric circulation, in *Cimetidine Symp. Westminster Hosp.,* Wastell, C. and Lance, P., Eds., Churchill Livingstone, London, 1979, 207.
147. Brigham, K. L., Bowers, R. E., and Owen, P. J., Effects of antihistamines on the lung vascular repsonse to histamine in unanesthetized sheep. Diphenhydramine prevention of pulmonary edema and increased permeability, *J. Clin. Invest.,* 58, 391, 1976.
148. Soter, N. A. and Austen, K. F., Urticaria, angioedema, and mediator release in humans in response to physical environmental stimuli, *Fed. Proc., Fed. Am. Soc. Exp. Biol.,* 36, 1736, 1977.
149. Haas, F. and Bergofsky, E. H., Role of the mast cell in the pulmonary pressor response to hypoxia, *J. Clin. Invest.,* 51, 3154, 1972.
150. Sullivan, T. J., Parker, K. L., Stenson, W., and Parker, C. W., Modulation of cyclic AMP in purified rat mast cells. I. Responses to pharmacologic, metabolic and physical stimuli, *J. Immunol.,* 114, 1473, 1975.
151. Orange, R. P., Kaliner, M. A., Laraia, P. J., and Austen, K. F., Immunological release of histamine and slow reacting substance of anaphylaxis from human lung. II. Influence of cellular levels of cyclic AMP, *Fed. Proc., Fed. Am. Soc. Exp. Biol.,* 30, 1725, 1971.
152. Beaven, M. A., Histamine, *N. Engl. J. Med.,* 294, 320, 1976.
153. Davis, V. E. and Walsh, M. J., Effect of ethanol on neuroamine metabolism, in *Biological Basis of Alcoholism,* Israel, Y. and Mardones, J., Eds., John Wiley & Sons, New York, 1971, 73.
154. Kaliner, M., Orange, R. P., and Austen, K. F., Immunologic release of histamine and slow reacting substance of anaphylaxis from human lung. IV. Enhancement by cholinergic and alpha adrenergic stimulation, *J. Exp. Med.,* 136, 556, 1972.
155. Kaliner, M. and Austen, K. F., Cyclic AMP, ATP, and reversed anaphylactic histamine release from rat mast cells, *J. Immunol.,* 112, 664, 1974.
156. Wilhelm, D. L., Chemical mediators, in *The Inflammatory Process,* Vol. 2, 2nd ed., Zweifach, B. W., Grant, L., and McCluskey, R. T., Eds., Academic Press, Orlando, Fla., 1973, 251.
157. Granger, D. N., Richardson, P. D. I., Kvietys, P. R., and Mortillaro, N. A., Intestinal blood flow, *Gastroenterology,* 78, 837, 1980.
158. Sparrow, E. M. and Wilhelm, D. L., Species differences in susceptibility to capillary permeability factors: histamine, 5-hydroxytryptamine, and compound 48/80, *J. Physiol.,* 137, 51, 1957.
159. Biber, B., Lundgren, O., and Svanvik, J., Studies on the intestinal vasodilation observed after mechanical stimulation of the mucosa of the gut, *Acta Physiol. Scand.,* 82, 177, 1971.
160. Page, I. H., Cardiovascular actions of serotonin (5-hydroxytryptamine), in *5-Hydroxytryptamine,* Lewis, G. P., Ed., Pergamon Press, London, 1957, 93.
161. Haddy, F. J., Gordon, P., and Emanuel, D. A., The influence of tone upon the responses of small and large vessels to serotonin, *Circ. Res.,* 7, 123, 1959.
162. McCubbin, J. W., Kaneko, Y., and Page, I. H., Inhibition of neurogenic vasoconstriction by serotonin, *Circ. Res.,* 11, 74, 1962.

163. Davies, B. N. and Withrington, P. G., The actions of drugs on the smooth muscle of the capsule and blood vessels of the spleen, *Pharmacol. Rev.*, 25, 373, 1973.
164. Ahlman, H., Dahlstrom, A., Kewenter, J., and Lundberg, J., Vagal influence on serotonin concentration in enterochromaffin cells in the cat, *Acta Physiol. Scand.*, 97, 362, 1976.
165. Westerfeld, W. W. and Schulman, M. P., Some biochemical aspects of the alcohol problem, *Q. J. Stud. Alcohol,* 20, 439, 1959.
166. Pas, E., Movat, H. Z., and Wasi, S., An aminopeptidase of human neutrophil leukocytes — its possible role in enhanced vascular permeability, *Agents Action,* 8, 91, 1978.
167. Maling, H. M., Webster, M. E., Williams, M. A., Saul, W., and Anderson, W., Jr., Inflammation induced by histamine, serotonin, bradykinin and compound 48/80 in the rat: antagonists and mechanisms of action, *J. Pharmacol. Exp. Ther.*, 191, 300, 1974.
168. Movat, H. Z., Kinins and the kinin cascade system as inflammatory mediators, in *Chemical Messengers of the Inflammatory Process, (Handbook of Inflammation,* Vol. 1.,) Houck, J. C., Ed., Elsevier/North-Holland, Amsterdam, 1979, 47.
169. Rocha e Silva, M., On the participation of polypeptides and biogenic amines in the acute inflammatory reactions, in *Endocrine Aspects of Disease Processes,* Jasmin, D., Ed., Warren H. Green, St. Louis, Mo., 1968, 74.
170. Nelson, N. A., Kelly, R. C., and Johnson, R. A., Prostaglandins and the arachidonic acid cascade, *Chem. Eng. News,* 60, 30, 1982.
171. Robert, A., Prostaglandins: effects on the gastrointestinal tract, *Clin. Physiol. Biochem.*, 2, 61, 1984.
172. Pennington, S. N., Biochemical interactions of ethanol with the arachidonic acid cascade, in *Recent Developments in Alcoholism,* Vol. 3., Calanter, M., Ed., Plenum Press, New York, 1985, 123.
173. Tepperman, B. L. and Jacobson, E. D., Mesenteric circulation, in *Physiology of the Gastrointestinal Tract,* Vol. 2, Johnson, L. R., Ed., Raven Press, New York, 1981, 1317.
174. Ferreira, S. H., Prostaglandins, in *Chemical Messengers of the Inflammatory Process, (Handbook of Inflammation,* Vol. 1,) Houck, J. C., Ed., Elsevier/North-Holland, Amsterdam, 1979, 113.
175. Manku, M. S. and Horrobin, D. F., Indomethacin inhibits responses to all vasoconstrictors in the rat mesenteric vascular bed: restoration of responses by prostaglandin E2, *Prostaglandins,* 12, 369, 1976.
176. Blumberg, A. L., Denny, S. E., Marshall, G. R., and Needleman, P., Blood vessel-hormone interactions: angiotensin, bradykinin, and prostaglandins, *Am. J. Physiol.*, 232, H305, 1977a.
177. Blumberg, A. L., Nishikawa, K., Denny, S. E., Marshall, G. R., and Needleman, P., Angiotensin (A I, A II, A III) receptor characterization. Correlation of prostaglandin release with peptide degradation, *Circ. Res.*, 41, 154, 1977b.
178. Crunkhorn, P. and Willis, A. L., Cutaneous reactions to intradermal prostaglandins, *Br. J. Pharmacol.*, 41, 49, 1971.
179. Williams, T. J. and Morley, J., Prostaglandins as potentiators of increased vascular permeability in inflammation, *Nature,* 246, 215, 1973.
180. O'Brien, P. E. and Carter, D. C., Effect of gastric secretory inhibitors on the gastric mucosal barrier, *Gut,* 16, 437, 1975.
181. Greenough, W. B., III, Pierce, N. F., Al Awqati, Q., and Carpenter, C. C. J., Stimulation of gut electrolyte secretion by prostaglandins, theophylline, and cholera exotoxin, *J. Clin. Invest.*, 48, 32a, 1969.
182. Pierce, N. F., Carpenter, C. C. J., Elliott, H. L., and Greenough, W. B., III, Effects of prostaglandins, theophylline and cholera exotoxin upon transmucosal water and electrolyte movement in the canine jejunum, *Gastroenterology,* 60, 22, 1971.
183. Kimberg, D. V., Field, M., Gershon, E., and Henderson, A., Effects of prostaglandins and cholera enterotoxin on intestinal mucosal cyclic AMP accumulation. Evidence against an essential role for prostaglandins in the action of toxin, *J. Clin. Invest.*, 53, 941, 1974.
184. Matuchansky, C. and Bernier, J. J., Effect of prostaglandin E_1 on glucose, water, and electrolyte absorption in the human jejunum, *Gastroenterology,* 64, 1111, 1973.
185. Robert, A., Prostaglandins and the gastrointestinal tract, in *Physiology of the Gastrointestinal Tract,* Vol. 2, Johnson, L. R., Ed., Raven Press, New York, 1981, 1407.
186. Robert, A., Nezamis, J. E., Lancaster, C., Davis, J. P., Field, S. O., and Hanchar, A. J., Mild irritants prevent gastric necrosis through "adaptive cytoprotection" mediated by prostaglandins, *Am. J. Physiol.*, 245, G113, 1983.
187. Morris, G. P., Are prostaglandins truly "cytoprotective"?, *J. Clin. Gastroenterol.*, 8, 326, 1986.
188. Malo, C. and Morin, C., personal communication.
189. Morris, G. P., personal communication.

Chapter 7

RADIATION INJURY AND THE SPLANCHNIC CIRCULATION

Lorris G. Cockerham and Robert N. Hawkins

TABLE OF CONTENTS

I. INTRODUCTION

Acute radiation sickness, which is characterized by variable degrees of weakness, exhaustion, lassitude, anorexia, nausea, and vomiting, has been defined for some time.[1] In man, the dose-survival curve of the acute radiation syndrome displays three distinct plateaus.[2] Death in the plateau regions of the curve is ascribed to hematopoietic depression, GI dysfunction, or failure of the CNS in the low-, mid-, and high-dose ranges. respectively.[2,3]

Radiation levels leading to GI dysfunction (10 to 120 Gy whole body) result in a survival time of 3 to 5 days, varying with the species.[3,4] These levels of exposure result in pathologic manifestations which are largely confined to the GI tract and this condition is referred to as the "gastrointestinal syndrome".[5]

However, limiting the definition of the acute radiation syndrome to these three plateaus or subsyndromes leads to a disregard of changes in the cardiovascular system at doses between 30 and 50 Gy, because this radiation level falls within that range which produces the GI syndrome.[6] Denudation of the intestinal mucosal epithelium is a well-known histopathologic sign of radiation exposure within the dose range associated with the GI syndrome. However, the responses of the intestinal microcirculation to radiation have received little attention, in spite of the fact that this may be an important factor in the development of the GI radiation syndrome.[7-10] Indeed, radiation effects on the GI microcirculation are significant complications in the radiation treatment of abdominal and pelvic malignancies.[11-13]

II. DOSIMETRY AND EXPOSURE

Before discussing the effects of ionizing radiation, some of the many factors that influence the toxicity of radiation should be reviewed.[14] One of the major factors related to the exposure is the dose or total amount of radiation received. The absorbed dose of radiation is the quotient dE/dm where dE is the differential energy deposited into a differential mass, dm. The unit of absorbed dose in the cgs system is the rad and 1 rad = 100 erg/g. In 1980 the International Commission on Radiological Units and Measurement (ICRU) introduced the Système International or SI units to express radiation dose.[3] The Gray (Gy), the SI unit for absorbed dose, corresponds to an energy absorption of 1 J/kg or 100 rad. This concept of energy absorption is useful for determining absorbed doses of X-rays and gamma rays. However, determination of the absorbed dose in tissues exposed to fast neutron radiation involves more elaborate calculations which are beyond the scope of this discussion. Suffice it to say that the absorbed dose of neutron radiation depends on the transfer of energy from neutrons to directly ionizing particles in the tissue and must be described by the kinetic energy released in the material. For general use, a quantity different from the rad or Gray has been introduced, i.e., the dose equivalent, which allows for the relative effectiveness of a particular type of radiation. Gamma rays and X-rays are regarded as the standard and a quality factor of 1 is multiplied times the dose to compute the dose equivalent. Therefore, the dose equivalent (Sieverts) for X-rays and gamma rays is equal to the dose (Grays). However, neutrons are thought to be roughly ten times more effective than X-rays in producing tissue damage and therefore are assigned a quality factor of 10. For this discussion, the absorbed dose of radiation, expressed as Grays, will be used. Another factor influencing the toxicity of radiation is the dose rate ($\dot{D} = dD/dt$, the differential dose with respect to time, or where there is no variability in dose [dE/dm], $\dot{D} = D/t$). When reviewing experiments in radiation biology, these variables, i.e., total dose, dose rate, type of radiation, and variability of the animal model, must be considered.

III. POSTRADIATION BLOOD FLOW

Studies which have addressed the effects of radiation on the splanchnic circulation are summarized in Tables 1 through 4. A review of the literature reveals much information concerning the effects of radiation on blood flow to the small intestine. On the other hand, there is less information concerning postradiation blood flow to the large intestine, liver, and spleen, and still less concerning the effects of radiation on pancreatic and stomach blood flow.

This discussion will present data according to the postradiation time of observed response of the splanchnic circulation, blood flow in individual organs, the species studied, and the type and amount of radiation exposure.

A. Immediate Changes

Utilizing the hydrogen clearance technique, Cockerham et al.[15] measured blood flow in the canine small intestine (ileum) after exposure to 90-Gy whole-body gamma radiation. Data obtained from 12 radiated beagles indicated an increase in intestinal blood flow by 10 min postradiation which lasted for at least 90 min. This study also reported a decreased mean systemic arterial blood pressure, an increased hematocrit, and significant histopathological lesions in the mucosal crypt cells of the radiated animals.

Two later studies demonstrated a 100% increase in intestinal (ileum) blood flow within 10 min postradiation with 100-Gy whole-body gamma radiation of beagles.[16,17] By 60 min postradiation, the blood flow had decreased to 24% above the control level. The apogee of the postradiation blood flow curve shortly followed the apex of the postradiation plasma histamine concentration. The latter of these two reports also demonstrated the successful blocking by antihistamines of the radiation-induced increase in intestinal blood flow. These data implicate histamine in the immediate postradiation changes in intestinal blood flow, and are compatible with the theory that a chemical mediator released immediately after radiation influences intestinal blood flow.

An earlier study[10] utilized a washout technique to estimate blood flow in the small intestine of rats exposed to both 5- and 10-Gy total-body gamma radiation. Volumetric blood-flow rate in intestinal vessels was determined using the clearance of ^{133}Xe. These data failed to demonstrate reliable changes in blood flow after radiation with 5 Gy; however, after exposure of 10 Gy, intestinal blood flow diminished in the first 2 hr but increased significantly by 6 hr postradiation. Analysis of data which characterized the functional state of the intestinal mucosa, e.g., absorption of glucose, albumin, etc. showed that there was postradiation impairment of correlation between the hemodynamic and absorption processes. In other words, the authors contend that the absorption changes in radiated animals are related to the functional state of the epithelium and functional impairment of the digestive and transport systems, and not necessarily due to the postradiation hemodynamic disorders.

Other studies, however, support the observation of an increased blood flow to the small intestine during the immediate postradiation period. In rats examined 4 hr after 15-Gy whole-body X-radiation, Janossy[19] found a significant increase in the fraction of blood flow going to the small intestine and an intense vasodilation in the small intestinal vascular system without affecting the coronaries in any significant degree. In support of the chemical mediator theory, Janossy speculated that vasodilator substances (e.g., bradykinin and/or histamine) induce general vasodilation which may assert itself primarily in the small intestine (or else their release is particularly intensive in the region), because the observed decrease in the vascular resistance in the small intestine was greater than the decrease in total peripheral resistance.

Table 1
SUMMARY OF REPORTS ON THE EFFECTS OF RADIATION ON BLOOD FLOW IN THE SMALL INTESTINE

Species	Radiation conditions: Type	Radiation conditions: Dose (Gy)	Time postexposure	Blood flow cf. control	Ref.
Dog	Gamma	90	10—90 min	Increased	15
	Gamma	100	10—60 min	Increased	16
	Gamma	100	10—60 min	Increased	17
	Gamma	20	12 days	Decreased	18
Rat	X-ray	14.6	72 hr	Decreased (suggested)	8
	X-ray	15	4 hr	Increased	19
			24 hr	Same	
			48 hr	Decreased	
			72 hr	Decreased	
	X-ray	15	72 hr	Decreased	20
Dog	Gamma-neutron	15	72 hr	Decreased	21
Rat	Gamma	10	72 hr	Decreased	22
	Gamma	5	1 hr	Same	10
			2 hr	Same	
			3 hr	Increased	
			6 hr	Decreased	
			24 hr	Increased	
	Gamma	10	1 hr	Decreased	10
			2 hr	Decreased	
			3 hr	Decreased	
			6 hr	Increased	
			24 hr	Decreased	
	Gamma	9	2 hr	Decreased	23
			4 hr	Same	
			6 hr	Increased	
			1 day	Same	
			2 days	Decreased	
			3 days	Decreased	
	Gamma	10	2 hr	Decreased	23
			4 hr	Same	
			6 hr	Increased	
			1 day	Same	
			2 days	Decreased	
			3 days	Decreased	
Rat (jejunum)	X-ray	28.71 (Fractionated @ 1.91 Gy/day)	Immed.	Same	24
			6 months	Decreased	
		5.74 (single)	6 months	Same	
Rat (ileum)	X-ray	28.7 (Fractionated @ 1.9 Gy/day)	Immed.	Decreased	24
			6 months	Increased	
		5.74 (single)	6 months	Same	
Rat (jejunum)	X-ray	28.7 (Fractionated @ 1.9 Gy/day)	12 months	Decreased	25
		5.3 (single)	12 months	Decreased	

Table 1 (continued)
SUMMARY OF REPORTS ON THE EFFECTS OF RADIATION ON BLOOD FLOW IN THE SMALL INTESTINE

Species	Radiation conditions: Type	Radiation conditions: Dose (Gy)	Time postexposure	Blood flow cf. control	Ref.
Rat (ileum)	X-ray	28.7 (Fractionated @ 1.9 Gy/day)	12 months	Decreased	25
		5.3 (single)	12 months	Decreased	
Rat	X-ray	30	5—75 hr (increments of 5 hr)	Increased	26

Table 2
SUMMARY OF REPORTS ON THE EFFECTS OF RADIATION ON BLOOD FLOW IN THE LARGE INTESTINE IN RATS

Radiation conditions (X-ray dose in Gy)	Time postexposure	Blood flow cf. control	Ref.
15	4 hr	Increased	19
	24 hr	Increased	
	48 hr	Increased	
	72 hr	Decreased	
15	72 hr	Decreased	20
28.71	Immed.	Increased	24
(Fractionated @ 1.91 Gy/day)	6 months	Increased	
5.74 (single)	6 months	Increased	24
28.7 (fractionated @ 1.9 Gy/day)	12 months	Decreased	25
5.3 (single)	12 months	Decreased	25

In a study of the postradiation blood flow in the small intestine, Suskevic and Uklonskaya[23] exposed rats to whole-body gamma radiation of either 9 or 10 Gy. Blood flow was measured utilizing the ^{133}Xe clearance technique. In the first hours after radiation, sharp fluctuations in blood flow were observed. An initial decrease was followed by a pronounced increase at 6 hr postradiation. This increase in blood flow was replaced at first by a smooth decrease, and then by a sharp decrease in the period from the end of the second to the end of the third day.

Blood flow to the small intestine during the immediate postradiation (<4 hr) period has been observed to increase, decrease, or remain unchanged. The preponderance of evidence, however, suggests an increase in flow to the small intestine during this time. The mechanisms of any radiation-induced change in flow remain to be established, although chemical mediation remains an attractive hypothesis.

Table 3
SUMMARY OF REPORTS ON THE EFFECTS OF RADIATION ON BLOOD FLOW IN THE SPLEEN IN RATS

Radiation conditions (X-ray dose in Gy)	Time postexposure	Blood flow cf. control	Ref.
15	72 hr	Decreased	20
28.71 (fractionated @ 1.91 Gy/day)	Immed. 6 months	Increased Increased	24
5.74 (single)	6 months	Increased	24
28.7 (fractionated @ 1.9 Gy/day)	12 months	Decreased	25
5.3 (single)	12 months	Same	25
30	5—20 hr 25—50 hr 55 hr 60—80 hr	Increased Decreased Increased Decreased	26

Table 4
SUMMARY OF REPORTS ON THE EFFECTS OF RADIATION ON BLOOD FLOW IN THE LIVER

Species	Radiation conditions: Type	Radiation conditions: Dose (Gy)	Time after postexposure	Blood flow cf. control	Ref.
Rat	X-ray	15	72 hr	(Increased % of cardiac output)	20
	X-ray	28.71 (fractionated @ 1.91 Gy/day)	Immed. 6 months	Same Same	24
	X-ray	5.74 (single)	6 months	Increased	24
	X-ray	28.7 (fractionated @ 1.9 Gy/day)	12 months	Increased	25
	X-ray	5.3 (single)	12 months	Same	25
	X-ray	30	5—75 hr	Increased	26
Mouse	X-ray	5—20	0.5—75 hr	Decreased	27
Rat	X-ray	15, 30	7—45 days	Decreased	27
Mouse	Beta/gamma	230, 310	0—7 days	Decreased	27
Rat	Alpha/gamma	5.4	2—23 days	Mod. decreased	27
Dog	Beta/gamma	570, 650	4 months	Decreased	27
Rat	X-ray	15, 30	9 months	Decreased	27
	Beta/gamma	15, 150	6 months	Decreased	27
Rabbit	Beta	16, 23	3.5, 9 months	Decreased	27
Mouse	Beta	75—375	3.5, 9 months	Decreased	27
	X-ray	11, 15	12 months	Same	27

B. Intermediate Changes

Radiolabeled microspheres have been utilized to estimate splanchnic blood flow during the more extended postradiation period (<72 hr). With this technique, Kabal et al.[21] subjected male beagles to 15-Gy whole-body, pulsed gamma-neutron radiation and then measured the distribution of intestinal (duodenum, jejunum, and ileum) capillary blood flow 72 hr postradiation using radioactive microspheres. The results showed that the intestinal capillary blood flow (as percent of cardiac output) of the radiated dogs was higher than that of the nonradiated dogs. The decreased weight of the mucosal layer, together with an unchanged capillary blood flow, indicated an increased capillary blood flow per unit weight in the remaining mucosa. Furthermore, the corresponding regional distribution of the mucosal capillary blood flow did not show any significant alteration.

Rats exposed to 30-Gy whole-body X-radiation were injected with labeled microspheres at various postexposure times to monitor changes in relative blood flow in various organs.[26] For the period of observation (0 to 75 hr), blood flow to the small intestine and liver increased above control levels. The increase in blood flow to the spleen in the first 20 hr postradiation was replaced by fluctuating levels at or just below control levels for the remainder of the observations.

Kudrjavcev and Suskevic[22] reported a marked decrease in blood supply to the small intestine of rats 72 hr after exposure to 10-Gy gamma-radiation. They suggested that this disturbed blood supply not only intensifies radiogenic destruction of the mucosal epithelium but also prevents, to a certain extent, the regeneration of the epithelial cells.

The early postradiation increase in blood flow reported by Janossy[19] had returned to control levels by 24 hr postradiation, and flow then displayed decreased levels at 48 and 72 hr postradiation. The blood flow in the large intestine, however, remained at an elevated level from 4 through 48 hr postradiation. It was not until 72 hr postradiation that the large intestine showed a decrease in blood flow below control levels.

In a second study Janossy[20] demonstrated that the cardiac output of rats exposed to whole-body X-radiation of 15 Gy had decreased 74% below that of control animals by 72 hr postradiation. The fractions of the cardiac output distributed to the small intestine and spleen were considerably reduced, while that to the large intestine showed no significant change, and the hepatic fraction showed a significant increase as compared to the controls.

Evidence has been furnished which suggests that the postradiation changes in intestinal blood flow during the 48- to 72-hour time period may result from altered intestinal vasoactivity. Kabal et al.[9] utilized an *in situ* jejunal loop preparation from beagles exposed to 1500 rad mixed neutron-gamma radiation to evaluate vasoactivity. Statistically, intestinal blood flow remained unchanged at 48 hr postradiation but, by 72 hr postradiation, intestinal flow had decreased. When compared to nonradiated controls, radiated intestines demonstrated an exaggerated vasoconstrictor response to infused norepinephrine. Moreover, the intestines of the radiated animals did not exhibit autoregulatory escape during norepinephrine infusion. These data support earlier observations of exaggerated responses of terminal arterioles and precapillaries in animals after whole-body radiation.[28]

More recent studies utilizing a rat model exposed to 20-Gy X-radiation have yielded different results. The experiments, carried out 1 to 3 days postradiation, suggested that the response of mesenteric blood flow to noradrenaline is enhanced.[29] Moreover, in contrast to the work of Kabal et al.,[9] an autoregulatory escape in the radiated intestine was observed in the latter studies. The autoregulatory escape occurred at even higher doses after radiation than in control animals, which indicated a possible involvement of alpha receptors. In addition, other biogenic amines were investigated, but the evidence supports the conclusion that the changes in response after radiation resulted from a greater reactivity to norepinephrine. Similar studies were performed in the same laboratory to investigate the involvement of the alpha receptors. In subsequent experiments, rats were exposed to only 8 Gy. Pressure and intestinal flow responses were again determined in response to infused biogenic amines (norepinephrine, dopamine, and serotonin), both with and without prior treatment with the alpha blocker, phenoxybenzamine. Similar but less severe changes in the response of pressure and intestinal flow to the infusion of the amines were observed when compared to the previous study. In addition, treatment with phenoxybenzamine indicated that a reduced activity of alpha receptors was responsible for the postradiation alteration in flow response.[30]

Blood flow to the small intestine, in general, seemed to remain above control levels for up to 72 hr postradiation, although some investigators[19] did find a decrease at approximately 24 hr. However, by 72 hr postradiation most investigators reported a decrease in blood flow to the small intestine. In contrast, blood flow to the large intestine and liver remained elevated through the 72-hr postradiation period. Blood flow to the spleen was above the control levels until 20 hr postradiation and then began fluctuating around control levels for the remainder of the observation period.

C. Late Changes

Eddy and Casarett[8] exposed either the exteriorized intestine or the whole body of rats to 14.6-Gy X-rays. Rats with intestinal radiation survived only long enough to permit daily sacrifice for angiographic examination for 5 days following exposure. Those receiving whole-body exposure survived long enough to allow angiographic examination of some at 3 days and histopathology of the remainder at 4 days. Although an actual measurement of blood flow was not attempted, the microangiographic examinations suggested that radiation may have caused a moderate to marked reduction in mucosal blood flow. Histopathological examination of radiated intestine revealed occlusive endothelial changes, especially in the submucosal arterioles.

Using radioactive microspheres to measure blood flow, Delgado et al.[18] reported an increased blood flow in the radiated segment of small intestine 12 days postradiation with 20 Gy. There was also an increase in blood flow in adjoining, nonradiated segments of the same intestines. Unfortunately, the investigators did not report the source of radiation for comparison purposes.

Volenec et al.[24] studied the microcirculations of rat small intestine, colon, spleen, and liver using the ^{86}Rb uptake technique following X-radiation of just the abdomen with either a fractionated (1.91 Gy/day) exposure of 28.71 Gy or a single exposure of 5.74 Gy. Blood-flow determination was completed immediately after the last fractionated exposure or 6 months later. This procedure was also used in the single-dose group. Blood flow in the jejunum was no different from control immediately after exposure for the fractionated group, but at 6 months it decreased. Blood flow in the single-dose group was not significantly different from control at 6 months. Conversely, blood-flow values for the ileum showed a decrease immediately after fractionated radiation and an increase 6 months later, while the single exposure did not change ileal blood flow after 6 months. Blood flows in the large intestine and spleen were increased for both methods of radiation with each of the determinations. Fractionated radiation did not seem to change blood flow to the liver, but the single dose resulted in an increased blood flow 6 months later.

In a later study, Volenec et al.[25] repeated the previous exposure schedule, but blood-flow observations were made after 12 months. In both the fractionated dose and the single-dose groups, blood flow in the small and large intestine decreased below control levels. Blood flow in the spleen decreased with the fractionated dose but remained the same with the single dose. Although the hepatic blood flow remained the same with the single dose, it increased with the fractionated dose.

Extended observations of postradiation blood flow to the small intestine showed a continued decrease at 6 and 12 months. However, both the jejunum and ileum exhibited control blood flows when exposed to only a single dose of 5.74-Gy X-radiation.[24] The large intestine continued to show an increased blood flow through the 6th month but began a decline to below control levels by the 12th month postradiation. Blood flow to the spleen behaved in a like manner, except that 12 months after a single exposure to 5.3-Gy X-radiation, flows in radiated and nonradiated spleens were similar. In general, hepatic blood flow and liver function were decreased after the first few days and up to 9 months postradiation. However, three studies showed blood flow at control levels at 6 and 12 months[24,25,27] and two showed increased flow at 6 and 12 months postradiation.[24,25]

Review of published reports on the effects of ionizing radiation on splanchnic circulation yields what at first appears to be often inconsistent and highly variable, if not conflicting, information. Some of the confusion may be cleared up if the factors influencing the toxicity of an agent are considered. As seen in this review, variations exist in species, organs, source of radiation, method of exposure (fractionated or single), technique of blood-flow measurement, and time of measurement after radiation. With these variables it becomes difficult, if not impossible, to make a single, all-inclusive statement concerning the effects of ionizing radiation on the splanchnic circulation.

IV. MICROCIRCULATION

Studies concerning the effects of radiation on the microcirculation consist of morphological observations and estimates of permeability changes. The permeability changes in whole-body radiated animals have been studied mainly by measuring the disappearance from the circulation of tracer molecules. Few data exist which delineate postradiation capillary dynamics.

Histological sections of dog small intestine, 72 hr postexposure to 15-Gy mixed neutron-gamma, indicate that the villous capillary network still appears to be intact and continuous despite mucosal cell destruction.[21] Eddy and Casarett[8] used a microradiographic examination of radiated intestine to reveal occlusive endothelial changes, especially in the submucosal arterioles in rats 4 days after exposure to 14.6-Gy X-radiation. Utilizing a smilar technique, clinical evidence of microvascular changes in humans with radiation bowel disease has been furnished by Carr et al.[7] Data from these studies indicated alterations in the mucosal vasculature in patients 1 to 28 months after radiotherapy.

Movement of Evans Blue out of the circulatory system in rabbits exposed to 1-Gy X-radiation was studied by Dunjic,[31] who demonstrated an increased permeability between 2 and 17 days postradiation. In addition to their observations on flow, Suskevic and Uklonskaya[23] estimated permeability changes in rats exposed to whole-body gamma-radiation of either 9 or 10 Gy. Permeability was estimated by tissue uptake of Evans Blue. Estimates of permeability at 3 days postradiation, as determined by the yield of protein-bound dye in the tissue, indicated that permeability had increased 3.5- to 4.0-fold.

Alterations in the microvasculature of the cat intestine were observed by Eriksson[32] 4 days to 4 months postradiation. The exteriorized cat intestine was exposed to doses of X-ray ranging from 15 to 30 Gy. After up to 15 Gy, the vascular pattern was found to be normal, but with 30 Gy decreased vascularity was observed in all layers of the bowel, including variations in luminal width and obstruction of vessels which occurred more frequently at the higher doses. Subsequent evidence has been furnished[33] which indicates that vascular changes may be responsible for decreased capillary filtration coefficient (CFC) which has been observed after radiation.[34] CFC has been measured in isolated small intestine of cats in separate groups exposed to 15-, 20-, and 25-Gy X-radiation. All three groups showed significant decreases in CFC at 4 days postradiation. These changes were dose related and could not be explained solely on the basis of loss of mucosal integrity. Although there was partial recovery after 4 months in the group exposed to 15 Gy, the groups exposed to 20 and 25 Gy exhibited a secondary decrease in CFC after 4 months.[34] Later experiments utilizing morphological procedures provided evidence of ultrastructural changes which correlated with changes in CFC.[33] These studies suggest that the early decrease in CFC results from endothelial damage, whereas the secondary decrease in CFC experienced by the groups exposed to 20 and 25 Gy may result from pericapillary fibrosis.

V. ISCHEMIA AND RADIOPROTECTION

As early as 1909, decreasing tissue oxygen tension during radiation was known as an effective mechanism for decreasing the sensitivity of tissue to ionizing radiation damage.[35,36] The radioprotective effect of tissue ischemia has been investigated utilizing several techniques to achieve ischemia, including arterial clamping,[37] interarterial infusion of vasopressin,[38] and arterial embolization with enzymatically degradable starch microspheres (DSM).[39-41] Lote and Myking[42] have furnished evidence that the utilization of starch microspheres induces severe temporary small intestinal ischemia without detectable late adverse effects. They have also studied the effects of radiation on mesenteric blood flow and vascular integrity in DSM-protected cats. Average mesenteric flow decreased from a control value of 109 mℓ/min to 0 during DSM administration and radiation (7-Gy X-radiation, abdominal). By 25 min postradiation, average mesenteric flow was 135 mℓ/min and returned to an average of 108 mℓ/min by 45 min postradiation. Moreover, the vascular response to intra-arterial infusion of vasopressin and isoproterenol indicated no change in vascular activity.[39]

The therapeutic benefit of radioprotection of healthy tissue during radiotherapy is obvious, and hypoxic radioprotection continued to receive considerable attention from the radiation research community.

The phenomenon of ischemic radioprotection may provide insight into the mechanism of radiation-induced vascular changes in the splanchnic circulation. The superoxide radical (O^{2-}) has long been of interest to radiation chemists.[43] Recognized as being an important radical species produced when living tissue is radiated, superoxide radicals have recently received a great deal of attention from investigators in the biological sciences.[44] A significant amount of circumstantial evidence has been gathered which implicates O^{2-} in the increased capillary permeability[45] and mucosal lesions[46] resulting from extended ($\geqslant$60 min) regional intestinal ischemia.

The association between radiation-induced superoxide production, vascular reactivity, and changes in permeability may be fortuitous. On the other hand, superoxide production may be intimately related to the established phenomenon of oxygen as a radiosensitizer. Between these boundaries, superoxide production may, in part, be responsible for many of the splanchnic circulatory responses to ionizing radiation. The relationship between radiation-induced superoxide production and radiation-induced changes in the splanchnic circulation deserves further investigation.

REFERENCES

1. Jenkinson, E. L. and Brown, W. H., Irradiation sickness, *Am. J. Roentgenol. Radium Ther. Nucl. Med.*, 51, 496, 1944.
2. Allen, R. G., Brown, F. A., Logie, L. C., Rovner, D. R., Wilson, S. G., Jr., and Zellmer, R. W., Acute effects of gamma radiation in primates, *Radiat. Res.*, 12, 532, 1960.
3. Hall, E. J., *Radiation and Life,* 2nd ed., Pergamon Press, Elmsford, N.Y., 1984, chap. 2, 3.
4. Zsebok, Z. and Petranyi, G., Changes in electrolyte balance in the gastro-intestinal syndrome, *Acta Radiol.*, 2, 377, 1964.
5. Handford, S. W., The acute radiation syndrome in dogs after total-body exposure to a supralethal dose of ionizing radiation, *Radiat. Res.*, 13, 712, 1960.
6. Kundel, H. L., The effect of gamma irradiation on the cardiovascular system of the rhesus monkey, *Radiat. Res.*, 27, 406, 1966.
7. Carr, N. D., Pullen, B. R., Hasleton, P. S., and Schofield, P. F., Microvascular studies in human radiation bowel disease, *Gut,* 25, 448, 1984.
8. Eddy, H. A. and Casarett, G. W., Intestinal vascular changes in the acute radiation intestinal syndrome, in *Gastrointestinal Radiation Injury,* Sullivan, M. F., Ed., Excerpta Medica, New York, 1968, 385.
9. Kabal, J., Baum, S. J., and Parkhurst, L. J., Canine intestinal vasoactivity during the development of the gastrointestinal radiation syndrome, *Radiat. Res.*, 50, 528, 1972.
10. Nesterenko, V. S., Piskarev, A. V., and Sushkevich, L. N., Effect of hemodynamic changes on postradiation functional state of the rat small intestine, *Radiobiologiya,* 19, 433, 1979.
11. Cornet, A., Barbier, J., Debesse, B., Elhadad, A., and Carnot, F., Lésions digestives après irradiation abdomino-pelvienne dans le traitement des cancers de l'appareil génital, *Sem. Hop.*, 52, 1965, 1973.
12. Egawa, J. and Ishioka, K., Radiation effects on the fine blood vessels in abdominal organs of mice, *Acta Radiol. Oncol. Radiat. Ther. Phys. Biol.*, 17, 414, 1978.
13. Stuart, M., Failes, D. G., Killingback, M. J., and De Luca, C., Irradiation injuries of the large intestine, *Dis. Colon Rectum,* 23, 94, 1980.
14. Doull, J., Factors influencing toxicology, in *Toxicology, the Basic Science of Poisons,* 2nd ed., Doull, J., Klaassen, C. D., and Amdur, M. O., Eds., Macmillan, New York, 1980, 70.
15. Cockerham, L. G., Doyle, T. F., Trumbo, R. B., and Nold, J. B., Acute postirradiation canine intestinal blood flow, *Intl. J. Radiat. Biol.*, 45, 65, 1984.
16. Cockerham, L. G., Doyle, T. F., Donlon, M. A., and Helgeson, E. A., Canine postradiation histamine levels and subsequent responses to Compound 48/80, *Aviat. Space Environ. Med.*, 55, 1041, 1984.
17. Cockerham, L. G., Doyle, T. F., Donlon, M. A., and Gossett-Hagerman, C. J., Antihistamines block radiation-induced intestinal blood flow in canines, *Fundam. Appl. Toxicol.*, 5, 597, 1985.
18. Delgado, G., Butterfield, A. B., Dritschilo, A., Hummel, S., Harbert, J., Petrilli, E. S., and Kot, P. A., Measure of blood flow by the multiple radioactive microsphere technique in radiated gastrointestinal tissue, *Am. J. Clin. Oncol.*, 6, 463, 1983.
19. Janossy, G., Intestinal blood flow in gastrointestinal irradiation syndrome in the rat, *Acta Med. Acad. Sci. Hung.*, 26, 13, 1969.
20. Janossy, G., Cardiac ouptut and its distribution in the terminal stage of the gastrointestinal irradiation syndrome ("radiation shock"), *Acta Med. Acad. Sci. Hung.*, 26, 23, 1969.
21. Kabal, J., Parkhurst, L. J., and Wyant, D. E., Measurement of Canine Intestinal Capillary Blood Flow in the Terminal Phase of the Gastrointestinal Radiation Syndrome, AFRRI SR73-18, U.S. Armed Forces Radiobiology Research Institute, Bethesda, Md., 1973.
22. Kudrjavcev, V. D. and Suskevic, L. N., Der Mechanismus der Zirkulationsstörungen in der Dunndarmwand und ihre Rolle bei der Entwicklung des Darmsyndroms, *Radiobiol. Radiother.*, 21, 771, 1980.
23. Suskevic, L. N. and Uklonskaya, L. I., Changes in certain functional properties of the vessels of the intestines in whole-body gamma irradiation at superlethal doses, *Radiobiologiya,* 15, 771, 1975.
24. Volenec, K., Vodicka, I., Chmelar, V., Brich, P., and Vavrova, E., Changes in regional blood flow at late intervals after single and fractionated X-ray irradiation in rats, *Sb. Ved. Pr. Lek. Fak. Karlovy Univ. Hradci Kralove,* 22, 459, 1979.
25. Volenec, K., Vodicka, I., Chmelar, V., Brich, P., and Vavrova, E., Late hemodynamic changes after a single and fractionated local irradiation of the abdomen in rats, *Sb. Ved. Pr. Lek. Fak. Karlovy Univ. Hradci Kralove, (Suppl.),* 23, 319, 1980.
26. Watters, C. and Gerber, G. B., Regional blood flow in rats exposed to supralethal doses of whole-body X-irradiation, *Radiat. Environ. Biophys.*, 12, 303, 1975.

27. Dunjic, A., Blood flow and permeability in liver, kidney and lung, *Curr. Top. Radiat. Res. Q.*, 10, 109, 1974.
28. Zweifach, B. W. and Kivy-Rosenberg, E., Microcirculatory effects of whole-body X-irradiation and radiomimetic procedures, *Am. J. Physiol.*, 208, 492, 1965.
29. Timmermans, R. and Gerber, G. B., Reaction of blood pressure and mesenteric blood flow to infusion of biogenic amines in normal and supralethally X-irradiated rats, *Radiat. Res.*, 82, 81, 1980.
30. Timmermans, R., Reaction of blood pressure and mesenteric blood flow to an infusion of biogenic amines in rats: influence of irradiation and alpha blockers, *Strahlentherapie*, 160, 513, 1984.
31. Dunkic, A., Blood flow and permeability after whole body irradiation, *Curr. Top. Radiat. Res. Q.*, 10, 170, 1974.
32. Eriksson, B., Microangiographic pattern in the small intestine of the cat after irradiation, *Scand. J. Gastroenterol.*, 17, 887, 1982.
33. Eriksson, B., Johnson, L., and Lundqvist, P. G., Ultrastructural aspects of capillary function in irradiated bowel. An experimental study in the cat, *Scand. J. Gastroenterol.*, 18, 473, 1983.
34. Eriksson, B. and Johnson, L., Capillary filtration in the small intestine after irradiation. An experimental study in the cat, *Scand. J. Gastroenterol.*, 18, 209, 1983.
35. Schwartz, G., Desensibilizierung Gegen Röntgen und Radiumstrahlen, *Muench. Med. Wochenschr.*, 56, 1217, 1909.
36. Larsson, B. and Stenson, S., Reduction of radiation damage to the intestinal mucous membrane by local hypoxia, *Nature*, 205, 364, 1965.
37. Suit, H. and Lindberg, R., Radiation therapy administered under conditions of tourniquet-induced local tissue hypoxia, *Am. J. Roentgenol.*, 102, 27, 1968.
38. Borgstrom, S., Aronsen, K. F., Dougan, P., Jacobsson, L., Lindstrom, C., and Nylander, G., A study of the radioprotective effect of vasopressin induced ischemia on the small intestine of the dog and its relation to circulatory parameters, *Br. J. Radiol.*, 55, 568, 1982.
39. Lote, K., Hypoxic radioprotection by temporary intestinal ischemia: degradable starch microsphere embolization in the cat, *Am. J. Roentgenol.*, 137, 909, 1981.
40. Forsberg, J. O. and Jung, B., Abdominal radiation response modified by hypoxia after intra-aortal injection of starch microspheres. Experiments in the rat, *Acta Radiol. Oncol. Radiat. Ther. Phys. Biol.*, 17, 353, 1978.
41. Forsberg, J. O., Jung, B., and Larsson, B., Mucosal protection during irradiation of exteriorized rat ileum. Effect of hypoxia induced by starch microspheres, *Acta Radiol. Oncol. Radiat. Ther. Phys. Biol.*, 17, 485, 1978.
42. Lote, K. and Myking, A. O., Starch Microsphere induced small intestinal ischaemia. Blood flow and morphologic investigations of late effects, *Acta Radiol. Oncol.*, 21, 353, 1982.
43. Czapski, G., Radiation chemistry of oxygenated aqueous solutions, *Annu. Rev. Phys. Chem.*, 22, 171, 1971.
44. Del Maestro, R. F., An approach to free radicals in medicine and biology, *Acta Physiol. Scand. Suppl.*, 492, 153, 1980.
45. Granger, D. N., Rutili, G., and McCord, J. M., Superoxide radicals in feline intestinal ischemia, *Gastroenterology*, 81, 22, 1981.
46. Parks, D. A., Bulkley, G. B., Granger, D. N., Hamilton, S. R., and McCord, J. M., Ischemic injury in the cat small intestine: role of superoxide radicals, *Gastroenterology*, 82, 9, 1982.

Chapter 8

INFLAMMATORY BOWEL DISEASE: ROLE OF THE INTESTINAL CIRCULATION

Ronald J. Korthuis*

TABLE OF CONTENTS

* Ronald J. Korthuis is the recipient of a New Investigator Research Award (HL-36069) from the National Heart, Lung, and Blood Institute.

I. INTRODUCTION

Inflammatory bowel diseases (IBD) constitute one of the major unsolved problems facing gastroenterologists and basic scientists interested in GI pathophysiology. Although these maladies have been the subject of intensive investigation for many years, there has been a tremendous increase in the pace of research, with well over 2000 articles concerned with various aspects of IBD published in the past 3 to 4 years alone. Nevertheless, the understanding of these diseases remains incomplete and their etiology unknown. In addition, comparatively little attention has been paid to the potential role of the intestinal circulation in the etiology and/or pathogenesis of IBD, despite the occurrence of rather remarkable vascular alterations in association with these disorders.

The objective of this review is to provide the reader with a contemporary description of the vascular alterations associated with IBD and to describe the various hypotheses which relate vascular factors to their etiology and pathogenesis. It is hoped that consideration of these observations will rekindle interest in the potential role of the circulation in IBD.

II. VASCULAR ALTERATIONS ASSOCIATED WITH IBD

A. Morphologic Alterations

By convention, the idiopathic IBD include ulcerative colitis and granulomatous enterocolitis or Crohn's disease. The vascular changes associated with these inflammatory disorders are often remarkable, but vary considerably and appear to be related to the severity of the inflammation. In active ulcerative colitis, for example, the submucosal arteries display a tortuous course and dilatation and congestion of the mucosal and submucosal microvessels is often striking (Figure 1).[1-11] Capillary proliferation also occurs, but is restricted to the granulation tissue of the mucosal ulcerations.[7] However, the vascular architecture of the muscular and serosal layers of the large bowel appears to be normal except in the severe, fulminant stages of the disease.[1,6,7,9] Studies employing microangiography, vascular casts, and mesenteric angiography have demonstrated widened arteries and a rapid venous return, suggesting that an increase in colonic blood flow occurs with active ulcerative colitis.[2-5,7,11,15] The early studies of Bacaneer[12] support this conclusion. They noted a high colonic blood flow in the majority (five of seven) of patients with ulcerative colitis examined in their studies. However, their data suggests that the increased colonic flow occurred through arteriovenous shunts rather than as nutritive flow, presumably reflecting an "instability of the vasomotor system".[11,12] Another apparently frequent vascular abnormality is vasodilation of the lymph node vasculature, including vessels of the nodal medulla, paracortex, cortex, and perinodal connective tissue.[13]

In Crohn's disease, the morphologic alterations are less uniform than described for ulcerative colitis and the vascular changes show considerable variation from patient to patient and even within the same resected specimen.[6] For example, angiographic examination of the small bowel in Crohn's disease indicates that the degree of dilation and engorgement of ileal and colonic microvessels may be as conspicuous as in active ulcerative colitis, although a reduced vascularity is also commonly reported.[2-5,7,14-16] In addition, in areas with mild alterations (deep lymphocytic infiltration but not ulcerative lesions or fissures), there is a distinct focal hypervascularity in the submucosa evidenced by numerous dilated arterial vessels which have a straight "broom-like" course (Figure 2). A different vascular pattern is present in areas characterized by more severe alterations, i.e., ulcerative lesions and fissures. There is again a marked hyper-

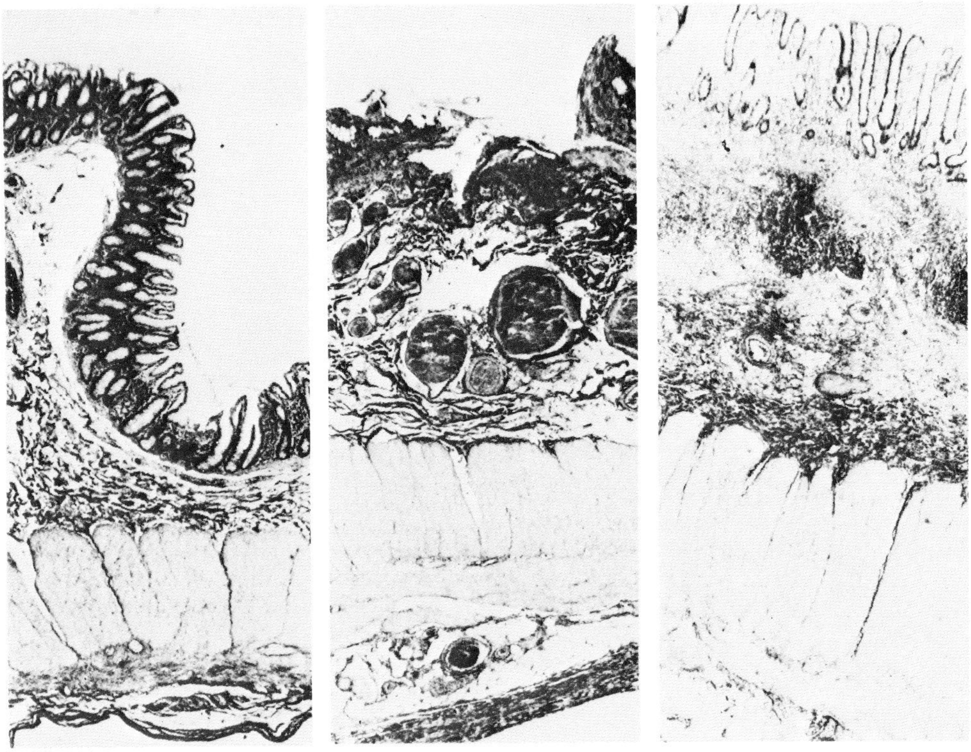

FIGURE 1. Photomicrographs from large-bowel preparations obtained from normal individuals (left) and patients with severe (center) and chronic mild (right) ulcerative colitis. Note the striking degree of vascular engorgement and dilation in severe colitis (center), and the apparently normal or focally decreased vascularity in chronic mild colitis (right). (From Hulten, L., Lindhagen, J., Lundgren, O., Fasth, S., and Ahren, C., *Gastroenterology,* 72, 388, 1977. With permission.)

vascularity, but the vessels are diffusely distributed throughout the damaged area and exhibit a tortuous, corkscrew appearance (Figure 3).[7] These vascular changes are most conspicuous in the submocosa.[1,6,7,14,17] Acute and chronic damage to vascular endothelium, including focal venular endothelial necrosis, is also prominent in the submucosal vessels of patients with Crohn's disease (Figure 4). Hemorrhage is apparent and extravasated red blood cells are present in the submucosal interstitium.[17] Obliterative arterial and venous lesions, owing to subintimal fibroelastic proliferation and medial hypertrophy, have also been reported.[7,14,17] In contrast to these changes, areas of the colon with morphologically intact intestinal walls exhibit no vascular alterations. Lymphatic vessels are markedly distended, especially in the submucosa, where the accumulation of edema fluid is most prominent. Large interendothelial gaps, which would allow free access of interstitial fluid to the lymphatic lumen, have been reported in association with Crohn's disease,[17] However, other studies have provided evidence to suggest that lymphatic intercellular junctions are closed.[18] Finally, it may be of interest to note that mucosal ulcerations associated with Crohn's disease are often localized to the dome of epithelium overlying Peyer's patches.[19] Ulceration here may allow the free access of luminal antigens to the immunorecognition site of the intestine.[20]

B. Alterations in Intestinal Blood Flow

The functional significance of these morphological alterations is largely unknown, although the results have been interpreted as suggesting an increased blood flow to the

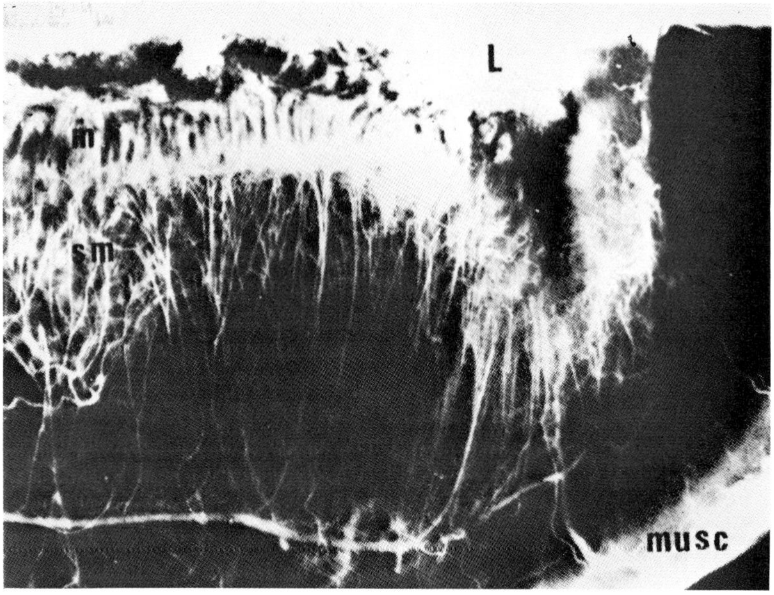

FIGURE 2. Microangiogram of the ileum obtained from a patient with Crohn's disease exhibiting mild intestinal alterations (no ulcerations or fissures). Note the focal hypervascularity in the submucosa with straight, "broom-like" arterial branches at left of angiogram. (L) lumen, (m) mucosa, (sm) submucosa, (musc) muscularis. (From Johansson, H., Krausse, U., and Olding, L., *Acta Chir. Scand.*, 138, 409, 1972. With permission.)

inflamed tissue. As outlined above, Bacaneer[12] provided the first quantitative evidence that flow was dramatically altered in different stages of ulcerative colitis. Hulten and co-workers[6] confirmed and extended these observations by employing an isotope washout technique to estimate regional intestinal blood flow and its intramural distribution in patients with ulcerative colitis and Crohn's disease. Their results indicate that in patients with IBD, blood flow in affected regions may increase two- to sixfold (Figure 5). In addition, determination of the intramural distribution of flow indicated that this increase is largely confined to the mucosa-submucosal layer. Based on these observations, Hulten and associates[6] estimated that blood flow to the inflamed colon corresponds to 25 to 30% of the resting cardiac output and suggested that these high flows may represent an important factor contributing to the physical deterioration often seen in these patients.

In contrast to the results obtained in active or exudative stages of ulcerative colitis and Crohn's disease, colonic blood flow decreases below normal in the late fibrosing stages (Figure 5).[6] A similar pattern is observed for the ileum in patients with Crohn's disease affecting this segment of the bowel. These findings correlate well with the observed reduced vascularity in this stage (Figure 6).[6,9,14]

Hulten and co-workers[6] also correlated their blood-flow measurements with the degree of vascular dilatation and engorgement and found good agreement between the alterations of blood flow and vascular morphology. In addition to these changes, a characteristic distention or clubbing of the villi occurs and, in a later phase, epithelial denudation and destruction of the villi (Figure 7).

Although the mechanisms underlying these alterations in colonic blood flow are un-

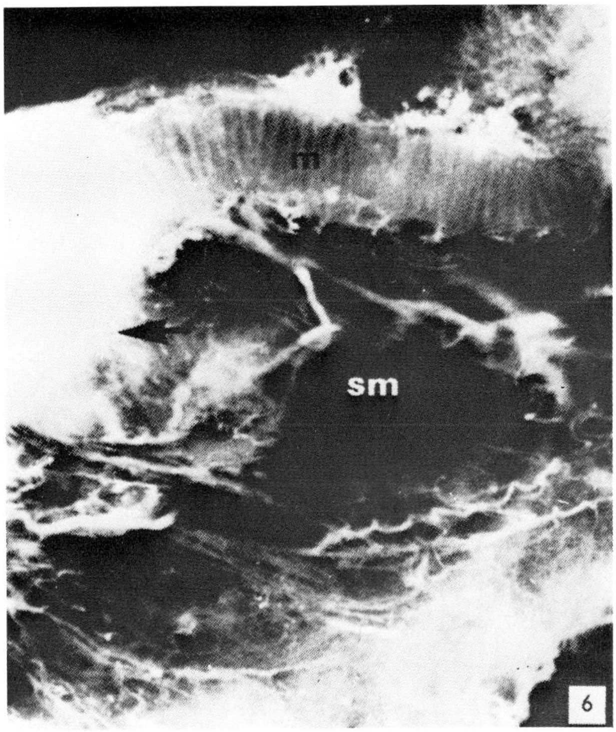

FIGURE 3. Microangiogram obtained from a patient with Crohn's disease exhibiting severe ulcerative lesions and fissures. Note the marked hypervascularity with irregular, tortuous vessels in the vicinity of the fissures located at the left of the angiogram. (sm) submucosa. (From Johansson, H., Krausse, U., and Olding, L., *Acta Chir. Scand.*, 138, 409, 1972. With permission.)

known, Zipser and co-workers[21] have proposed that arachidonic acid metabolites, derived through the cyclooxygenase pathway, may be important. They point out that the results of many studies indicate that the synthesis and release of prostaglandins and thromboxanes are elevated in experimental colitis and in patients with IBD.[22-26] In general, prostaglandins induce vasodilation and thromboxanes induce vasoconstriction. Based on these observations, they postulated that the relative release rates of these eicosanoids may vary during the course of these disorders and thus may play a role in the variable pattern of colon blood flow seen in IBD.[21]

III. FACTORS INVOLVED IN THE FORMATION OF EDEMA IN IBD

A major consequence in the pathogenesis of IBD is enhanced transvascular fluid filtration, with the subsequent accumulation of interstitial fluid (edema).[27,28] Although interstitial edema is a cardinal histopathological sign of these disorders, the mechanisms underlying the increases in interstitial fluid volume remain undefined. Under normal physiological conditions, a balance between steady-state transvascular (J_V) and lymphatic (J_L) fluid fluxes exists such that[29,30]

$$J_V = k_f\,[P_c - P_t - \sigma\,(\pi_c - \pi_t)] = J_L$$

where k_f represents the microvascular filtration coefficient (which, in turn, represents

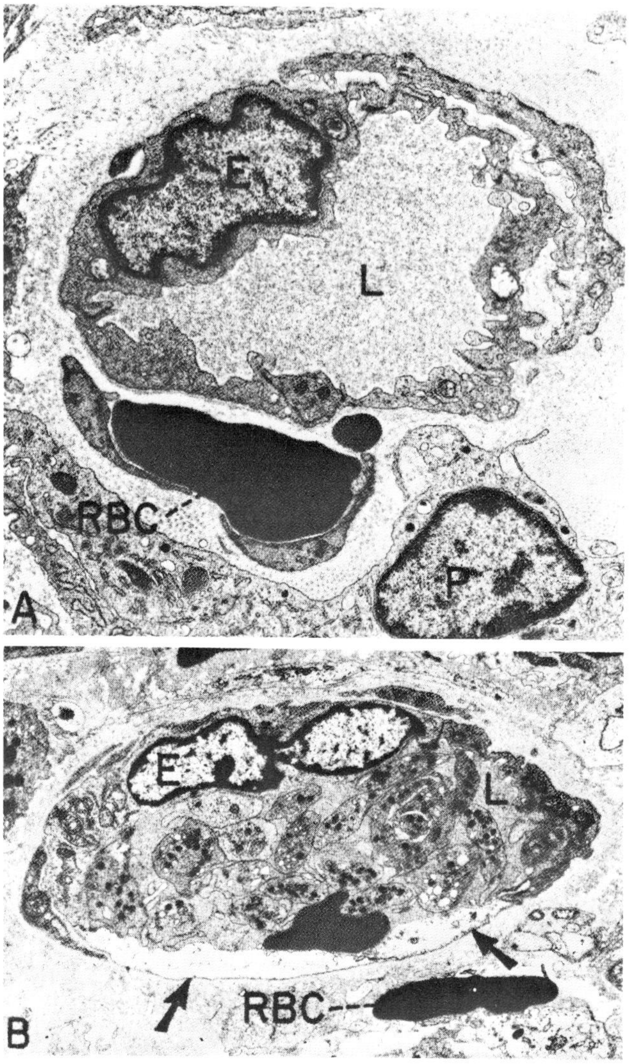

FIGURE 4. Photomicrograph of submucosal vessels obtained from a patient with Crohn's disease. Note the presence of extravasated red blood cells (RBC) and focal endothelial cell (E) necrosis. (L) lumen, (P) pericyte. (From Dvorak, A. M., Monahan, R. A., Osage, J. E., and Dickersin, G. R., *Hum. Pathol.*, 11, 606, 1980. With permission.)

a product of microvascular surface area and permeability), P_c represents microvascular hydrostatic pressure, P_t represents interstitial fluid pressure, σ represents the osmotic reflection coefficient for total plasma proteins (a measure of vascular permeability), π_c represents plasma colloid osmotic pressure and π_t represents tissue colloid osmotic pressure. From a consideration of the Starling relation, it is apparent that several pathophysiologic alterations may initiate the accumulation of excess interstitial fluid in IBD. These include (1) increased microvascular permeability and/or surface area, (2) increased microvascular hydrostatic pressure, (3) obstruction of lymphatic drainage, and (4) hypoproteinemia.

A. Vascular Permeability

It is generally believed that an increase in vascular permeability plays an important

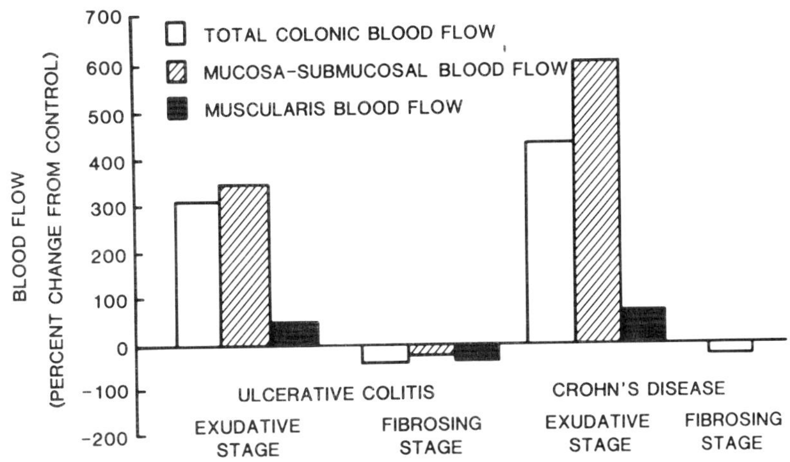

FIGURE 5. Colonic blood flow alterations in IBD. Blood flow is expressed as the percent change in blood flow in patients with IBD relative to blood flow in normal individuals. (Figure constructed using the data of Hulten, L., Lindhagen, J., Lundgren, O., Fasth, S., and Ahren, C., *Gastroenterology*, 72, 388, 1977.)

FIGURE 6. Photomicrographs of an ileal preparation obtained from patients in the early exudative (left) and late fibrosing (right) stages of Crohn's disease. Note reduced number of vessels and prominent thickening of all layers of the bowel wall in the late fibrosing stage (right). (From Hulten, L., Lindhagen, J., Lundgren, O., Fasth, S., and Ahren, D., *Gastroenterology*, 72, 388, 1977. With permission.)

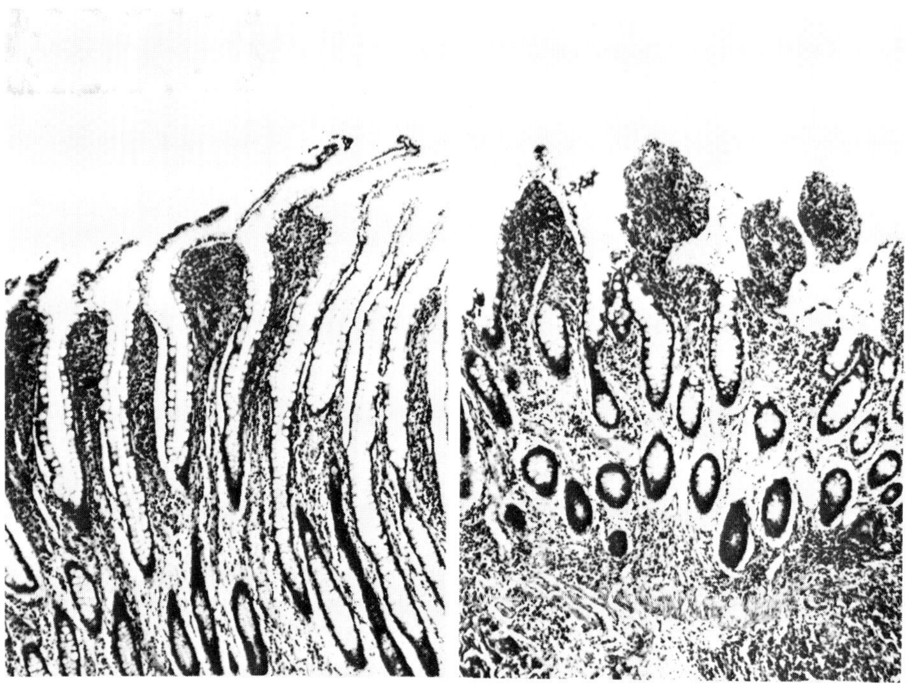

FIGURE 7. Photomicrograph of intestinal mucosa in the early exudative stages of Crohn's disease. Typical mild changes in the mucosa include inflammatory obliteration and clubbing of villi (left), while more advanced changes include endothelial denudation of the villi (right). (From Hulten, L., Lindhagen, J., Lundgren, O., Fasth, S., and Ahren, C., *Gastroenterology,* 72, 388, 1977. With permission.)

role in producing the interstitial edema and lymphatic dilation associated with IBD.[27,28] Although scant information is available, it has been suggested that histamine, serotonin, bradykinin, and other agents known to increase microvascular permeability are released in the inflamed tissue.[6,17,27,28] A role for histamine in this response is particularly appealing for several reasons. For example, histamine is known to increase intestinal vascular permeability.[31] Furthermore, mast cells and basophils, both of which contain histamine, accumulate in large numbers in the submucosa of diseased areas of the colon in patients with Crohn's disease (Figure 8).[17] Many of these cells undergo complete degranulation with release of histamine to the submucosal interstitium. Histamine may then cause endothelial cells to contract, creating interendothelial gaps, and thus increasing vascular permeability.[17] Inasmuch as histamine is a vasodilator, release of this agent during the active stages of IBD may also contribute to the vasodilation reported in these disorders. It may also be relevant that the accumulation and degranulation of mast cells and basophils in Crohn's disease occur primarily in the submucosa, which is also the most prominent site of fluid accumulation and vascular dilatation.

It has also been suggested that the mucosal ulcerations accompanying IBD allow bacterial toxins and caustic substances normally confined to the bowel lumen to gain access to the interstitial space and increase vascular permeability.[27,28,32] Support for the contention that bacterial endotoxins contribute to this increase is provided by the observation that approximately one half of the patients with IBD have elevated antibody titers to antigens derived from *Escherichia coli* and other bacteria.[27]

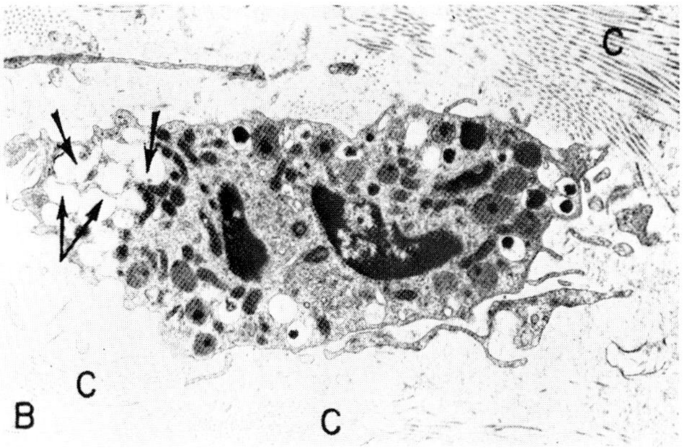

FIGURE 8. Photomicrograph of the ileum in Crohn's disease showing the presence of degranulated mast cells in the submucosa. (From Dvorak, A. M., Monahan, R. A., Osage, J. E., and Dickersin, G. R., *Hum. Pathol.*, 11, 606, 1980. With permission.)

Granger and Barrowman[28] have proposed that oxygen-derived free radicals may be involved in the increased vascular and mucosal permeability associated with IBD. This notion is based on the observation that infiltration of leukocytes,[6,17] which are known to produce oxygen radicals,[33] is a common histopathological feature of these disorders. Since oxygen radicals increase intestinal vascular permeability,[35] it is feasible that these substances may play an important role in the genesis of edema in IBD. This hypothesis is especially appealing since (1) there is evidence in support of a role for intestinal ischemia as a causative factor in the pathogenesis of IBD (see below) and (2) ischemia-induced increases in intestinal vascular permeability appear to be due, in large part, to generation of oxygen radicals.[34-37] In this regard, it is of interest to note that the morphologic alterations associated with IBD are similar, in many respects, to those that occur in association with hemorrhagic shock or ischemic disorders of the small intestine and colon.[28,38] Finally, Wei and co-workers[34] have recently demonstrated that generation of oxygen radicals can produce irreversible vasodilation due to vascular smooth muscle damage. If oxygen radicals are involved in the pathogenesis of IBD, this observation may provide an explanation for the pronounced increase in colonic blood flow and the striking degree of microvessel dilation associated with the active stages of these disorders.

Arachidonic acid metabolites, derived from the lipoxygenase and cyclooxygenase pathways, have been implicated as mediators of some of the manifestations of IBD including increased anion secretion, smooth muscle dysfunction, vasodilation, and inflammation.[40-42] Inflammation of the colon is associated with increased production of prostaglandins and thromboxanes, and elevated levels of these compounds have been reported in the colonic mucosa, plasma, and feces of patients with these disorders.[22-26] Furthermore, the levels of prostaglandins and their metabolites in patients with IBD decline after treatment with sulfasalazine or corticosteroids.[23,24,26] Zipser and co-workers[21] have demonstrated increased release of prostaglandins and thromboxanes in response to angiotensin II and bradykinin, peptide hormones which may be present in elevated levels at sites of inflammation. From these data, they concluded that these peptides may augment any putative eicosanoid-mediated manifestations of colitis.

Although the aforementioned results appear to support a role for prostaglandins in the pathogenesis of inflammation in IBD, a major objection to this hypothesis is that agents which block prostaglandin synthesis (e.g., indomethacin) have not proven useful in the treatment of IBD.[23] While a role for prostaglandins in IBD remains uncertain, these compounds may participate in the formation of edema through their actions as vasodilators (increased capillary pressure). Although prostaglandins appear to increase vascular permeability,[87] they may also act to potentiate the actions of other inflammatory mediators known to increase permeability.[44]

A role for lipoxygenase products of arachidonic acid in the pathogenesis of edema formation in IBD has also been suggested.[45] Levels of leukotriene B_4 are increased more than 50-fold in the colonic mucosa of patients with Crohn's disease and ulcerative colitis.[45] Leukotriene B_4 is a potent chemotactic agent for inflammatory cells, especially neutrophils and macrophages.[43] With regard to the contention that oxygen radicals may play a role in the increased vascular permeability associated with IBD, it may be relevant that leukotriene B_4 induced neutrophil aggregation and degranulation and increases microvascular permeability in the presence of neutrophils.[46] This latter effect may be mediated by oxygen radicals,[33] although release of lysosomal enzymes has also been implicated.[47] Additional support for a role of lipoxygenase metabolites in IBD is provided by the observation that sulfasalazine, a useful therapeutic agent for these disorders, blocks human neutrophil 5-lipoxygenase, and thus the synthesis of leukotriene B_4.[48] In addition, the corticosteroids have also proven efficacious in the treatment of IBD. These compounds inhibit phospholipase A_2, and thus reduce the release of arachidonic acid from phospholipids and may potentially limit the availability of substrate for the 5-lipoxygenase pathway.[49]

Levels of another lipoxygenase product, 5-hydroxyeicosatetraenoic acid (5-HETE), are increased in the colonic mucosa of patients with IBD.[45] 5-HETE induces chloride secretion and thus may contribute to the diarrhea seen in patients with these disorders.[40] The observations that (1) leukotriene B_4 and 5-HETE are the major arachidonic acid metabolites of neutrophils[48] and (2) neutrophil infiltration is one of the major histologic features of these disorders[6,17] provide additional support for the notion that these substances may be involved in the pathogenesis of IBD. While there is no evidence that these metabolites of arachidonic acid initiate IBD, these data suggest they may mediate some of its manifestations.

B. Microvascular Hydrostatic Pressure

Although increased vascular permeability is a likely cause of edema in IBD, there is evidence that microvascular hydrostatic pressure may be elevated.[28] As outlined above, colonic blood flow may be increased as much as sixfold and may comprise as much as 25 to 30% of the resting cardiac output.[6] Assuming that the increased blood flow results from arteriolar dilation, microvascular hydrostatic pressure may increase by as much as 10 to 40 mmHg.[28] Such an increase in microvascular pressure could account for the interstitial edema associated with IBD.

C. Hypoproteinemia and Lymphatic Obstruction

Hypoproteinemia, especially hypoalbuminemia, is an important clinical feature in IBD.[50,51] For example, Soergel and Ingelfinger[50] have measured the concentrations of various protein fractions and total proteins in serum obtained from normal individuals and patients suffering from ulcerative colitis (Table 1). Their results indicate that a significant reduction in total protein concentration occurs in association with these disorders which is almost entirely attributable to a reduction in plasma albumin concentration, since the concentration of globulins was unaltered.[50] Calculation of plasma colloid osmotic pressure for total proteins (π_P) from these data indicates that π_p may be reduced by as much as 9 to 11 mmHg (Table 1). Such a reduction may contribute substantially to the formation of interstitial edema associated with these disorders.

Table 1
CONCENTRATIONS (C) AND COLLOID OSMOTIC PRESSURES (π) FOR TOTAL PROTEINS (P), ALBUMIN (A), AND GLOBULINS (G) IN NORMAL INDIVIDUALS AND PATIENTS WITH ULCERATIVE COLITIS

		Ulcerative colitis		
	Normal	Active	Severely ill	Remission
C_P	8.00	6.44	6.04	7.48
π_P	31.65	22.56	20.50	28.43
$\Delta\pi_P$	—	9.09	11.15	3.22
C_A	4.86	3.09	2.56	3.81
π_A	19.24	10.72	8.54	13.94
$\Delta\pi_A$	—	8.52	10.70	5.3
C_G	3.14	3.35	3.39	3.67
π_G	6.69	7.27	7.38	8.19
$\Delta\pi_G$	—	−0.58	−0.69	−1.50

Note: Plasma total protein (C_P), albumin (C_A), and globulins (C_G) concentrations obtained from Soergel, K. H. and Ingelfinger, F. J., *Gastroenterology,* 40, 37, 1961. Colloid osmotic pressures for total proteins (π_P), albumin (π_A), and globulins (π_G) were calculated from respective concentrations using the equations for human plasma obtained from Landis, E. M. and Pappenheimer, J. R., in *Handbook of Physiology: Circulation, Section 2, the Cardiovascular System,* Vol. 2, Hamilton, W. F. and Dow, P., Eds., Williams & Wilkins, Baltimore, 1963, 961. $\Delta\pi$ represents the difference between colloid osmotic pressures measured in normal individuals and in patients with ulcerative colitis.

Since this decrease in plasma colloid osmotic pressure appears to be due, in large part, to protein leakage across the inflamed epithelial surface, it would seem likely that this reduction augments, rather than initiates, the formation of edema in IBD. However, there is evidence to suggest that another mechanism, lymphatic obstruction, may contribute to edema formation in Crohn's disease.[52] Such obstruction may contribute to the hypoproteinemia seen in these disorders by impairing the return of extravasated plasma proteins to the circulation. In addition, hypoproteinemia may occur as a consequence of a shift in metabolism to favor net catabolism of protein in patients with IBD. Finally, liver cell dysfunction and nutritional deficiencies, especially in the severely ill patient, may contribute to the reduction in plasma oncotic pressure in IBD.

From the foregoing discussion, it is apparent that the pathogeneis of edema formation of the intestinal submucosa and mucosa in IBD is complex since changes in vascular permeability, blood flow (microvascular pressure), and plasma protein concentration all appear to play a role. The formation of mucosal edema in IBD may increase the diffusion distance from the blood to parenchymal cells for oxygen and other nutrients, and thus may represent an important contributory factor to the formation of ulcerative lesions. In light of this potential problem, it is essential that future investigations be directed at more precisely defining, in quantitative terms, the relative contribution of these pathophysiologic mechanisms of edema formation in IBD to facilitate identification of appropriate therapeutic regimens.

IV. VASCULAR FACTORS IN THE ETIOLOGY AND PATHOGENESIS OF IBD

Many diverse hypotheses have been formulated to provide a basis for the etiology and pathogenesis of IBD, including autoimmunity, viral or bacterial infection, food allergy, lymphatic obstruction, excessive mast cell accumulation with subsequent histamine release, Paneth cell proliferation followed by release of proteolytic enzymes, enhanced sympathetic activity, and psychological factors.[1,9,10,20,27,32,54-60] By comparison, little attention has been focused on the potential role that vascular factors may play in these diseases. In fact, although several vascular hypothesis have been considered,[1,9,27,32,54,56,57,59] they are often ignored in discussion of putative mechanisms underlying the etiology and pathogenesis of IBD. Perhaps this is related to the fact that while nearly all the vascular hypotheses invoke mucosal ischemia as the primary circulatory event underlying these disorders, little attention has been given to the possible mechanism(s) that may give rise to this impairment in flow.

Based on the early observations of Lium,[55] Wolf,[60] and Drury and co-workers,[61] Fairburn[54] has proposed that the mucosal alterations associated with ulcerative colitis arise as a result of impaired microcirculatory flow to this layer of the large bowel. It is his contention that high intraluminal pressures are generated by the colonic musculature which result in a mechanical impairment of blood flow to the metabolically highly active mucosa which, in turn, gives rise to the mucosal alterations associated with ulcerative colitis.[54] Thus, it might be expected that if colonic muscular contraction is important in the pathogenesis of ulcerative colitis, the pathological changes would begin in segments of the colon with the most powerful musculature.[55] In fact, the disease most often begins in the rectum (which contains the strongest muscle) and progresses along the tenial bonds (whose strength exceeds that of the circular fibers).[55] One potential criticism of this notion is that another important colonic disorder, diverticulosis coli, is thought to be due to excessive tension development in colonic smooth muscle. However, there does not appear to be any particular correlation between the two diseases, in that one seldom sees them occurring together.

In support of his hypothesis, Fairburn[54] points out that in patients with diarrhea, total colonic motility is reduced. With loss of normal rhythmic activity, mass movement results when a long portion of the colon contracts simultaneously or segmentally. Such contractions can increase intraluminal pressure 60 to 75 mmHg and are sustained for as long as 2 to 4 min. In fact, this activity was first reported in symptomatic ulcerative colitis, where such contractions may occur as often as every 3 min.[54] High intraluminal pressures (40 to 70 mmHg) also occur with partial bowel obstruction, which often leads to a colitis proximal to the obstruction that is similar in many respects to ulcerative colitis.[62,63] In addition, several other factors may give rise to an externally applied force to the mucosal vasculature, including intussusception, strangulated hernias, and volvulus. Finally, it appears likely that a variety of psychological factors, including stress, cause increased colonic motility and intraluminal pressure in patients with severe ulcerative colitis (Figure 9).[64] This latter observation may be of some importance in view of the evidence in support of a role for psychologic or emotional factors in the pathogenesis of IBD.[53,61,64]

Central to Fairburn's hypothesis[54] is the notion that increased intraluminal pressure impairs blood flow to the mucosa of the colon. The resultant reduced delivery of nutrients and diminished removal of waste products leads to parenchymal damage and ultimately tissue necrosis. The results of several studies indicate that increases in intraenteric pressure above 30 to 40 mmHg are associated with progressive reductions in colonic blood flow.[62,65-72] However, luminal distending pressures of less than 40 mmHg

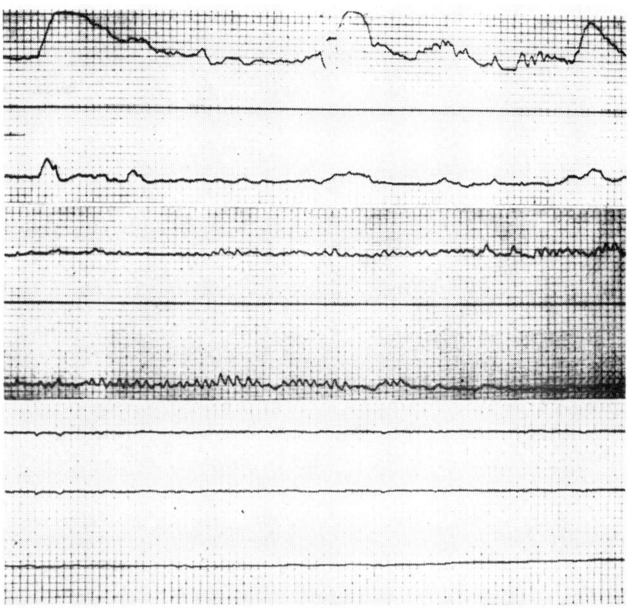

FIGURE 9. Effect of discussing emotional topics on colonic intraluminal pressure in patients with ulcerative colitis when symptoms were severe (upper panel) or mild (middle panel). Bottom panel depicts intraluminal pressure during the discussion of emotional topics when the patient was symptom-free. Each large square represents 10 mmHg. (From Chaudhuary, N. A. and Truelove, S. C., *Gastroenterology,* 40, 27, 1961. With permission.)

apparently reduce colonic blood flow only if a concomitant bowel obstruction is present.[62,63] Examination of the intramural distribution of blood flow in the colon indicates that when intraluminal pressure exceeds 30 to 60 mmHg, mucosal flow is significantly reduced.[63,65,68,71] In concert with the progressive reduction in blood flow produced by increased intraluminal pressure, a progressive reduction in colonic oxygen extraction and consumption occurs, suggesting that flow is diverted from the metabolically active mucosa.[65,66,68] In addition to reducing colonic blood flow and oxygen consumption, luminal distention produces interstitial edema and a marked increase in lymph flow. The formation of edema with luminal distention apparently results from enhanced capillary filtration secondary to elevated microvascular hydrostatic pressure. Increased microvascular surface area and permeability may also play a role in this response.[72] As outlined above, interstitial edema may contribute to impaired mucosal nutrition by increasing nutrient diffusion distance. Thus, these results not only provide support for Fairburn's hypothesis but may also explain the mucosal edema associated with ulcerative colitis.

Bolcy and co-workers[65,66] and Tunick et al.[68] have examined the effects of intermittent bowel distention on intestinal blood flow. Alternate distention of the bowel to 45 mmHg for 5 min followed by 5 min of decompression over a period of 1 to 2 hr is associated with a fall in blood flow during the distention period (Figure 10). During each succeeding period of distention, the decrease in flow was greater than recorded in the immediately preceding period, and during the last distention, flow was reduced by an average of 64%.[66,68] Furthermore, a flow reduction of 55% persisted for as long as 2 hr after release of the final distention.[66,68] When the bowel was distended to 45 mmHg and perfused with silicone rubber, only the submucosal and serosal vessels

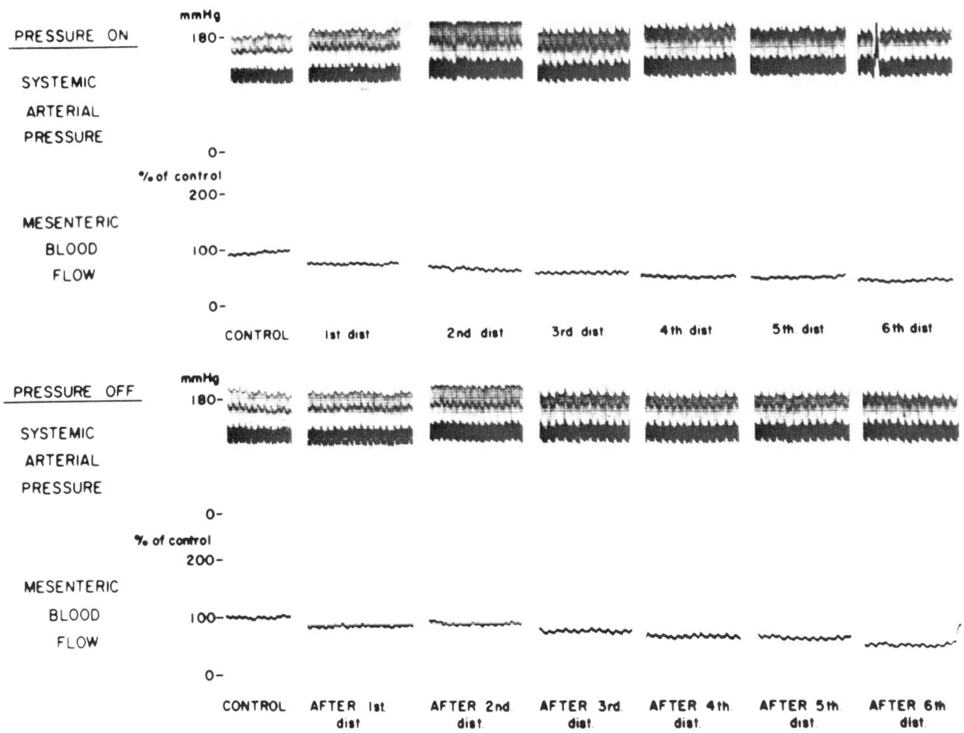

FIGURE 10. Effect of intermittent bowel distention (5 min distention followed by 5 min with no distention) to 45 mmHg over a 1-hr period. Upper panel depicts fall in blood flow during distention period, while lower panel depicts blood flow changes during the intervening periods with no distention. Note the progressive reduction in flow that occurs during both periods over the 1-hr protocol. Flow after release of the final distention was reduced to 50% of control. (From Tunick, P. A., Treiber, W. F., Frank, M., Veith, F. J., Gliedman, M. L., and Boley, S. J., *Curr. Top. Surg. Res.*, 2, 59, 1970. With permission.)

filled, whereas those in the mucosa and muscularis were almost devoid of injectate.[65,66,68] These results lend support to Fairburn's suggestion[54] that the intermittent increases in intraluminal pressure associated with symptomatic ulcerative colitis may result in impaired mucosal flow.

An elegant study conducted by Shikata and co-workers[73] graphically depicts the effects of elevated intraluminal pressure on mucosal capillarity. These investigators increased intraluminal pressure on mucosal capillarity. These investigators increased intraluminal pressure to simulate bowel obstruction and outlined the vasculature with a resin cast. Results of these studies indicate that a progressive vascular derecruitment occurs as a result of increased intraluminal pressure (Figure 11). The reduction in vascular transmural pressure due to luminal distention results in an apparent increase in vascular resistance.[67] However, if the concept of a vascular waterfall (vascular resistance calculated from the difference between arterial minus intraluminal pressure) is taken into consideration, this reduction in mucosal capillary flow occurs in the face of a reduced total vascular resistance.[70,72,74]

Further support for the hypothesis that ischemia, leading to impaired energy metabolism of the intestinal mucosa, underlies the development of ulcerative lesions and edema in IBD is provided by the observations of Roediger and associates.[75,76] They have demonstrated that the increased luminal concentrations of *n*-butyrate (which colonic enterocytes use for 86% of their aerobic energy requirements[75]) and potassium and the reduction in luminal pH associated with ulcerative colitis correlate with the

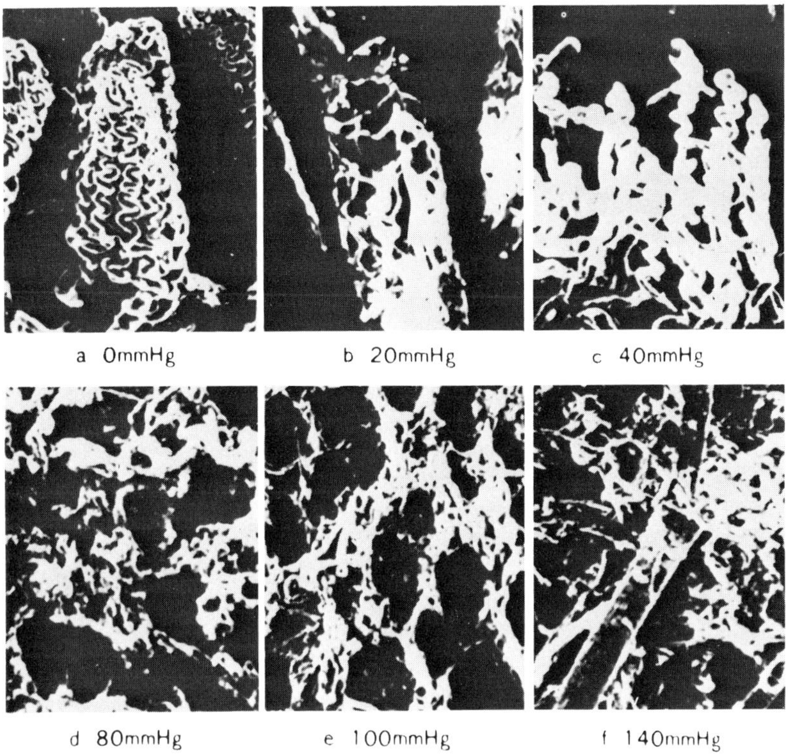

FIGURE 11. Effect of elevated intraluminal pressure over a range of 0 to 140 mmHg on mucosal capillarity, demonstrating progressive reduction in number of perfused capillaries as intraenteric pressure increases. (From Shikata, J., Shida, T., Amino, K., and Ishioka, K., *Surg. Gynecol. Obstet.*, 156, 155, 1983. With permission.)

degree of mucosal injury in this disorder.[76] These findings have been interpreted to suggest that a deficit in colonic mucosal energy metabolism occurs, leading to a progressive impairment in the regulation of ionic fluxes by the colon in ulcerative colitis.[76]

In summary, Fairburn[54] has presented a vascular hypothesis to explain the etiology of the mucosal lesions seen in IBD. According to this hypothesis, the mucosal lesions associated with ulcerative colitis arise as a result of mucosal ischemia caused by contractions of the colonic musculature. These contractions cause increases in intraluminal pressure of high amplitude and relatively long duration which, in turn, are proposed to mechanically impair blood flow to the metabolically highly active mucosa.

Nielsen[56] and Fasth and Hulten[77] have criticized Fairburn's contention that mucosal ischemia is caused by contractions of the colonic musculature. They point out that although the parasympathetic pelvic nerves are involved in active contraction and emptying of the colon, they also induce a concomitant colonic vasodilation.[70,71,78] Thus, impairment of colonic mucosal flow as a result of colonic contraction per se does not appear to provide a likely explanation for the etiology and/or pathogenesis of IBD. This objection does not preclude the possibility that other mechanisms (e.g., intussusception, volvulus, strangulated hernias) may give rise to an externally applied force to the mucosal vasculature and thus mechanically impair flow. In fact, as outlined above, the results of several studies indicate that increases in intraenteric pressure are associated with reduction in colonic blood flow and oxygen consumption. This effect may be particularly important if a rise in distending pressure occurs in the presence of obstruction, because lower intraluminal pressures are required to derecruit capillaries in the face of obstruction.

Mucosal ischemia with subsequent ulceration may also result from altered central sympathetic activity, since it is known that stimulation of the sympathetic nerves supplying the colon increases vascular resistance and reduces mucosal blood flow by as much as 50%.[70,71,78] On the other hand, section of the sympathetic postganglionic fibers to the colon results in a colitis similar to active ulcerative colitis.[79] With regard to Fairburn's hypothesis, it may be relevant to point out that removal of sympathetic inhibition of colonic motility is associated with an intensification of propulsive activity in the colon.[60] In addition, immunosympathectomy greatly reduces the turnover rate of jejunal epithelium.[88]

Recently, it has been demonstrated that i.v. nicotine, infused to produce blood concentrations similar to those seen in smokers after one cigarette, reduces intestinal blood flow by approximately 40%.[80] A 50% reduction in flow was produced by a dose of nicotine equivalent to an individual smoking five to six cigarettes in 1 hr. This effect is apparently indirect, since local intra-arterial infusion of nicotine did not alter mesenteric resistance. Since nicotine administration decreased arterial pressure by approximately 20%, the increase in intestinal resistance appears to be the result of α-adrenergic receptor stimulation secondary to haroreceptor activation.[80] In view of this observation and the contention that mucosal ischemia as a result of altered sympathetic activity may underlie the pathogenesis of IBD, it might be expected that smoking may predispose certain individuals to IBD. However, epidemiologic evidence suggests that smokers have a reduced incidence of these disorders.[81] The significance of this finding, however, remains obscure.

In light of potential neural mechanisms, it may be relevant to note that vagotomy is associated with a significant increase in the proliferative rate of the large intestinal epithelium.[82] This observation suggests that an increase in the level of parasympathetic activity may reduce the proliferative rate of the large intestinal epithelium which, in turn, may explain why vagal section has proven useful in the treatment of IBD.[83] Inasmuch as parasympathetic activity also increases colonic blood flow, it has been suggested that an autonomic imbalance may represent an important etiologic factor in these disorders.[32]

Another vascular factor which may play a role in IBD relates to the presence of 19S gamma globulin capable of producing vasospasm in serum and leukocyte extracts obtained from patients with active ulcerative colitis and also in apparently healthy relatives of patients with this disorder.[84,85] It has been suggested that this protein may produce insufficient microcirculatory perfusion which may lead to ulceration.[27]

The importance of mucosal ischemia as a factor in the etiology or pathogenesis of IBD should not be overstressed nor should it be dismissed until it can be determined whether ischemia arises during the days, weeks, or even months preceding a clinical attack. That this crucial evidence is not currently available probably relates to the difficulty inherent in obtaining colonic blood flows in asymptomatic patients. However, techniques for the early detection of intestinal ischemia have been developed recently,[74] and retrospective studies of cases in which these techniques were employed may provide important clues to the relation between prior intestinal ischemia and subsequent development of IBD. In addition, it should be stressed that although the hemorrhagic, edematous, ulcerating lesions associated with IBD are reminiscent of the early changes in intestinal ischemic disease, they differ in as many ways as they are similar. Also, mucosal ischemia with subsequent infarction followed by healing per se does not lead to the development of IBD. Therefore, if impaired mucosal flow is, in fact, important in the etiology and/or pathogenesis of IBD, it would appear likely that this mechanism cannot represent the sole pathogenetic factor in the disease.

V. SUMMARY

Despite a wealth of information regarding their varied clinical, angiographic, morphologic, and immunologic features, Crohn's disease and ulcerative colitis remain enigmatic in terms of their etiologic and pathogenetic mechanisms. The occurrence of gross vascular changes in association with IBD suggests a role for the intestinal circulation in these disease processes. Based on the evidence presented above, the following working hypothesis can be used to summarize the potential role that various factors may play in the pathogenesis of IBD (Figure 12). According to this scheme, the basic vascular event underlying the pathogenesis of these disorders is impaired mucosal nutrition. Reduced substrate delivery to the metabolically highly active mucosa may result from intestinal ischemia and/or mucosal edema (increased nutrient diffusion distance). Mucosal blood flow may be reduced early in the course of these disorders (i.e., before the disease becomes clinically evident) as a result of enhanced colonic activity concomitant with bowel obstruction (Figure 12). This increase in activity coupled with the presence of an obstructed mass may produce an increase in intraenteric pressure sufficient to mechanically impair flow. This may be especially important in the pathogenesis of Crohn's ileitis, since bowel obstruction is commonly associated with this disorder. Because bowel obstruction rarely occurs in association with Crohn's colitis and almost never with ulcerative colitis, it would seem unlikely that obstruction plays an important role in these disorders. Although it is possible that forces externally applied to the intestinal vasculature and subsequent mucosal ischemia may also arise with intussusception, the development of a volvulus, or strangulated hernias, or by the direct effects of intraluminal distention (Figure 12), these conditions are not generally associated with IBD. In addition to mechanical impairment of flow, altered CNS activity or an enhanced colonic vascular response to vasoconstrictor stimuli may also play a role in producing mucosal ischemia. Ultimately, the insufficient mucosal microcirculatory perfusion leads to tissue necrosis and ulceration.

Although interstitial edema is a cardinal sign of IBD, the mechanisms underlying the excessive accumulation of tissue fluid remain uncertain. It is generally believed that an increase in vascular permeability plays an important role in producing the intestitial edema and lymphatic dilation associated with these disorders (Figure 12). This increase in vascular permeability may arise as a result of intestinal ischemia or perhaps through increased release of one or more of the putative chemical mediators of inflammation. However, the stimulus for this increased release, if it occurs, remains obscure. In addition to altered vascular permeability, it seems likely that an increase in microvascular hydrostatic pressure and lymphatic obstruction may also be important. Hypoproteinemia, as a result of protein loss across the inflamed epithelial surface, probably augments rather than initiates the excessive accumulation of interstitial fluid in these disorders. Whatever the mechanism, the formation of mucosal edema may result in an increased diffusion distance for nutrients, thereby impairing mucosal nutrition with subsequent tissue necrosis and ulceration.

It should be apparent that almost every aspect of the aforementioned hypothesis is highly speculative, in that the evidence in support of each point is at best only suggestive. Indeed, the proposition that vascular mechanisms may underlie the pathogenesis of these disorders is based, in large part and perhaps unfortunately, on advanced secondary histologic alterations. In addition, it would seem highly unlikely that impaired nutrition is the sole pathogenetic event in these disorders, since mucosal ischemia and edema followed by healing per se do not lead to the development of IBD.

Despite this observation, the vascular hypothesis is appealing in many respects. Chief among these is that the hypothesis provides an attractive explanation for the

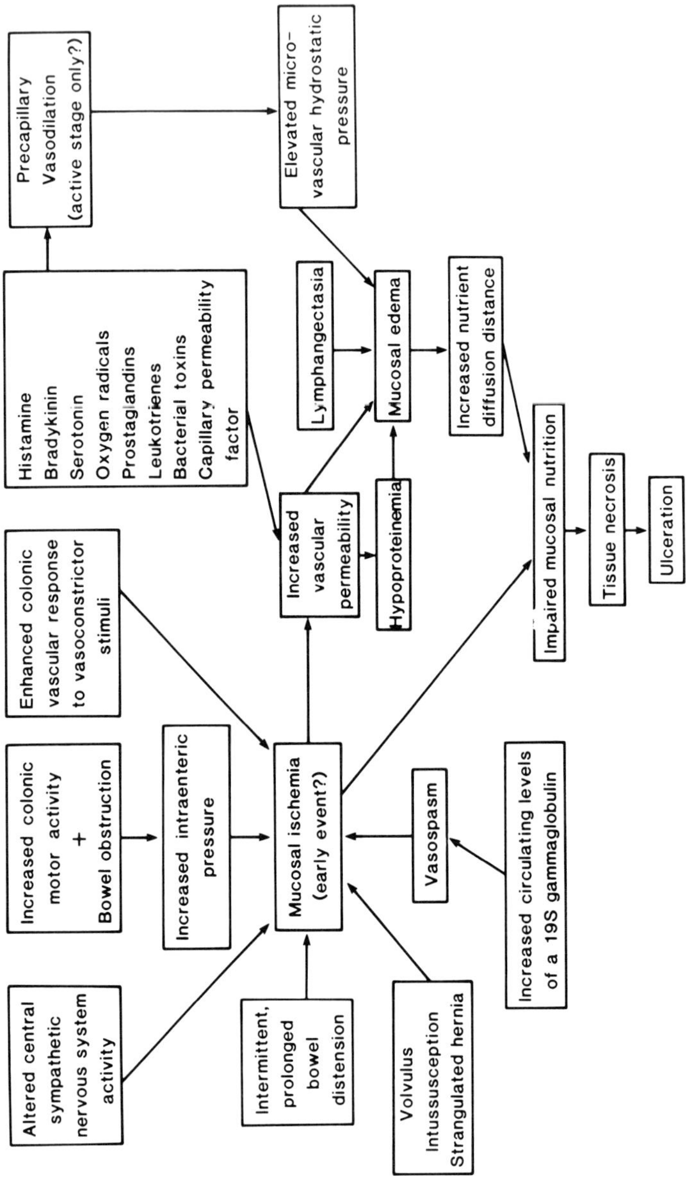

FIGURE 12. Potential role of vascular factors in the pathogenesis of IBD.

formation of interstitial edema and mucosal ulcerations associated with IBD. However, the crucial evidence required to evaluate the vascular hypothesis properly is lacking, perhaps owing to the difficulty inherent in obtaining colonic flows in asymptomatic patients. Moreover, the lack of appropriate animal models that reliably reproduce human inflammatory bowel disorders has further hampered significant new developments in this area. Perhaps application of newly developed techniques available for use in patients for the early detection of intestinal ischemia will circumvent this difficulty and yield an answer to the crucial question of whether mucosal ischemia is involved in the pathogenesis of these enigmatic disorders. Clearly, much more investigation will be required to clarify the role of the intestinal circulation in IBD, and it is hoped that this presentation will challenge investigators to explore the validity and implications of the working hypothesis outlined above.

REFERENCES

1. Allen, A. C., A unified concept of the vascular pathogenesis of enterocolitis of varied etiology. A pathophysiologic analysis, *Am. J. Gastroenterol.*, 57, 347, 1971.
2. Boisjen, E., Mesenteric angiography in the evaluation of inflammatory and neoplastic diseases of the intestine, *Radiology*, 87, 1028, 1966.
3. Brahme, F. and Lindstrom, C., A comparative radiographic and pathological study of intestinal vasoarchitecture in Crohn's disease and in ulcerative colitis, *Gut*, 11, 928, 1970.
4. Eriksson, U., Fagerberg, S., Krausse, U., and Olding, L., Angiographic studies in Crohn's disease and ulcerative colitis, *Am. J. Roentgenol.*, 110, 385, 1970.
5. Farman, J., The radiologic features of colonic vascular disease, in *Vascular Disorders of the Intestine*, Boley, S. J., Schwartz, S. S., and Williams. L. F., Eds., Appleton-Century-Crofts, East Norwalk, Conn., 1971, 229.
6. Hulten, L., Lindhagen, J., Lundgren, O., Fasth, S., and Ahren, C., Regional intestinal blood flow in ulcerative colitis and Crohn's disease, *Gastroenterology*, 72, 388, 1977.
7. Johansson, H., Krausse, U., and Olding, L., Microangiographic studies in Crohn's disease and ulcerative colitis, *Acta Chir. Scand.*, 138, 409, 1972.
8. Lunderquist, A. and Lunderquist, A., Angiography in ulcerative colitis, *Am. J. Roentgenol.*, 99, 18, 1967.
9. Morson, B. C., Pathology of ulcerative colitis, in *Inflammatory Bowel Disease*, Kirsner, J. B. and Shorter, R. G., Eds., Lea & Febiger, Philadelphia, 1980, 281.
10. Morson, B. C. and Dawson, I. M. P., *Gastrointestinal Pathology*, Blackwell, London, 1972, 448.
11. Tsuchiya, M., Miura, S., Asakura, H., Hibi, T., Tanaka, T., Aiso, S., and Hiramatsu, K., Angiographic evaluation of vascular changes in ulcerative colitis, *Angiology*, 31, 147, 1980.
12. Bacaneer, M. B., Quantitative measurement of regional colon blood flow in the normal and pathological human bowel, *Gastroenterology*, 51, 764, 1966.
13. Lott, M. F. and Davies, J. D., Lymph node hypervascularity: hemangiomatoid lesions and pan-nodal vasodilation, *Pathology*, 140, 209, 1983.
14. Knutson, H., Lunderquist, A., and Lunderquist, A., Vascular changes in Crohn's disease, *Am. J. Roentgenol.*, 103, 380, 1968.
15. Lunderquist, A., Lunderquist, A., and Knutson, H., Angiography in Crohn's disease of small bowel and colon, *Am. J. Roentgenol.*, 101, 338, 1967.
16. Whitehead, R. C., Pathology of Crohn's disease, in *Inflammatory Bowel Disease*, Kirsner, J. B. and Shorter, R. G., Eds., Lea & Febiger, Philadelphia, 1980, 261.
17. Dvorak, A. M., Monahan, R. A., Osage, J. E., and Dickersin, G. R., Crohn's disease: transmission electron microscopic studies. II. Immunologic inflammatory response. Alterations of mast cells, basophils, eosinophils, and the microvasculature, *Hum. Pathol.*, 11, 606, 1980.
18. Kovi, J., Duong, H. D., and Hoang, C. T., Ultrastructure of intestinal lymphatics on Crohn's disease, *Am. J. Clin. Pathol.*, 76, 385, 1981.
19. Otto, H. F. and Gebbers, J. O., Electron microscopic ultracytochemical and immunohistochemical observations in Crohn's disease of the ileum and colon, *Virchows Arch. Pathol. Anat. Physiol.*, 391, 489, 1981.

20. Singleton, J. W., Inflammatory bowel disease, in *The Gastroenterology Annual*, Vol. 1, Kern, F. and Blum, A. L., Eds., Elsevier, Amsterdam, 1983, 268.
21. Zipser, R. D., Patterson, J. B., Kao, H. W., Hauser, C. J., and Locker, R., Hypersensitive prostaglandin and thromboxane response to hormones in rabbit colitis, *Am. J. Physiol.*, 249, G457, 1985.
22. Gould, S. R., Assay of prostaglandin-like substances in feces and their measurement in ulcerative colitis, *Prostaglandins*, 11, 489, 1976.
23. Gould, S. R., Brash, A. R., Conolly, M. E., and Lennard-Jones, J. E., Studies of prostaglandins and sulphasalazine in ulcerative colitis, *Prostagl. Leukotr. Med.*, 6, 165, 1981.
24. Ligumsky, M., Karmeli, F., Sharon, P., Zar, U., Cohen, F., and Rachmilewitz, D., Enhanced thromboxane A_2 and prostacyclin production by cultured rectal mucosa in ulcerative colitis and its inhibition by steroids and sulfasalazine, *Gastroenterology*, 81, 444, 1981.
25. Rampton, D. S., Sladen, G. E., and Youlten, L. J. F., Rectal mucosal prostaglandin E_2 release and its relation to disease activity, electrical potential difference, and treatment in ulcerative colitis, *Gut*, 21, 591, 1980.
26. Sharon, P., Ligumsky, M., Rachmilewitz, D., and Zar, U., Role of prostaglandins in ulcerative colitis. Enhanced production during active disease and inhibition by sulfasalazine, *Gastroenterology*, 75, 638, 1978.
27. Kirsner, J. B., Observations on the etiology and pathogenesis of inflammatory bowel disease, in *Gastroenterology*, Bockus, H. L., Ed., W. B. Saunders, Philadelphia, 1976, 521.
28. Granger, D. N. and Barrowman, J. A., Gastrointestinal and liver edema, in *Edema*, Staub, N. C. and Taylor, A. E., Eds., Raven Press, New York, 1984, 615.
29. Starling, E. H., On the absorption of fluids from the connective tissue spaces, *J. Physiol.*, 19, 312, 1896.
30. Taylor, A. E., Capillary fluid filtration. Starling forces and lymph flow, *Circ. Res.*, 49, 557, 1981.
31. Mortillaro, N. A., Granger, D. N., Kvietys, P. R., Rutilli, G., and Taylor, A. E., Effects of histamine and histamine antagonists on intestinal capillary permeability, *Am. J. Physiol.*, 240, G381, 1981.
32. Melnyk, C. S., Experimental enteritis and colitis, in *Inflammatory Bowel Disease*, Kirsner, J. B. and Shorter, R. G., Eds., Lea & Febiger, Philadelphia, 1980, 25.
33. McCord, J. M. and Fridovich, I., The biology and pathology of oxygen radicals, *Ann. Intern. Med.*, 89, 122, 1978.
34. Korthuis, R. J. and Granger, D. N., Ischemia-reperfusion injury: role of oxygen radicals, in *Oxygen Radicals*, American Physiological Society, Bethesda, Md., in press.
35. Parks, D. A., Shah, A. K., and Granger, D. N., Oxygen radicals: effect on intestinal vascular permeability, *Am. J. Physiol.*, 247, G167, 1984.
36. Granger, D. N., Rutili, G., and McCord, J. M., Superoxide radicals in feline intestinal ischemia, *Gastroenterology*, 81, 22, 1981.
37. Granger, D. N., Hollwarth, M. A., and Parks, D. A., Ischemia-reperfusion injury: role of oxygen-derived free radicals, *Acta Physiol. Scand.*, in press.
38. Schwartz, S., Boley, S., Lash, J., and Sternhill, V., Roentgenologic aspects of reversible vascular occlusion of the colon and its relationship to ulcerative colitis, *Radiology*, 80, 625, 1963.
39. Wei, E. P., Christman, C. W., Kontos, H. A., and Povlishock, J. T., Effects of oxygen radicals on cerebral arterioles, *Am. J. Physiol.*, 249, H157, 1985.
40. Musch, M. W., Miller, R. W., Field, M., and Siegel, M. I., Stimulation of colonic secretion by lipoxygenase metabolites of arachidonic acid, *Science*, 217, 1255, 1982.
41. Hunt, R. H., Dilawari, J. B., and Misiewicz, J. J., The effect of intravenous prostaglandin F_2 and E_2 on the motility of the sigmoid colon, *Gut*, 16, 47, 1975.
42. Goodwin, J. S. and Ceuppens, J., Regulation of the immune response by prostaglandins, *J. Clin. Immunol.*, 3, 295, 1983.
43. Ford-Hutchinson, A. W., Bray, M. A., Doig, M. V., Shipley, M. E., and Smith, J. H., Leukotriene B, a potent chemotactic and aggregating substance released from polymorphonuclear leukocytes, *Nature*, 266, 264, 1980.
44. Williams, T. J. and Morley, J., Prostaglandins as potentiators of increased vascular permeability in inflammation, *Nature*, 246, 215, 1973.
45. Sharon, P. and Stenson, W. F., Enhanced synthesis of leukotriene B_4 by colonic mucosa in inflammatory bowel disease, *Gastroenterology*, 86, 453, 1984.
46. Bjork, J., Hedqvist, P., and Arfors, K.-E., Increase in vascular permeability induced by leukotriene B_4 and the role of polymorphonuclear leukocytes, *Inflammation*, 6, 189, 1982.
47. Bokach, G. M. and Ried, P. W., Effect of various lipoxygenase metabolites of arachidonic acid on degranulation of polymorphonuclear leukocytes, *J. Biol. Chem.*, 256, 5317, 1981.
48. Stenson, W. F. and Lobos, E., Sulfasalazine inhibits the synthesis of chemotactic lipids by neutrophils, *J. Clin. Invest.*, 69, 494, 1982.

49. Flower, R. J. and Blackwell, G. J., Anti-inflammatory steroids induce biosynthesis of a phospholipase A_2 inhibitor which prevents prostaglandin generation, *Nature,* 278, 456, 1979.
50. Soergel, K. H. and Ingelfinger, F. J., Proteins in serum and rectal mucus of patients with ulcerative colitis, *Gastroenterology,* 40, 37, 1961.
51. Steinfeld, J. L., Davidson, J. D., and Gordon, R. S., A mechanism for hypoalbuminemia in patients with ulcerative colitis and regional enteritis, *J. Clin. Invest.,* 36, 931, 1957.
52. Kalima, T. V., The structure and function of intestinal lymphatics and the influence of impaired lymph flow on the ileum of rats, *Scand. J. Gastroenterol.,* 6 (Suppl. 10), 1, 1971.
53. de Dombal, F. T., Ulcerative colitis: definition, historical background, aetiology, diagnosis, natural history and local complications, *Postgrad. Med. J.,* 44, 684, 1968.
54. Fairburn, R. A., On the aetiology of ulcerative colitis. A vascular hypothesis, *Lancet,* 1, 697, 1973.
55. Lium, R., Etiology of ulcerative colitis. II. Effect of induced spasm on colonic explants in dogs, with comment on relation of muscular spasm to ulcerative colitis, *Arch. Int. Med.,* 63, 210, 1939.
56. Nielsen, S. L., Aetiology of ulcerative colitis, *Lancet,* 1, 1180, 1973.
57. Rappaport, H., Burgoyne, F. H., and Simetana, H. F., The pathology of regional enteritis, *Mil. Surg.,* 109, 463, 1951.
58. Singleton, J. W., Inflammatory bowel disease, in *The Gastroenterology Annual,* Vol. 2, Kern, F. and Blum, A. L., Eds., Elsevier, Amsterdam, 1984, 214.
59. Warren, S. and Summers, S. C., Pathology of regional ileitis and ulcerative colitis, *JAMA,* 154, 189, 1954.
60. Wolf, S., The central nervous system regulation of the colon, *Gastroenterology,* 51, 810, 1966.
61. Drury, A. N., Florey, H., and Florey, M. E., The vascular reactions of the colonic mucosa of the dog to fright, *J. Physiol.,* 68, 173, 1929.
62. Enochsson, L., Nylander, G., and Ohman, U., Effects of intraluminal pressure on regional blood flow in obstructed and unobstructed small intestines in the rat, *Am. J. Surg.,* 144, 558, 1982.
63. Wangensteen, O. H., *Intestinal Obstruction,* Charles C Thomas, Springfield, Ill., 1955.
64. Chaudhuary, N. A. and Truelove, S. C., Human colonic motility: a comparative study of normal subjects, patients with ulcerative colitis, and patients with the irritable bowel syndrome. III. Effects of emotions, *Gastroenterology,* 40, 27, 1961.
65. Boley, S. J. and Veith, F. J., Effects of bowel distension on intestinal blood flow, in *Vascular Disorders of the Intestine,* Boley, S. J., Schwartz, S. S., and Williams, L. F., Eds., Appleton-Century-Crofts, New York, 1971, 429.
66. Boley, S., Agrawal, G. P., Warren, A. R., Veith, F. J., Levowitz, B. S., Treiber, W., Doughterty, J., Schwartz, S. S., and Gliedman, M. L., Pathophysiologic effects of bowel distension on intestinal blood flow, *Am. J. Surg.,* 117, 228, 1969.
67. Hanson, K. M. and Moore, F. T., Pressure-volume relationships and blood flow in the distended colon, *Am. J. Physiol.,* 217, 1969.
68. Tunick, P. A., Treiber, W. F., Frank, M., Veith, F. J., Gliedman, M. L., and Boley, S. J., Pathophysiologic effects of bowel distension on intestinal blood flow. II, *Curr. Top. Surg. Res.,* 2, 59, 1970.
69. Noer, R. J., Robb, H. J., and Jacobson, L. F., Circulatory disturbances produced by acute intestinal distension in the living animal, *Arch. Surg.,* 63, 520, 1951.
70. Kvietys, P. R. and Granger, D. N., Regulation of colonic flow, *Fed. Proc., Fed. Am. Soc. Exp. Biol.,* 41, 2106, 1982.
71. Kvietys, P. R. and Granger, D. N., Physiology, pharmacology, and pathology of the colonic circulation, in *Physiology of the Intestinal Circulation,* Shepherd, A. P. and Granger, D. N., Eds., Raven Press, New York, 1984, 131.
72. Granger, D. N., Kvietys, P. R., Mortillaro, N. A., and Taylor, A. E., Effect of luminal distension on intestinal transcapillary fluid exchange, *Am. J. Physiol.,* 238, G516, 1980.
73. Shikata, J., Shida, T., Amino, K., and Ishioka, K., Experimental studies on the hemodynamics of the small intestine following increased intraluminal pressure, *Surg. Gynecol. Obstet.,* 156, 155, 1983.
74. Granger, D. N., Barrowman, J. A., and Kvietys, P. R., Vascular physiology and pathophysiology, in *The Gastroenterology Annual,* Vol. 2, Kern, F. and Blum, A. L., Eds., Elsevier, Amsterdam, 1984, 240.
75. Roediger, W. E. W., Utilization of nutrients by isolated epithelial cells of the rat colon, *Gastroenterology,* 82, 424, 1982.
76. Roediger, W. E. W., Heyworth, M., Willoughby, C. P., and Truelove, S. C., Luminal ions and short chain fatty acids as markers of functional activity of the mucosa in ulcerative colitis, *J. Clin. Pathol.,* 35, 323, 1982.
77. Fasth, S. and Hulten, L., On the etiology of ulcerative colitis, *Gastroenterology,* 68, 618, 1975.

78. Hulten, L., Extrinsic nervous control of colonic motility and blood flow. An experimental study in the cat, *Acta Physiol. Scand.,* Suppl. 335, 1, 1969.
79. Berger, R. L. and Lium, R., Abdominal postganglionic sympathectomy: a method for the production of an ulcerative colitis-like state in dogs, *Ann. Surg.,* 152, 266, 1960.
80. Gallavan, R. H., Tsuchiya, Y., and Jacobsen, E. D., Effects of nicotine on canine intestinal blood flow and oxygen consumption, *Am. J. Physiol.,* 246, G195, 1984.
81. Harries, A. D., Baird, A., and Rhodes, J., Non-smoking: a feature of ulcerative colitis, *Br. Med. J.,* 284, 706, 1982.
82. Silen, W., Peloso, O., and Jaffe, B. F., Kinetics of intestinal epithelial proliferation: effect of vagotomy, *Surgery,* 60, 127, 1966.
83. Dennis, C., Eddy, F. D., Frykman, H. M., McCarthy, A. M., and Westover, D., Response to vagotomy in idiopathic ulcerative colitis and regional enteritis, *Ann. Surg.,* 128, 479, 1948.
84. Auersperg, M. and Skalova, M., The "p" phenomenon associated with ulcerative lesions of the colon in rats, *Acta Chir. Scand.,* 134, 147, 1969.
85. Polcak, J. and Skalova, M., The "p" phenomena associated with ulcerative colitis, *Wien. Med. Wochenschr.,* 119, 323, 1969.
86. Landis, E. M. and Pappenheimer, J. R., Exchange of substances through the capillary walls, in *Handbook of Physiology: Circulation, Vol. 2, Section 2, The Cardiovascular System,* Hamilton, W. F. and Dow, P., Eds., Williams & Wilkins, Baltimore, 1963, 961.
87. Granger, D. N., Schackelford, J. S., and Taylor, A. E., Prostaglandin E_1-induced filtration secretion in the feline ileum, *Am. J. Physiol.,* 236, E788, 1979.
88. Dupont, J. R., Biggers, D. C., and Prinz, H., Intestinal renewal and immunosympathectomy, *Arch. Pathol. Lab. Med.,* 80, 357, 1965.

Chapter 9

ROLE OF THE CIRCULATION IN SECRETORY DIARRHEA

David Mailman

TABLE OF CONTENTS

I. INTRODUCTION

Diarrhea has been defined as an increase in fecal water excretion above the normal 200 mℓ/day. Secretory diarrhea implies a net volume addition to the GI contents above that ingested or that due to "normal" GI secretions.[1] For example, diarrhea could be caused by increased intestinal motility even though net absorption could be occurring and would not be secretory diarrhea. Secretion is also a normal phenomenon; for example, hypertonic meals are diluted by fluid entry into the lumen and herbivores also secrete fluid.[2] The ultimate source of diarrheic secretions must be the effective mucosal circulation, and from this point alone the circulation could have a major influence on diarrhea. However, there are several other aspects of the circulation which could also influence the level of intestinal secretions.

In secretory diarrhea there is a driving force exerted on the volume entering the gut lumen. The driving force most frequently considered is active, energy-dependent transcellular secretion which can be observed in vitro, and the classic example is enterotoxin-induced secretion. Starling forces such as mucosal interstitial fluid pressure can also act as driving forces, as could an excessive osmotic load in the intestinal lumen. A corollary to the effects of driving forces on secretion is the conductance or resistance through which these forces act and which, if altered, can influence the rate of fluid translocation (Figure 1).

The anatomical site of secretion is also a factor. Both the large and small intestine can absorb and secrete fluid independently.[1] The large intestine can abosrb 5 to 6 ℓ of fluid per day and therefore diarrhea may not occur even with a major secretory malfunction of the small intestine.[3] Alternatively, a relatively small amount of large intestinal secretion could cause diarrhea even if the small intestine was functioning well and absorbing a normal 10 ℓ/day.[2]

II. SECRETORY MECHANISMS

A. Active Secretion

Transcellular secretion implies an energy-, and therefore oxygen-dependent cellular process (Figure 2). The driving force for active secretion is thought to depend on the same cellular mechanism required for active absorption, namely the Na^+-K^+ pump.[4] Active absorption, overall, requires solute entry at the apical membrane and exit at the basolateral membrane, with water following passively through transcellular and/or paracellular pathways. Apical entry of solutes is generally due to movement down an electrochemical gradient either directly or coupled by co-transport.[5-8] Apical entry of Na^+ occurs through pores, especially in the large intestine, or coupled to the entry of Cl^- or organic molecules such as sugars or amino acids by carrier molecules, especially in the small intestine. However, there is some evidence arguing against a simple Na/Cl co-transport mechanism.[9] The electrochemical driving forces for Na^+ entry at the apical membrane, which also supplies the gradient for co-transport, are the low intracellular Na^+ concentration and the negative cytoplasmic potential created by active transport of Na^+ out of the cell, and the K^+ diffusion potential created after K^+ entry in exchange for Na^+ at the basolateral membrane. Other transport mechanisms can involve Na^+/H^+ and Cl^-/HCO_3^- exchange, and these processes can lead to reduced absorption or increased secretion because of altered acid-base balance in the body.[10]

The major mechanism for secretion in both the large and small intestine seems to involve an increased permeability to Cl^- at the apical membrane. The Cl^- enters at both the apical and basolateral membranes primarily coupled to Na^+ and thus is concentrated above its electrochemical equilibrium potential. An increased apical permeabil-

A. NUTRITIVE BLOOD FLOW

1. O_2 /SUBSTRATE DELIVERY
2. CO_2 /H^+ REMOVAL

B. WASHOUT

C. STARLING FORCES

1. PASSIVE ULTRAFILTRATION
2. CONDUCTANCE CHANGES

FIGURE 1. Summary of local blood-flow mechanisms which can affect absorption or secretion.

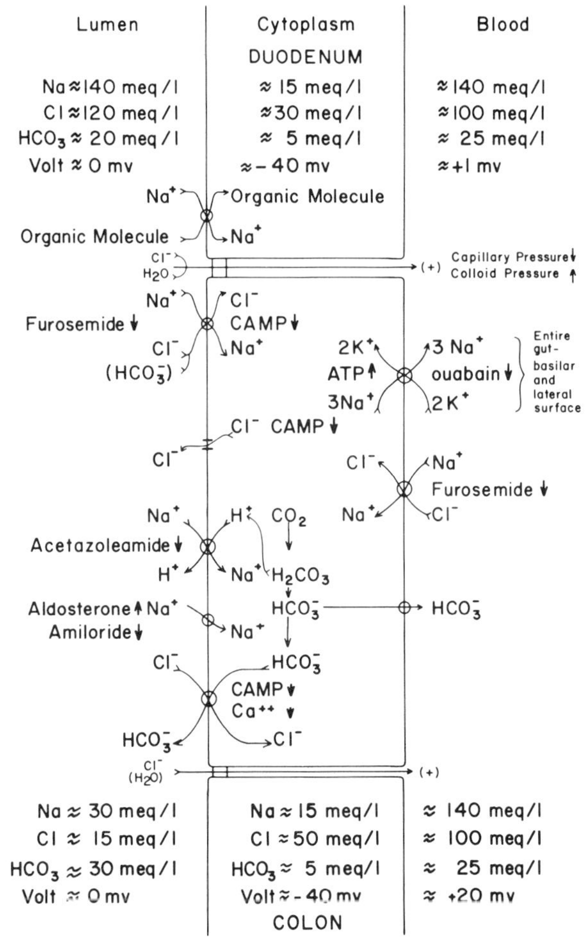

FIGURE 2. A diagram of several transport carriers in the small intestine. The diagram represents the relative importance of the pumps from proximal (top) to distal intestine. Also shown are drugs or hormones that stimulate (↑) or inhibit (↓) these carriers.

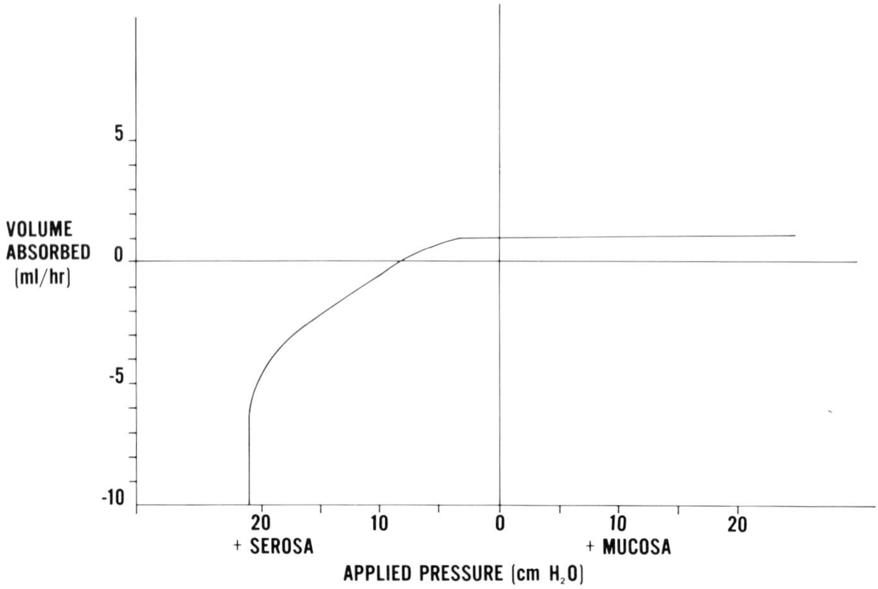

FIGURE 3. Illustration of how serosal pressure increases secretion but mucosal pressure does not affect absorption in vitro. (Redrawn from Hakim, A. A. and Lifson, N., *Am. J. Physiol.*, 216, 276, 1969.)

ity to Cl^- causes a shift in the direction of net Cl^- transport such that more begins to enter the lumen and less exits at the basolateral membrane. In addition, neutral NaCl absorption is also inhibited. In the large intestine there is Cl^- absorption coupled to HCO_3^- secretion and also to K^+ secretion.[11]

The cellular sites for secretion may be different than those for absorption. There is evidence that secretion occurs primarily in crypt cells and absorption from surface cells.[12] The intracellular stimulus for secretion seems to be primarily cyclic AMP and/or Ca^{++}, and a wide variety of secretagogues can stimulate an increase in one or both of these substances.

B. Hydraulic (Filtration) Secretion

Secretion can also be driven across the mucosa by changes in serosal tissue pressure, but not mucosal pressure, due to altered Starling forces in the interstitial tissue and/or capillaries analogous to the same forces which govern fluid translocation across capillaries (Figure 3).[13] Tissue Starling forces can, in turn, alter and be altered by the direction of net mucosal and capillary fluid translocation.

Entry of fluid into the interstitial spaces raises tissue pressure, first quickly and then more slowly, and also increases tissue conductance.[14-17] Fluid can enter the interstitial space because of either leakage from the capillaries or increased absorption from the lumen. Increased tissue pressure will, in turn, tend to cause ultrafiltration of fluid into both the circulation and the lumen. The overall direction of net fluid movement will be determined by the interactions among mucosal transport, capillary translocation, and mucosal ultrafiltration.

The blood flow directly concerned with secretion, both through O_2 delivery or wash-out of absorbed solutes and through Starling forces effects, is the mucosal blood flow. Measuring this blood flow and the local forces created in the mucosa is difficult. Measurements of mucosal blood flow have been made with a variety of techniques including microspheres, luminal clearance of highly permeable compounds, and microscopic observations. Estimates range from about 5 to 80% of total intestinal blood flow depending on the technique. The smaller values, measured by luminal clearance, probably represent villous blood flow in contact with the luminal solution, and the larger values, measured with microspheres, probably represent blood flow to the crypts and villi. If absorption takes place in the villi and secretion in the crypts,[12] then blood flow to these regions would have to be determined independently, which cannot be done at the present time. The values for mucosal blood flow measured by most techniques are in fairly good agreement, ranging from about 50 to 100 $\mu\ell$/g gut · min in cat and dog, which have a relatively larger fraction of muscularis, to 200 to 250 $\mu\ell$/g gut · min in the rat, which has a thinner muscularis layer.[14]

A net loss of fluid from the circulation into the interstitial space, which would in turn promote secretion, can occur if there are increases in capillary hydrostatic pressure or tissue colloid osmotic pressure and/or decreases in plasma colloid osmotic pressure or tissue hydrostatic pressure. An increase in capillary pressure could occur because of precapillary vasodilation and/or postcapillary vasoconstriction, although autoregulation of intestinal blood flow may tend to maintain blood flow and pressure at constant levels.[18] A decrease in tissue colloid osmotic pressure would occur when fluid enters the interstitium because of mucosal absorption or capillary transudation. The relative changes in estimated tissue pressure and colloid osmotic pressure as volume absorption increases suggest that the increased hydrostatic pressure is the major contributor moving fluid into capillaries at lower mucosal absorption rates, but as mucosal absorption increases the decrease in interstitial colloid osmotic pressure becomes more important.[19] More recent work suggests that tissue hydrostatic pressure and colloid osmotic pressure are about equal in moving fluid into capillaries during absorption.[20] The reverse situation would seem likely with active transcellular secretion.

Since changes in blood flow will also change Starling forces in the mucosa, separating these effects on fluid secretion would be difficult. In one series of experiments, blood flow and pressures were changed by mesenteric arterial or venous occlusion, both of which reduce blood flow but have opposite effects on capillary pressure.[21] Blood flow was measured by luminal clearance of ^3H_2O and capillary pressure estimated from resistance changes. Blood flow primarily affected the absorptive fluxes of Na and H_2O, and capillary pressure affected mainly the secretory fluxes. Blood flow affected the absorptive Na flux mainly through O_2 delivery to support active transport, but affected the absorptive H_2O flux mainly by a washout effect on diffusional exchange. Capillary pressure acted on the secretory fluxes primarily through changes in ultrafiltration.

Certain complications exist in quantitating the physical forces involved in mucosal fluid translocation. Tissue hydrostatic pressure in the mucosa is difficult to measure. Lee[22] measured central lacteal pressure while varying fluid absorption and found that pressures increased from about 1 to 7 mmHg as absorption increased to a maximum. Over rates of absorption commonly encountered, tissue (lacteal) pressure increased by only about 0.4 mmHg. Tissue colloid osmotic pressure has been estimated from the protein content of total lymph flow, which is a mixture from all layers of the gut, and found to decrease from about 10 to about 3 mmHg as absorption increases.[23] Capillary hydrostatic pressure in rat villi has been measured as 14 mmHg, and in the muscularis layer as 24 mmHg.[24] This latter observation indicates significant heterogeneity in the value of Starling forces in different regions of the gut, and therefore values derived from whole gut measurements may not reflect the significant values affecting secretion. A recent study has also shown differences in responsiveness of the microcirculation, with submucosal arterioles constricting and muscularis arterioles dilating when venous pressure was elevated.[25] Indeed, Yablonski and Lifson[26] and Granger[17] have suggested

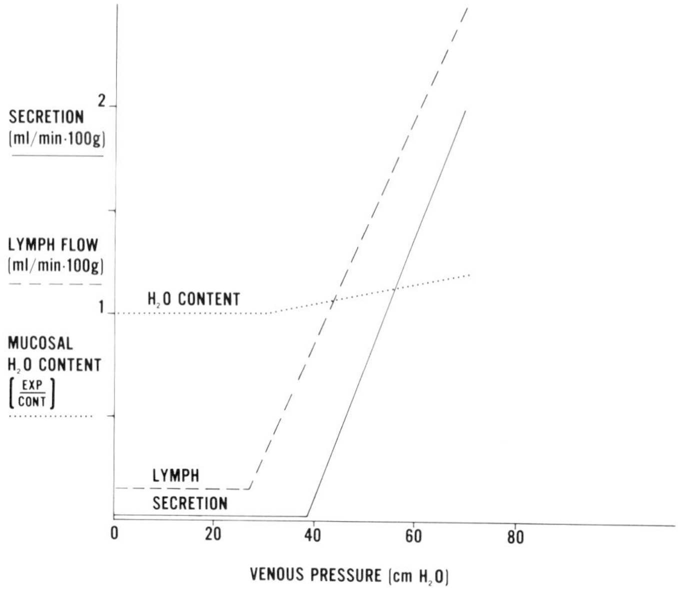

FIGURE 4. Illustration of threshold increase in secretion, mucosal H_2O content, and lymph flow as venous pressure is mechanically increased. (Redrawn from Yablonski, M. E. and Lifson, N., *J. Clin. Invest.*, 57, 904, 1976.)

that the interstitial region controlling translocation between the lumen and blood may be only the volume between the mucosal cell basolateral membrane and the subvillous capillaries which have fenestrations only at their surface facing the epithelial cells. An additional aspect of intestinal heterogeneity is that tissue hydration increases in direct proportion to venous pressure in nonmucosal regions of the gut, but in the mucosal tissue hydration increases only after a threshold of venous pressure, which is also when lymph flow and secretion increase (Figure 4).[26] These observations suggest mucosal autoregulation of pressure. Another complication is that, because of physical interactions between colloids and the mucopolysaccharides of the interstitial space, the change in effective colloid osmotic pressure is approximately twice the change in interstitial protein concentration, thus amplifying the effects of local colloid concentration changes.[27]

The permeability characteristics of the mucosal capillaries will also affect fluid translocation. The effective colloid osmotic pressure of tissue and plasma colloids is determined by the reflection coefficient of the capillary wall. In the small intestine the reflection coefficient is relatively high, about 0.9, and thus 90% of the maximum colloid osmotic rpessure can be exerted across the capillary wall (Figure 5). Changes in the reflection coefficient can change the contribution of colloid osmotic pressure relative to hydrostatic pressure in determining fluid translocation between the interstitium and blood.

There are some differences between the mucosal microcirculation in the large and small intestine. Colloid osmotic pressure gradients and reflection coefficients across the submucosal capillaries of the large intestine are similar to those in the small intestine. However, the hydrostatic pressure gradient is smaller across the large intestinal capillaries and the capillaries are also closer to the mucosal surface, thus favoring capillary absorption.[19]

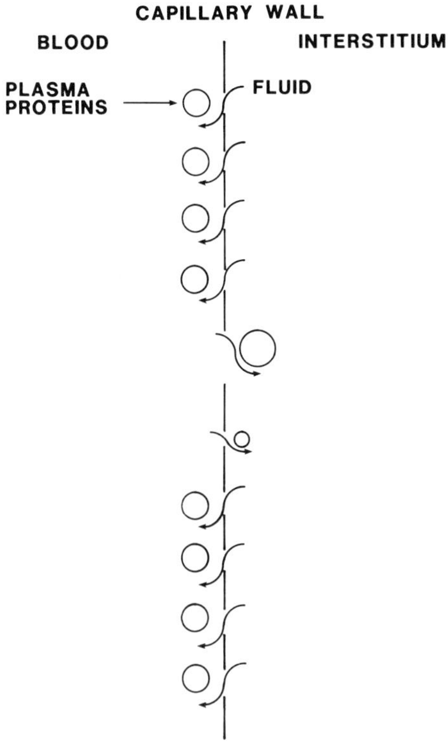

FIGURE 5. Illustration of how a reflection coefficient of 0.8 for proteins by the capillary wall can influence fluid movement by colloid osmotic pressure between plasma and interstitium. Proteins can cross the capillary endothelium through larger than average pores or because they are smaller than average proteins, and thus not generate an effective osmotic pressure.

C. Conductance Pathways

The pathways through which fluid moves between the intestinal lumen and the blood are essentially the same whether the driving forces originate in the cell or in the vascular system. The pathways include the lateral spaces between the epithelial cells, the interstitial space, and the capillary endothelium. Transcellular transport has an additional path through the apical membrane, cytoplasm, and basolateral membrane, but once solutes and water leave the cell they are subject to the same physical forces as fluid which by-passed the cell (Figure 6).

Fluid entry into the interstitium, whether across the mucosa or the capillary endothelium, expands the interstitial space of the matrix (Figure 7), thus increasing its conductance up to 1000-fold.[16] The increased conductance facilitates transfer between the mucosa and the capillaries and lymphatics. The lateral spaces between the cells of the small but not the large intestine are a relatively conductive pathway for fluid movement. Secretory stimuli frequently result in increased permeability of the mucosa which seems to involve both the paracellular and transcellular pathways.[8,28]

Transcellular absorption of solute, mainly NaCl, is thought to be coupled to water transport through the lateral spaces by solute being pumped into these spaces, thus causing a localized osmotic pressure increase which is dissipated by the entry of water through the tight junctions and lateral cell membranes.[29] The entry of water, in turn,

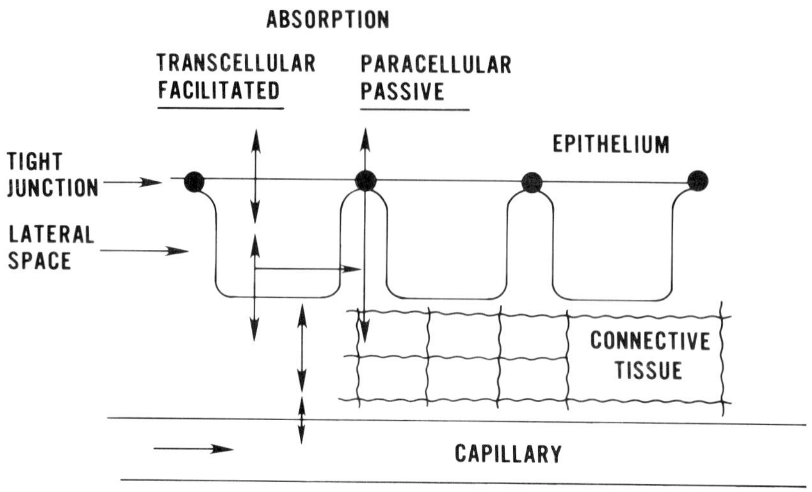

FIGURE 6. Diagram of sites of solute and H_2O movement in the intestinal mucosa.

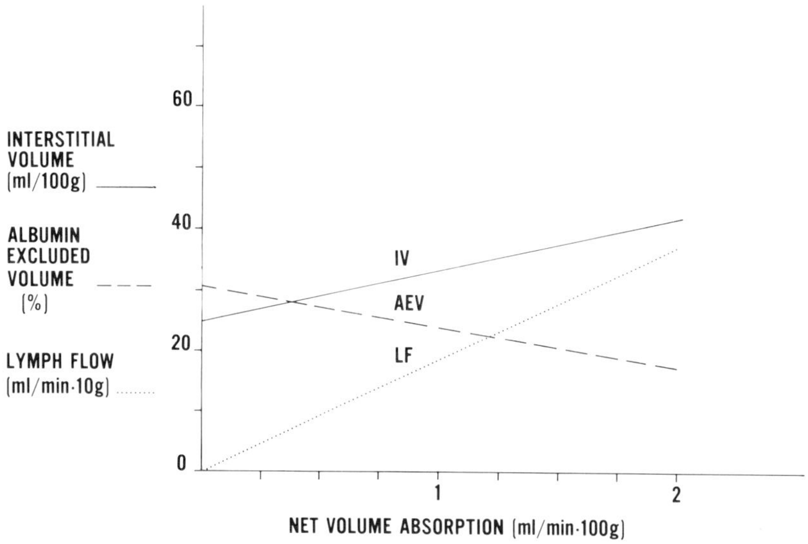

FIGURE 7. Illustration of how absorbed fluid can expand the interstitial space accessible to colloids and increase lymph flow. (Redrawn from Granger, D. N., Mortillaro, N., Kvietys, P., Rutili, G., Parker, J., and Taylor, A., *Am. J. Physiol.*, 238, G183, 1980.)

raises the hydrostatic pressure in the lateral spaces, which then forces fluid into the interstitium. The direction of movement of fluid through the lateral spaces is therefore, in part, determined by interstitial hydrostatic pressure.

D. General Interactions Between Circulation and Secretion

The circulation can affect intestinal secretion through (1) its delivery of oxygen to support active absorption or secretion, (2) changing Starling forces, (3) changing the ease of fluid movement across the mucosa, and (4) the delivery of solutes and water to the absorptive cells. It is difficult to predict or interpret cause/effect relationships between changes in blood flow and changes in secretion. A change in blood flow could reflect a primary event and secondarily alter intestinal secretion, or primary changes in

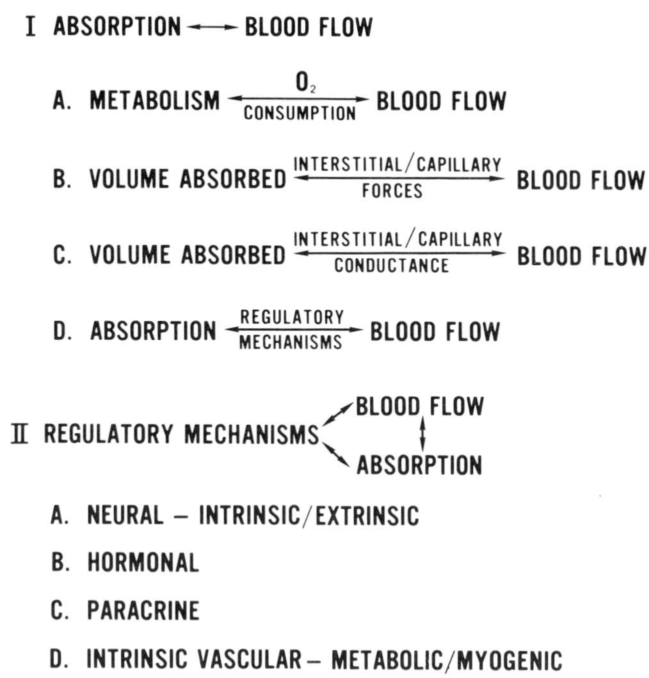

FIGURE 8. Diagram of possible interactions between mucosal blood flow and absorption which can feed back to mutually alter each other.

intestinal function could secondarily alter blood flow through metabolic, neural, or hormonal regulatory mechanisms (Figure 8).

Oxygen consumption is increased during both induced absorption and secretion.[30,31] Oxygen delivery can be met by increased oxygen extraction and/or increased blood flow. Increased blood flow was relatively more important in the small intestine, and increased oxygen extraction in the large intestine.[32] Blood flow can be reduced by 50% by mechanical means without affecting oxygen consumption, indicating that even if blood flow is somewhat decreased, oxgyen delivery may still be adequate to support increased absorption.[33,34] This may be especially true since decreased blood flow would tend to increase the H^+ and CO_2 levels in the mucosa, and these changes would stimulate absorption in both the small and large intestine.[10,35]

Although both increased secretion and absorption can increase O_2 consumption, there is not necessarily a proportional increase. In the small intestine, when secretion was stimulated by several secretagogues, only theophylline, cholera toxin, and PGE_1 caused a positive correlation between secretion rate and O_2 consumption, but there was no such correlation when secretion and O_2 consumption were increased by mesenteric venous occlusion, glucagon, histamine, vasoactive intestinal polypeptide, or intraluminal ricinoleic acid.[30] Oxygen consumption per milliliter of fluid absorbed was about 50% higher in the large as compared to the small intestine, and secretion required about 400% more O_2 than did absorption per milliliter of translocated fluid in the small intestine.[30,32]

Since secretion seems to depend on the degree of active Na^+ absorption, the net effect of reducing O_2 delivery to absorptive cells is not easily predicted. If both absorption and secretion were reduced equally there would be no changes in net absorption. This type of response has been observed in the colon when blood flow was mechanically reduced.[36] A primary increase in active secretion would probably cause an increase in

Table 1
SUMMARY OF EFFECTS OF SECRETAGOGUES ON GUT FUNCTIONS

Secretagogue	Active secretion	Mucosal blood flow	Mucosal capillary pressure	Blood-lumen conductance
VIP	↑	↓	↓?	↑?
Serotonin	↑	—?	?	?
Neurotensin	↑	—	—	↑
CCK	?	↑?	?	?
Glucagon	?	↑	↑	↑
Histamine	↑?	↑?	?	↑
Substance P	↑?	↑	?	?
PGE_1	↑	↑?	↑?	↑
Acetylcholine	↑	?	?	?
Adenosine	↑?	↑?	?	—?
Gastrin	↑?	↓	?	?
Bradykinin	↑	↑?	?	↑?
Calcitonin	↑?	?	?	?
Bacterial toxins	↑	?	?	?
Laxatives	↑	↑?	?	↑?

Note: Increased (↑), decreased (↓), or unchanged (—) functions; (?) questionable, conflicting, or unknown changes.

O_2 consumption by the mucosa because of cellular regulatory mechanisms which respond to intracellular ion concentrations.[6]

A problem arises in interpreting the mechanism of drugs or regulatory agents which cause secretion since many of these substances could have both direct vasoactive and absorptive effects, making cause/effect interpretations difficult (Figure 8). Also, since visceral muscle contraction can alter O_2 consumption, measurements of O_2 consumption which are based on total blood flow may be confounded by that contribution to the total volume of O_2 consumed.

A basic question then is: do the various causes of secretory diarrhea act through changing transcellular secretion, physical forces, or both, and do changes in mucosal blood flow support or limit the diarrhea? In addition, there is the question of whether secretagogues act directly or through other mediators (Table 1).

III. SECRETAGOGUES

A. Vasoactive Intestinal Polypeptide

Vasoactive intestinal polypeptide (VIP) is found in nerves primarily in the lamina propria of the mucosa, and to a lesser extent in the submucosa and muscularis.[37] Of particular interest are the presence of and sensitivity to VIP in the muscularis mucosa of the small and large intestine.[38] Motility of the muscularis mucosa could alter the surface area of the absorbing or secreting surfaces as well as mechanically occluding blood flow to the mucosa. Hypertrophy and contraction of the muscularis mucosa are characteristic of ulcerative colitis and ileitis, and VIP-containing nerves are highly immunoreactive in the former. This may be especially important since VIP is secreted into and has effects from the lumen.[39] Elevated levels of VIP are associated with pancreatic tumors (watery diarrhea — Verner Morrison — pancreatic cholera syndrome) and the accompanying diarrhea.[40]

VIP causes secretion in vitro in both the large and small intestine (2 $\mu g/\ell$;[41] 10^{-9} to 10^{-7} M;[42] 10^{-11} to 10^{-9} M[43]) through a cyclic AMP-sensitive mechanism. However, in vivo, although VIP (400 pmol/kg · hr, i.v.) causes a small amount of intestinal secretion in humans, it frequently does not cause diarrhea.[39,40] In vitro, VIP-induced secretion can be inhibited by somatostatin both before and after the process, which increases cyclic AMP,[44] but in vivo somatostatin acts through reducing VIP secretion by pancreatic tumors.[40] In vivo, VIP (30 pmol/kg · min, i.v.) produced secretion in the jejunum but not the colon, and the secretion was not associated with changes in cyclic AMP in the rabbit.[45] An effect of VIP (80 ng/kg · min, i.a.) which is partially mediated through increased capillary ultrafiltration is also suggested by capillary dilation and a slight increase in protein losses into the canine lumen, which were not seen with cholera toxin.[46]

Intravenous VIP (17.5 to 175 ng/min) causes intestinal secretion in the dog primarily by decreasing the absorptive fluxes of Na and H_2O.[47] Pretreatment with guanethidine did not alter the effect of VIP, but pretreatment with atropine abolished the VIP-induced secretion. VIP (10^{-9} to 10^{-7} *M*) has been shown to increase acetylcholine release in other studies in vitro.[48] VIP also decreased effective mucosal blood flow and arterial pressure and increased mucosal resistance, which resulted in decreased estimated capillary pressure. The decreased effective mucosal blood flow accounted for part of the decreased absorptive fluxes, but there was another component which could represent an effect on transcellular absorption. Changes in capillary pressure could not account for changes in secretory fluxes, and thus VIP may have increased transcellular secretion but also caused a simultaneous reduction in ultrafiltration across the capillaries. Direct observation in the rat showed that i.v. VIP (5 μg/kg · min) did not change villous blood flow but did dilate the villous arterioles. Blood pressure was decreased, but total intestinal blood flow was only transiently decreased. Bolus injections of 70 μg/kg did reduce villous blood flow.[49] The authors suggested the blood flow was shunted to the crypt region. VIP (1 μg/kg · min, i.a.) also decreased lymph flow in the cat, which is characteristic of active secretion.[50]

Considering both the in vivo and in vitro data, it seems likely that VIP does increase active secretion by the epithelial cells. In vivo the reduced effective mucosal blood flow and capillary pressure would tend to blunt the active secretory effect.

B. Serotonin

Serotonin is one of several substances released in carcinoid syndrome, which is characterized by diarrhea.[51] Serotonin has also been implicated as an intermediate in the diarrhea of amebiasis.[52] Serotonin is found in large amounts in the mucosa and to a lesser extent in the myenteric plexus. Serotoninergic neurons comprise only about 2% of myenteric neutrons and serotonin coexists with other regulatory agents in the same nerves, which makes its role in the regulation of gut function more difficult to determine.[53,54] A serotonin barrier between the two areas has been proposed.[55] Serotonin seems to move across the gut relatively easily, but in vivo blood flow to the two areas would likely reduce effective diffusion.[56] Therefore, mucosal and myenteric serotonin would have independent effects.

Serotonin increases secretion both in vivo and in vitro in both the large and small intestine (30 μg/kg · min, i.v., dog;[51,53,57] 10^{-8} to 10^{-5} *M*;[58] 20 μg/kg · min, i.v., rabbit[59]). Serotonin acts through a Ca^{++}-mediated process rather than through cyclic AMP.[60] However, epithelial cells do not have serotoninergic receptors, suggesting that serotonin may act through an intermediate.[61] In rabbit small intestine, the presence of glucose in the luminal fluid abolished the secretory effect of serotonin.[59] Serotonin (100 μ*M*) inhibits neutral NaCl absorption and stimulates active Cl^- secretion.[62] Serum from carcinoid patients reduces lymph flow, also suggesting an increase in active secretion, but net secretion was not observed.[50] In these studies, net absorption was observed to decrease in a few experiments, but only when blood flow was not changed.

The effects of serotonin on blood flow are highly variable.[18] Intravenous serotonin, (33 to 100 μg/kg · min), increased jejunal vascular resistance and caused precapillary constriction in the cat as judged by a decrease in capillary filtration coefficient.[63] These findings would suggest a fall in capillary pressure. Other investigators, however, found an increase in capillary filtration coefficient.[64] In both the large and small intestine the vasoconstrictor effects of relatively large doses of serotonin (50 to 100 μg/min, i.a., cat) are probably mediated through adrenergic stimulation.[65,66] The vasodilator effects of lower doses of serotonin (5 μg/min) were also nerve-mediated. Serotonin (3.3 to 333 μg/min, either i.a. or i.v.) had relatively little effect on absorption from dog ileum or on effective mucosal blood flow measured by luminal ^3H_2O clearance.[230] Several manipulations such as mechanical stimulation of the mucosa or electrical field stimulation in vivo, which were associated with serotonin release, increased mucosal blood flow as judged by visual observation or ^{85}Kr clearance.[67] Serotonin-induced secretion (52 μmol/kg × 14 days) was not associated with changes in mucosa-submucosal blood flow in rabbits.[68]

The secretory processes stimulated by serotonin in vivo have been difficult to elucidate, but some investigators have suggested that serosal hydrostatic pressure may be one of them.[57] Serotonin does seem to increase active secretion, but its variable effects on blood flow in vivo make the role of physical forces difficult to evaluate. Also, the stimulation of other regulatory agents by serotonin could potentiate or inhibit the direct secretory effect of serotonin in vivo.

C. Neurotensin

Neurotensin is found primarily in the ileal mucosa, and to a much lesser extent in the ileal muscularis.[69] It is released by luminal fat through nerve stimulation.[70]

Neurotensin causes intestinal secretion in the dog, human, and rat (0.67 μg/kg·min, i.v., dog;[71] 3 pmol/kg · min, i.v., human;[72] 50 pmol/kg · min, i.v., rat[73]) in vivo and in vitro (10^{-9} to 10^{-7} *M*[74]). The secretion is not associated with an increase in cyclic AMP, but probably depends on intracellular Ca^{++}.[60] Neurotensin (0.75 to 7.5 μg/min, i.a., i.v.) increases canine intestinal secretion in the dog in vivo due to increased secretory fluxes and decreased absorptive fluxes.[230]

Neurotensin (2.5 to 40 pmol/kg · min, i.v., dog) is a vasodilator in the mesenteric circulation and selectively increases blood flow to the muscularis of the gut, especially the ileum, as determine by microspheres.[75] Neurotensin (0.75 to 7.5 μg/min, i.a., i.v.) caused only slight increases in effective mucosal blood flow as judged by ^3H_2O clearance, and at the higher dose, a decrease in blood pressure and mucosal resistance.[230] The changes in capillary pressure and blood flow did not seem sufficient to explain the changes in fluxes. Since neurotensin had the same effects during both i.a. and i.v. infusion at the same dose, a direct effect on the gut does not seem likely. One observation which may be significant was that there were reversible changes in hematocrit during neurotensin infusion, suggesting an increased permeability of the vasculature since capillary pressure was not greatly changed. An increase in large-pore size of the intestinal vasculature during neurotensin infusion (180 p*M*) has been observed by others.[76]

It seems likely, therefore, that neurotensin increases active secretion, which is potentiated in vivo by an increase in tissue hydrostatic pressure due to fluid leakage from the capillaries.

D. Cholecystokinin

Cholecystokinin (CCK) or its analogues decrease intestinal absorption or increase secretion in humans and experimental animals (10 to 40 U/kg, i.a., rat;[77] 6 U/kg · hr, i.v., human;[78] 4 U/kg · hr, i.v., dog[79]). However, an analogue, caerulein (5 μg/kg, i.m.), which causes diarrhea, did not alter small or large intestinal absorption of fluid in the rat[80] nor did CCK-OP (octapeptide) (0.3 μg/min, i.v.) in conscious dogs.[81] CCK (1 U, i.v., rat) increased lymph flow, which is suggestive of an increase in fluid transudation across the capillaries.[82]

CCK increases blood flow to the intestinal mucosa but not the combined mucosa-submucosa, with no change to the muscularis in cats.[83] CCK (0.1 μg/kg · min, i.a., dog) also increases O_2 consumption by the intestine.[84] Atropine blocks the vasodilation and increased O_2 consumption due to CCK.

The mechanism of action of CCK has not been well determined, nor has an effect on active secretion been well established. The vasoactive properties of CCK are consistent with a partial cardiovascular origin of the secretion.

E. Glucagon

Glucagon has variable effects on gut absorption in vivo and in vitro. Glucagon (4 to 256 μg/kg, i.v.[85]) increased absorption in the rat but decreased it in the dog (10 μg/min, i.v.[81]) and human (0.6 μg/kg · hr, i.v.[86]) in vivo. In conjunction with gastrin (20 μg/kg · hr), glucagon (60 μg/kg · hr, i.v.) can cause diarrhea.[87] Glucagon (0.05 to 0.5 μg/kg · min) did not change absorption when directly infused intra-arterially into a segment of canine intestine, but increased the unidirectional secretory and absorptive fluxes of Na and H_2O. Glucagon decreased net absorption and the unidirectional fluxes when infused into an adjacent gut segment.[88] Glucagon (90 to 880 pg/mℓ[89]) in vitro did not change transport in human small intestine or in rat large intestine (10^{-6} *M*;[43] 10^{-5} *M*[90]), but did increase secretion in mouse intestine only in the absence of glucose (30 μg/mℓ[91]). Also, mucosal cyclic AMP is not increased by glucagon (10^{-5} *M*).[92] Enteroglucagon (70 p*M*) was also associated with the malabsorption of celiac disease.[93]

Glucagon (0.5 μg/kg · min, i.a.) increases intestinal blood flow and O_2 consumption in the dog.[84] At the microcirculatory level, glucagon (50 ng/kg · min, i.a.) increases capillary pressure, interstitial pressure, and capillary filtration coefficient, which were associated with mucosal damage and protein losses into the lumen of cats.[94] Effective mucosal blood flow was increased by local arterial glucagon but decreased by glucagon infused into an adjacent gut segment.[88] Villous blood flow, measured by microscopy, was markedly increased by glucagon (1 μg/kg·min, i.v.), while total blood flow was unchanged in the cat.[49]

Glucagon does not seem to have any pronounced effect on active transcellular secretion. The cardiovascular effects of glucagon suggest that the intestinal secretion observed in vivo is due mainly to physical forces.

F. Histamine

Chloride secretion was increased by histamine (10^{-4} *M*, H_1 receptors[95]) in guinea pig ileum but not in rabbit ileum (10^{-4} *M*[96]), although in the latter alkali secretion was increased. Chloride secretion by rabbit colon was also increased by histamine (10^{-5} *M*[97]) through a Ca^{++}-mediated effect. In other studies, however, alkali secretion was decreased by histamine (10^{-4} *M*[98]). Local histamine infusion increased intestinal secretion in vivo which contained a large concentration of protein (2 mg/hr, i.a., dog;[99] 1 μg/kg · min, i.a., cat[50]). Lymph flow and its protein concentration were also increased.

Histamine (0.5 μg/kg · min, i.a., dog), through H_1 receptors, caused an initial vasodilation which was maintained by H_2 receptors and also caused a delayed increase in muscularis flow through H_1 receptors, relative to mucosa-submucosal flow, although the latter was still slightly above control levels.[100] Microvascular permeability of serosal intestinal capillaries was increased by H_1 stimulation (5×10^{-4} *M*[101]). However, the microvascular permeability increase of the gut as a whole was due to H_2 receptor stimulation (10 μg/mℓ, i.a., cat[102]). This discrepancy between the histamine receptors which cause increased vascular permeability may be due to the sites which were studied or to species or technical differences. The permeability of the serosal capillaries was studied by the leakage of fluorescent proteins, which tends to measure more rapid responses.

Although histamine increases active secretion in vitro, it is most likely that the secretory effects in vivo are due to increased capillary permeability and blood flow leading to ultrafiltration driven by increased interstitial pressure.

G. Substance P

NaCl secretion is transiently increased by relatively high (10 μg/mℓ) levels of substance P in vitro,[103,104] but absorption is increased in vivo.[73] Cyclic AMP is not increased by substance P. Substance P (0.74 to 7.4 pmol/min, i.a., dog[105]) increases total blood flow and mucosal blood flow from the luminal surface (4 ng/mℓ[106]). At the present time neither the net effect on secretion nor a mechanism of action for substance P is well defined.

H. Prostaglandins

Intestinal secretion is increased by i.a. prostaglandins PGE_1, PGA_1, and PGF_2 (2 μg/min, i.a.[107]) by canine jejunum, and mucosal PGE_2 (0.1 μg/mℓ · kg[108]) causes secretion by human jejunum. PGE_1 (10^{-9} to 10^{-8} *M*) caused secretion by extracorporeally perfused rat jejunum, but PGE_2 or $PGF_{2\alpha}$ did not significantly alter absorption, although there was a tendency toward secretion.[109] Rats injected with a PGE_2 analogue had diarrhea even with the ileocecal junction tied, and the site of fluid secretion was localized to the cecum.[110] Both PGE_1 and PGA_1 increased secretion and cyclic AMP in large and small intestine in vitro (10^{-7} to 10^{-4} *M*;[111] 5×10^{-7} to 5×10^{-5} *M*;[112] 10^{-5} *M*[113]). However, PGE_2 increased intestinal secretion at a concentration (10^{-10} to 10^{-8} *M*) well below the level which increased cyclic AMP in vitro, and $PGF_{2\alpha}$ was much less effective.[114] In general, prostaglandins of the E or A type can cause secretion, but it is questionable whether cyclic AMP is involved.

Prostaglandins are synthesized by the GI tract and are released by a wide variety of stimuli including vasoactive agents, mechanical stimuli, and hypertonicity.[115] PGE_1, PGE_2, and PGI_2 are vasodilators, but $PGF_{2\alpha}$ is a vasoconstrictor. However, a precursor of prostaglandins, arachidonic acid, inhibited the increased blood flow following placement of food in the gut.[116] PGI_2 increased mucosal blood flow, but PGD_2 decreased it during increased total blood flow.[115] Luminal PGE_1 at a low concentration and $PGF_{2\alpha}$ at a much higher concentration increased intestinal secretion but reduced absorption of ^3H_2O. At higher concentrations of PGE_1, blood flow and both the secretion and absorption of ^3H_2O all were increased.[117] The increased secretion and decreased absorption of ^3H_2O seen with low concentrations of PGE_1 (0.1 μg/mℓ) and high concentrations (50 μg/mℓ) of $PGF_{2\alpha}$ are consistent with reduced mucosal blood flow and increased capillary pressure or conductivity.[21] Local arterial infusion of PGE_1 (5 μg/min) into cat ileum increased lymph flow (characteristic of passive secretion due to capillary fluid losses), blood flow, and protein losses into the lymph and lumen.[118] The magnitude of the changes in lymph flow and protein losses was smaller than that observed with purely physical secretion, and it was suggested that active secretion was occurring simultaneously. There was marked mucosal damage during PGE_1 infusion in these experiments, with tips of villi disappearing and desmosomal damage, but mucosal damage of itself is not necessarily associated with intestinal secretion.[119] PGE_2 analogues have similar effects on large and small intestine in vitro, including increased Na and Cl secretory fluxes and reduced electrical resistance, suggesting a leakier mucosa (10^{-6} *M*[114,120]).

The evidence seems consistent with PGE_1 and probably PGI_2 causing secretory diarrhea through effects on both active transcellular secretion and physical fluid transudation across mucosal capillaries, due to both increased capillary pressure and conductance.

I. Cholinergic Stimulation

Neural regulation of intestinal transport is of importance in its own right as well as being a probable intermediate in the effects of many other agents on the intestine. For example, the effects on secretion and blood flow of histamine, cholera toxin, pentagastrin, and VIP, among others, can be markedly changed by neurotransmitter antagonists.[47,84,95,121,122] Tapper[123] has suggested that the direction of net fluid transport may be controlled by the balance between cholinergic and adrenergic stimuli, with many hormones or paracrine agents acting as neuromodulators. In general, cholinergic stimuli cause secretion by the intestine.

There is evidence for nerve-like cells within the mucosa[124] and for cholinergic nerves and muscarinic receptors on colonic enterocytes[125,126] and small intestine,[127-129] but muscarinic receptors were not found in the mucosa of the small intestine in a radioautographic study.[130] The muscarinic binding was similar for crypt and villous cells.[126] Noradrenergic nerves were also found in close proximity to mucosal cells.[131]

Cholinergic agents caused intestinal secretion in humans (neostigmine, 6.25 μg/hr, i.v.[132]) and experimental animals (pilocarpine, 20 mg/kg, i.v., rat;[133,134] bethanechol, 0.04 mg/min, i.v., dog[135]). β-Adrenergic blockade in humans also increased intestinal secretion.[136] Muscarinic cholinergic stimuli were responsible for about 50% of Cl^- secretion observed in vitro induced by electric field stimulation or depolarizing agents[137-139] in human and guinea pig mucosa, but no effect was observed in rabbit ileum.[140] Human ileal responses to electric field stimulation were reduced by about 90% by atropine (10^{-5} *M*[141]). Electric field stimulation increased Cl^- secretion in both the large and small intestine.[142] The intracellular mediator for cholinergic-induced secretion is probably Ca^{++} rather than cyclic AMP.[60] Paradoxically, a low dose of atropine (10^{-8} to 10^{-7} mol/kg) can increase bethanechol (10^{-4} pmol/kg, i.p.) secretion in vivo.[143] Cholinergic stimuli have mixed effects on both the large and small intestine in vitro (1 μ*M* to 1 m*M* carbachol, 0.1 m*M* DMPP).[144,145] At low levels of cholinergic stimulation a muscarinic effect on the enterocyte predominated which caused Cl^- secretion, but at higher levels a nicotinic effect predominated which caused increased Na absorption and which was mediated indirectly through adrenergic nerves. However, vagotomy is frequently characterized by diarrhea, which is not consistent with acetylcholine-induced secretion and suggests an indirect mechanism. Vagotomized patients had ileal secretion caused primarily by reduced absorptive fluxes and secondarily by increased secretory fluxes. Increased xylose absorption suggested that mucosal permeability had increased.[146]

The direct effect of cholinergic stimuli on intestinal blood flow is vasodilatory, but this effect can be reduced by motility which can mechanically occlude blood vessels.[147] Intra-arterial acetylcholine (0.05 to 0.6 mg/min, i.a., dog) infusion reduced effective mucosal blood flow by about 35% at both the highest and lowest total blood flow rates.[148] Pilocarpine caused villous blood flow to decrease in conjunction with venous engorgement as determined visually.[145] However, vagotomy decreased blood flow to the villi as determined by microscopy.[149] Intravenous injections of atropine or neostigmine suggested that cholinergic stimuli either decreased or did not affect mucosal blood flow and increased mucosal capillary pressure.[150,151] In contrast, studies using the clearance of ^{125}I from the lumen showed that effective mucosal blood flow was increased by acetylcholine (1 μg/kg·min, i.a., dog) in proportion to total blood flow.[152]

The influence of cholinergic stimuli on intestinal secretion is relatively complex. Generally, the secretion can be attributed to stimulation of transcellular secretion, which could be blunted by a reduction in effective mucosal blood flow and O_2 delivery and by concomitant adrenergic stimuli. The secretion, however, would tend to be increased by any increase in capillary pressure.

J. Adenosine

Adenosine has been implicated as a local regulator of blood flow.[153] Active Cl^- secretion of rabbit colon is stimulated by adenosine (0.5 m*M*) in vitro through cyclic AMP,[154] but adenosine (0.1 mg/min, i.a., dog) does not decrease absorption across canine colon in vivo, although the unidirectional absorptive and secretory fluxes of H_2O are increased, as is total and effective mucosal blood flow.[36] Adenosine does not affect lymph flow or oncotic pressure in the small intestine, indicating no change in fluid movement across capillaries. Oxygen consumption is decreased by adenosine due to both a direct cellular effect and a redistribution of blood flow from the mucosa-submucosa to the muscularis (10 μg/mℓ, i.a., cat;[153] 9 ng/mℓ, i.a., dog[155]).

Information on the secretory effects of adenosine is limited but, assuming that a small intestinal transcellular secretion would be increased, as is large intestinal secretion, the reduced mucosal blood flow could counteract the cellular secretion. In the large intestine, there are active secretion and increased mucosal blood flow and capillary pressure, both of which should increase secretion which, however, was not observed. Possibly, the increased blood flow supplies sufficient O_2 to maintain an increased active absorption which balances the increased secretion.

K. Gastrin

Hypersecretion of gastrin has been associated with diarrhea.[156] Gastrin (160 mg/ℓ) decreased absorption in the hamster ileum in vitro, but not in more proximal portions of the intestine.[157] Gastrin (800 pg/mℓ) reduced absorption across human colon in vitro due to reduced absorptive and increased secretory fluxes.[156] However, pentagastrin (10^{-5} *M*) did not alter fluid absorption across rat colon either by itself or in combination with glucagon.[158] Pentagastrin (10 to 200 μg/kg, i.a.) decreased ileal absorption but increased duodenal absorption in rats in vivo.[77] Patients with Zollinger-Ellison syndrome who had elevated gastrin levels had greatly increased small and large intestinal absorption, which reduced the large volume of fluid entering the jejunum from the stomach and duodenum to almost normal fecal volume.[159] Pentagastrin (10 μg/min, i.v.) decreased absorption across the dog gut in vivo due to increased secretory fluxes and decreased absorptive fluxes.[122] Atropine inhibited while guanethidine potentiated the effects of pentagastrin. Pentagastrin (4 to 8 μg/kg · hr, i.v.) reduced absorption in the ileum but not the jejunum or colon of conscious dogs, and did not have consistent effects on unidirectional fluxes.[160] Pentagastrin (5.0 μg/kg · hr, i.v.) inhibited absorption in both ileum and jejunum in anesthetized dogs.[161] Gastrin is a vasodilator at high doses.[18] At doses which decreased absorption (10 μg/min, i.v.) in the dog, pentagastrin did not change ileal blood flow but decreased effective mucosal blood flow.[122]

Gastrin reduces intestinal absorption, probably through both a direct effect on transcellular secretion and decreased blood flow. A portion of these effects is neurally mediated.

L. Bradykinin

Bradykinin (10^{-10} to 10^{-8} *M*) stimulates secretion in vitro in both ileum and colon of rabbit and guinea pig, mainly through a prostaglandin mechanism.[162] Bradykinin (10^{-12}

to 10^{-10} *M*) inhibited absorption at both the mucosal and serosal surfaces, but could increase absorption at the serosal surface when basal absorption was low in rat jejunum in vitro.[163] Bradykinin is a potent vasodilator and increases the permeability-surface area product at relatively low concentrations (36 ng/mℓ, i.a.).[164] It also increases capillary protein permeability at higher concentrations (680 ng/mℓ, i.a.).

The effects of bradykinin on intestinal secretion in vivo have not been well defined. If secretion occurs in vivo, both an increased active secretion and mucosal blood flow would contribute.

M. Calcitonin

Hypersecretion of calcitonin by tumors of the pancreas,[165] adrenal medulla,[166] and thyroid[167] has been associated with diarrhea. However, as is the case with many clinical associations of hypersecretion of hormones with GI symptoms, there frequently are several hormones with elevated levels also present. Calcitonin (10 μg/mℓ) caused Cl^- secretion and reduced Na^+ absorption across rat ileum in vitro.[103] The decreased Na absorption was due to decreased absorptive fluxes and the increased Cl^- secretion was due to decreased absorptive and increased secretory fluxes. Cyclic AMP concentrations in the tissue were not changed by calcitonin. However, calcitonin (10 μg/mℓ) did not alter absorption across rabbit ileum in vitro.[103] Intravenous calcitonin increased secretion in man[167,168] (1 U/kg · hr) and rabbit[169] (0.18 μg/kg · hr), but in other studies calcitonin (0.55 μg/kg · hr) did not alter absorption in the rabbit.[170] The increased Na secretion across the rabbit jejunum was due to increased secretory fluxes, and across the ileum was due also to decreased absorptive fluxes. In the rabbit ileum, luminal glucose blocked the calcitonin-induced decrease in the absorptive flux. Calcitonin (3 μg/kg · hr, i.v.) did not affect absorption across the ileum of conscious dogs.[171] Information pertinent to the effects of calcitonin on intestinal blood flow could not be found, and hence the possible influence of altered mucosal hemodynamics on calcitonin-induced secretion could not be determined. Calcitonin does cause active secretion in vitro and in vivo in some species, and therefore altered mucosal blood flow may not be a necessary contributor to the secretion.

N. Bacterial Toxins

Several species of bacteria produce toxins which cause intestinal secretion both in vivo and in vitro. The proximal small intestine is most affected, with relatively little effect on the colon.[172] Cl^-, HCO_3^-, Na^+, and K^+ secretion are increased,[173] accompanied by reduced absorptive fluxes of Na^+ and/or Cl^-[174,175] and increased secretory Na^+ fluxes[176,177] in vitro and in vivo. Cholera toxin increases the secretory but not the absorptive Na fluxes in vivo. The increased secretion is associated with increased levels of cellular cyclic AMP,[172] although some studies, both in vivo and in vitro, have not found a correlation between cyclic AMP and secretion.[178,179] In addition, there is evidence for nerves as intermediates in the effects of cholera toxin, accounting for about 60% of the secretion.[121]

The vascular effects of bacterial toxins on mucosal blood flow have not been well defined. Increased, decreased, and unchanged flows have been measured.[180-182] The rate of secretion is also relatively independent of blood flow.[182] Local differences in the appearance of the vasculature have been observed with villous capillaries distended and crypt capillaries constricted.[183] Lymph flow is decreased by cholera toxin and the secreted fluid is protein-free, which suggests that the secretion is active.[184]

Many bacterial toxins which cause intestinal secretion apparently act through stimulation of active transcellular secretion. Cardiovascular changes, although they are variable, do not seem to influence the rate of secretion.

O. Laxatives

There are a number of substances which cause diarrhea and are generally grouped together as laxatives.[185] These include diphenolic compounds such as phenolphthalein, organic acids such as ricinoleic acid or bile acids, and magnesium salts. Bile acids, ricinoleic acid, and fats produced during steatorrhea have a number of similarities.[28] In general their mode of action, although studied for many years, is still poorly defined.

Phenolphthalein causes diarrhea in monkeys.[186] When mucosal tissues from these same animals were studied in vitro, mucosal phenolphthalein (10^{-3} *M*) caused Na^+ secretion but not Cl^- secretion in jejunal mucosa, and both Na^+ and Cl^- secretion in colonic mucosa. The unidirectional absorptive and secretory fluxes of Na and Cl were generally increased, although at a relatively low dose the absorptive fluxes of Na and Cl were decreased in colonic mucosa. Paradoxically, serosal phenolphthalein (10^{-4} to 10^{-3} *M*) increased net Na^+ and Cl^- absorption in the jejunum but not the colon, which was also associated with increased unidirectional fluxes. Similar effects were observed in rabbit ileum in vitro, but luminal phenolphthalein (10^{-4} *M*) caused only a transient decrease in absorption.[187] The tissue effects did not seem dependent on cyclic AMP or on Na,K-ATPase. Ricinoleic acid (5 m*M*), the active ingredient of castor oil, deoxycholic acid (5 m*M*), anthraquinone sennosides (75 mg/kg p.o.), and the osmotic laxative mannitol (22 m*M*) all increased H_2O entry into the lumen of rat colon.[188] PGE release into the lumen was also increased by these laxatives, with the exception of mannitol. However, inhibition of PGE synthesis with indomethacin could reduce PGE entry, but not the effect on H_2O entry into the lumen, for some of the laxatives. Ricinoleate and deoxycholate are Ca^{++} ionophores and therefore may cause transcellular secretion through raising intracellular Ca^{++}.[189] In perfused human ileum, bile acids (2.5 m*M*) increased secretion due to reduced absorptive fluxes.[190]

Studies on the effect of laxatives on mucosal permeability or integrity have yielded variable results. Mucosal damage, detected microscopically, has been observed with bile salts (0.1 to 10 m*M*) or their analogues,[191-193] but ricinoleic acid (10 m*M*) did not cause junctional disruption.[194] A distinction between active transcellular secretion and passive permeability was assessed by the plasma clearance of ^{51}CrEDTA in the rat colon[195] and by the ability of chlorpromazine (suggested to act by decreasing active secretion) in the rat small and large intestine.[196] Deoxycholic acid (1.8 m*M*) was concluded to have its effect mainly through increases in passive permeability, but oxyphenisatin (16 to 32 m*M*) and bisacodyl (28 to 83 m*M*) increased secretion only secondarily through increases in passive permeability. Dodecyl sulfate (1.7 m*M*), assumed to act analogously to bile acids, increased the rate at which Na and H_2O moved down their concentration gradients in both directions between plasma and luminal solution, suggesting an effect on mucosal permeability.[197] An opiate which reduced the secretion induced by deoxycholate also reduced intestinal permeability but did not alter the changes in cyclic AMP or Na,K-ATPase caused by the laxative.[198] In the rat colon, ricinoleic acid causes an increase in permeability as judged by increased inulin and creatinine clearance.[199,200]

A mixture of bile-glucose increased mucosal blood flow and whole bowel O_2 consumption.[201] Bile-oleic acid (20 m*M*) also increased total blood flow and O_2 consumption.[119] Ricinoleic acid (5 m*M*) increased lymph flow, indicating an increase in capillary fluid loss.[50] Bile-oleic acid also caused major structural damage to the intestinal mucosa. It was of interest in these experiments that atropine (0.2 mg/kg) reversed the bile-oleic acid-induced secretion, but not the mucosal damage or the increase in blood flow and O_2 consumption.[119] Whatever the mechanism by which atropine reverses secretion, it seems that mucosal damage per se does not invariably lead to increased secretion. Hexamethonium (20 mg/kg, i.v.) has also been shown to reduce the secretion caused by deoxycholate (8 m*M*) in the rat.[202] The neural component of laxative-induced secretion could be due to an increase in active secretion or it may represent a mucosal vascular effect.

Osmotic laxatives such as $MgSO_4$ are thought to act by providing an osmotic pressure gradient for H_2O movement from blood to lumen. However, recent studies could not account for fluid entry into luminal $MgSO_4$ (50 m*M*) solutions by physical or effective osmotic pressures or by changes in mucosal permeability, morphology, or cyclic AMP levels.[203] Since hypertonic solutions cause vasodilation, a local effect of osmotic laxatives to increase blood flow may also increase tissue pressure.[204] This possible effect would seem localized to only a portion of the mucosa, since hypertonic mannitol (450 m*M*) does not increase mucosa-submucosal blood flow.[68]

Although the mechanism of laxative action is still not clear, it seems that physical forces acting at the level of the mucosal capillaries and conductance can account for much of the secretion, particularly for bile acids. Other laxatives may have an additional component of active secretion.

IV. PHYSICAL FACTORS

Several of the physical factors such as plasma colloids or capillary pressure which can influence intestinal secretion have been mentioned above. One clinically interesting example of the possible contribution of Starling forces to secretory diarrhea is the very rapid reversal of the diarrhea associated with extreme malnutrition, and the concomitant reduction in plasma proteins, by the infusion of plasma colloids. The reversal has been attributed to the oncotic properties of the colloids.[205] The involvement of these physical factors in the pathophysiology of intestinal secretion, due to disease states which would be expected to act through altering cardiovascular function directly rather than through hormonal or neural mechanisms (which also could act indirectly by modifying physical forces), has not been well defined.

A. Portal Hypertension

An increase in mesenteric venous pressure such as is found in the portal hypertension of cirrhosis would be expected to cause diarrhea, not only because of an increase in mesenteric venous pressure of as high as 55 mmHg, but also because of marked splanchnic vasodilation.[206,207] However, diarrhea is rare even though intestinal edema is common, indicating fluid transudation across capillaries. Lymph flow is increased but capillary permeability to proteins is normal.[208] Villous edema, dilated intercellular spaces, and mucosal damage were associated with cirrhosis, although there was not a good correlation between histologic abnormalities and hepatic portal pressure and no secretion.[209] There is little change in net absorption because, even though secretory fluxes are increased, there is also a concomitant increase in absorptive fluxes. Similar observations were made on rats; volume expanded 5 or 10% of body weight with saline.[210] Volume expansion at 5% of body weight reduced net Na absorption due to a significant increase in the secretory flux and a nonsignificant decrease in the absorptive fluxes, with no change in effective mucosal blood flow. There was a decrease in the width of the intercellular space and in the large dilations of the intercellular space observed in luminally perfused segments but not in nonperfused segments. At 10% volume expansion the net Na flux returned to control values because of an increase in the absorptive Na flux, and the width of the lateral spaces increased back toward control levels. Effective mucosal blood flow was increased by 10% volume expansion. The adaptation from acute to chronic hepatic portal venous pressure elevation involves a decrease in protein flux into the lymph.[211] In both acute and chronic hepatic portal hypertension, lymph flow, permeability-surface area product, and protein reflection coefficient all were similarly increased. Many of the vascular changes in chronic portal hypertension as well as the long-term adaptation may be due to humoral factors,[209] especially glucagon, which increased threefold to 450 pg/mℓ.[207] Apparently there are interactions among mucosal blood flow, venous pressure, and perhaps colloid osmotic pressure, as well as ongoing absorption, which can modify secretion and which are associated with effects on the paracellular transport pathways.

B. Intestinal Obstruction

Secretion is associated with intestinal obstruction and the accompanying distention.[212,213] Lee[214] studied the effect of distention pressure in rat jejunum in vivo and found that with glucose-free luminal solutions, distention increased absorption up to a distending pressure of 10 mmHg. With further increases of pressure up to 40 mmHg, absorption fell toward control, but only at 70 mmHg was there a tendency for absorption (but still no net secretion) to decrease below control levels, although it was not significant. With glucose-containing fluid, absorption was increased by luminal pressures from 3 to 70 mmHg. Lymph flow was decreased only at the higher (>20 mmHg) distending pressure. Other investigators also found that distention did not cause secretion in the dog,[215,216] although it did in the rabbit.[217] Increased absorption up to a luminal pressure of 30 cm saline was also observed in dog ileum and attributed to increased surface area.[218] Large intestinal obstruction can result in pressures up to 50 mmHg, and up to 10 mmHg in the small intestine.[219,220] The increased secretion during distention is due to an increase in the secretory flux in rat colon,[221] canine ileum,[212] and man.[222] Recovery of absorption after distention or portal vein constriction is slow, and the prolonged effect of ischemia has been suggested as the cause.[221,229]

Blood flow to the mucosa is decreased and to the muscularis increased as distending pressures are increased in the large and small intestine in piglets with closed abdomens.[223] In dogs, distention to a pressure of 105 mmHg had no effect on arterial blood flow or on O_2 saturation after about 1 min.[224] Morphologic studies on the effects of intestinal obstruction compared to ischemia induced by mesenteric arterial occlusion indicated that the early changes (<45 min) in the mucosa were due to ischemia.[225] In the large intestine, both distention (<30 mmHg) and hypotension were required to produce mucosal lesions, although these lesions were produced by greater distention pressures (60 mmHg) alone. The potentiating effect of reduced pressure on injury produced by distention suggests that reduced blood flow and ischemia, rather than increased capillary pressure, are the major contributors to mucosal damage.[226] In other studies which used distention with silicone oil rather than absorbed saline, an additional increase in capillary protein permeability was noted,[227] and this could also account for the edema which is frequently observed.[206] Distention of a gut segment, rather than luminal pressure per se, has been shown to be the major stimulus to the increased blood flow resistance.[228]

The variable effects of luminal distention on secretion suggest that vascular pressure per se, with the possibility of increased capillary ultrafiltration, is not the cause of fluid entry into the lumen. More likely ischemia, with an accompanying increase in capillary protein losses, alters the balance of Starling forces and leads to secretion through conductive mucosa.

V. SUMMARY

Secretion by the intestine can be stimulated by primary changes in transcellular fluid transport and/or in mucosal Starling forces. Transcellular and hydraulic secretion can interact with each other to potentiate or inhibit the effect of the primary secretory mechanism. Secretagogues can affect transcellular and/or hydraulic secretion. For many secretagogues the mechanism of action is poorly defined and requires further study. Both unidirectional fluxes and an estimate of mucosal Starling forces in vivo would be required to assess their contributions to the net secretion.

REFERENCES

1. **Binder, H. J.**, Net fluid and electrolyte secretion: the pathophysiologic basis for diarrhea, in *Mechanisms of Intestinal Secretion*, Binder, H. J., Ed., Alan R. Liss, New York, 1979, 1.
2. **Mailman, D.**, Fluid and electrolyte absorption, in *Gastrointestinal Physiology*, 2nd ed., Johnson, L. R., Ed., C. V. Mosby, St. Louis, Mo., 1981, 107.
3. **Phillips, S. F.**, Functions of the large bowel: an overview, *Scand. J. Gastroenterol. Suppl.*, 93, 1, 1984.
4. **Kaplan, J. H.**, Sodium ions and the sodium pump: transport and enzymatic activity, *Am. J. Physiol.*, 245, G327, 1983.
5. **Kimmich, G. A. and Randles, J.**, Sodium-sugar coupling stoichiometry in chick intestinal cells, *Am. J. Physiol.*, 247, C74, 1984.
6. **Schultz, S. G.**, A cellular model for active sodium absorption by mammalian colon, *Annu. Rev. Physiol.*, 46, 435, 1984.
7. **Stevens, B. R., Kaunitz, J. D., and Wright, E. M.**, Intestinal transport of amino acids and sugars: advances using membrane vesicles, *Annu. Rev. Physiol.*, 46, 417, 1984.
8. **Frizzell, R. A., Field, M., and Schultz, S. G.**, Sodium-coupled chloride transport by epithelial tissues, *Am. J. Physiol.*, 236, F1, 1979.
9. **Liedtke, C. M. and Hopper, U.**, Mechanism of Cl^- translocation across small intestinal brush-border membrane. I. Absence of Na^+-Cl^- cotransport, *Am. J. Physiol.*, 242, G263, 1982.
10. **Charney, A. N. and Feldman, G. M.**, Systemic acid-base disorders and intestinal electrolyte transport, *Am. J. Physiol.*, 247, G1, 1984.
11. **Smith, P. L. and McCabe, R. D.**, Mechanism and regulation of transcellular potassium transport by the colon, *Am. J. Physiol.*, 247, G445, 1984.
12. **Welsh, M., Smith, P., Fromm, M. J., and Frizzell, R. A.**, Crypts are the site of intestinal fluid and electrolyte secretion, *Science*, 218, 1219, 1982.
13. **Hakim, A. A. and Lifson, N.**, Effects of pressure on water and solute transport by dog intestinal mucosa in vitro, *Am. J. Physiol.*, 216, 276, 1969.
14. **Mailman, D.**, Tritiated water clearance as a measure of intestinal absorptive site and total blood flow, in *Measurement of Blood Flow*, Granger, D. N. and Bulkley, G., Eds., Williams & Wilkins, Baltimore, 1981, 339.
15. **Mailman, D.**, Blood flow and intestinal absorption, *Fed. Proc., Fed. Am. Soc. Exp. Biol.*, 41, 2096, 1982.
16. **Granger, D. N., Mortillaro, N., Kvietys, P., Rutili, G., Parker, J., and Taylor, A.**, Role of the interstitial matrix during intestinal volume expansion, *Am. J. Physiol.*, 238, G183, 1980.
17. **Granger, D. N.**, Intestinal microcirculation and transmucosal fluid transport, *Am. J. Physiol.*, 240, G343, 1981.
18. **Granger, D. N., Richardson, P. D. I., Kvietys, P. R., and Mortillaro, N. A.**, Intestinal blood flow, *Gastroenterology*, 78, 837, 1980.
19. **Granger, D. N., Perry, M. A., and Kvietys, P. R.**, The microcirculation and fluid transport in digestive organs, *Fed. Proc., Fed. Am. Soc. Exp. Biol.*, 42, 1667, 1983.
20. **Granger, D. N., Perry, M. A., Kvietys, P. R., and Taylor, A. E.**, Capillary and interstitial forces during fluid absorption in the cat small intestine, *Gastroenterology*, 86, 267, 1984.
21. **Mailman, D.**, Cardiovascular and flux relationship in canine ileum, *Am. J. Physiol.*, 247, G357, 1984.
22. **Lee, J. S.**, Lymph capillary pressure of rat intestinal villi during fluid absorption, *Am. J. Physiol.*, 237, E301, 1979.
23. **Granger, D. N. and Taylor, A. E.**, Effects of solute coupled transport on lymph flow and oncotic pressures in cat ileum, *Am. J. Physiol.*, 235, E429, 1978.
24. **Gore, R. and Bohlen, H.**, Microvascular pressures in rat intestinal muscle and mucosal villi, *Am. J. Physiol.*, 233, H685, 1977.

25. Davis, M. J. and Gore, R. W., Capillary pressures in rat intestinal muscle and mucosal villi during pressure elevation, *Am. J. Physiol.*, 249, H174, 1985.
26. Yablonski, M. E. and Lifson, N., Mechanism of production of intestinal secretion by elevated venous pressure, *J. Clin. Invest.*, 57, 904, 1976.
27. Diana, J. W., Transcapillary water flux, *Physiologist*, 25, 365, 1982.
28. Phillips, S. F. and Gaginella, T. S., Effects of fatty acids and bile acids on intestinal water and electrolyte transport, in *Mechanisms of Intestinal Secretion*, Binder, H. J., Ed., Alan R. Liss, New York, 1979, 287.
29. Diamond, J. M., The mechanism of solute transport by the gall bladder, *J. Physiol.*, 161, 474, 1962.
30. Granger, D. N., Kvietys, P. R., Perry, M. A., and Taylor, A. E., Relationship between intestinal volume secretion and oxygen uptake, *Dig. Dis. Sci.*, 27, 42, 1982.
31. Valleau, J., Granger, D., and Taylor, A., Effect of solute coupled volume absorption on oxygen consumption in cat ileum, *Am. J. Physiol.*, 236, E198, 1979.
32. Kvietys, P. R. and Granger, D. N., Effects of solute-coupled fluid absorption on blood flow and oxygen uptake in the dog colon, *Gastroenterology*, 81, 450, 1981.
33. Kvietys, P. R. and Granger, D. N., Relation between intestinal blood flow and oxygen uptake, *Am. J. Physiol.*, 242, G207, 1982.
34. Groszman, R. J., Blei, A. T., Storer, E. H., and Conn, H. O., Intestinal O_2 consumption during mechanical and pharmacological reduction in portal pressure, *Am. J. Physiol.*, 238, G502, 1980.
35. Kurtin, P. and Charney, A. N., Effect of arterial carbon dioxide tension on amiloride-sensitive sodium absorption in the colon, *Am. J. Physiol.*, 247, G537, 1984.
36. Granger, D., Kvietys, P., Mailman, D., and Richardson, P., Intrinsic regulation of functional blood flow and water absorption in canine colon, *J. Physiol.*, 307, 443, 1980.
37. Ferri, G. L., Adrian, T. E., Ghatei, M. A., O'Shaughnessy, D. J., Probert, L., Lee, Y. C., Buchan, A. M. J., Polak, J. M., and Bloom, S. R., Tissue localization and relative distribution of regulatory peptides in separated layers from the human bowel, *Gastroenterology*, 84, 777, 1983.
38. Angel, F., Schmalz, P. F., Morgan, K. G., Go, V. L. W., and Szurszewski, J. H., Innervation of the muscularis mucosa in the canine stomach and colon, *Scand. J. Gastroenterol. Suppl.*, 93, 71, 1984.
39. Sninsky, C. A., Wolfe, M. M., Martin, J. L., Howe, B. A., O'Dorisio, T. M., McGuigan, V. E., and Mathias, J. R., Myoelectric effects of vasoactive intestinal peptide on rabbit small intestine, *Am. J. Physiol.*, 244, G46, 1983.
40. Krejs, G., Effects of somatostatin infusion on VIP induced transport changes in the human jejunum, *Peptides*, 5, 271, 1984.
41. Schwartz, C. J., Kimberg, D. V., Sheerin, H. E., Field, M., and Said, S. I., Vasoactive intestinal peptide stimulation of adenylate cyclase and active electrolyte secretion in intestinal mucosa, *J. Clin. Invest.*, 54, 536, 1974.
42. Racusen, L. C. and Binder, H. J., Alteration of large intestinal electrolyte transport by vasoactive intestinal polypeptide in the rat, *Gastroenterology*, 73, 790, 1977.
43. Waldman, D. B., Gardner, J. D., Zfass, A. M., and Makhlouf, G. M., Effects of vasoactive intestinal peptide, secretin, and related peptides on rat colonic transport and adenylate cyclase activity, *Gastroenterology*, 73, 518, 1977.
44. Carter, R. F., Bitar, K. N., Zfass, A. M., and Makhlouf, G. M., Inhibition of VIP-stimulated intestinal secretion and cyclic AMP production by somatostatin in the rat, *Gastroenterology*, 74, 726, 1978.
45. Camilleri, M., Cooper, B. T., Adrian, T. E., Bloom, S. R., and Chadwick, V. S., Effect of vasoactive intestinal peptide and pancreatic polypeptide in rabbit intestine, *Gut*, 22, 14, 1981.
46. Krejs, G. J., Barkley, R. M., Read, N. W., and Fordtran, J. S., Intestinal secretion induced by vasoactive intestinal polypeptide, *J. Clin. Invest.*, 57, 1337, 1978.
47. Mailman, D., Effects of vasoactive intestinal polypeptide on intestinal absorption and blood flow, *J. Physiol.*, 279, 121, 1978.
48. Cohen, M. L. and Landry, A. S., Vasoactive intestinal polypeptide: increased tone, enhancement of acetylcholine release, and stimulation of adenylate cyclase in intestinal smooth muscle, *Life Sci.*, 26, 811, 1980.
49. Holliger, C., Radzyner, M., and Knoblauch, M., Effects of glucagon, vasoactive intestinal peptide, and vasopressin on villous microcirculation and superior mesenteric artery blood flow of the rat, *Gastroenterology*, 85, 1036, 1983.
50. Granger, D. N., Cross, R., and Barrowman, J. A., Effects of various secretagogues and human carcinoid serum on lymph flow in the cat ileum, *Gastroenterology*, 83, 896, 1982.
51. McFadden, D., Jaffe, B. M., and Zinner, M. J., Secretory effects of intravenous serotonin on the proximal jejunum of the awake dog, *Am. J. Surg.*, 149, 60, 1985.
52. McGowan, K., Kane, A., Asarkof, N., Wicks, J., Guerina, V., Kellum, J., Baron, S., Gintzler, A. R., and Donowitz, M., *Entamoeba histolytica* causes intestinal secretion. Role of serotonin, *Science*, 221, 762, 1983.

53. Ormsbee, H. S. and Fondacaro, J. D., Action of serotonin on the gastrointestinal tract, *Proc. Soc. Exp. Biol. Med.*, 178, 333, 1985.
54. Legay, C., Saffrey, M. J., and Burnstock, G., Coexistence of immunoreactive substance P and serotonin in neurones of the gut, *Brain Res.*, 302, 379, 1984.
55. Gershon, M. D. and Tamir, H., Release of endogenous 5-hydroxytryptamine from resting and stimulated enteric neurons, *Neuroscience*, 6, 2277, 1981.
56. Cooke, H. J., Montakhab, M., Wade, P. R., and Wood, J. D., Transmural fluxes of 5-hydroxytryptamine in guinea pig ileum, *Am. J. Physiol.*, 244, G421, 1983.
57. Donowitz, M., Charney, A. N., and Tai, Y. H., A comprehensive picture of serotonin-induced ileal secretion, in *Mechanisms of Intestinal Secretion*, Binder, H. J., Ed., Alan R. Liss, New York, 1979.
58. Donowitz, M., Tai, Y. H., and Asarkoff, N., Effect of serotonin on active electrolyte transport in rabbit ileum, gallbladder, and colon, *Am. J. Physiol.*, 239, 463, 1980.
59. Kisloff, B. and Moore, E., Effect of serotonin on water and electrolyte transport in the in vivo rabbit small intestine, *Gastroenterology*, 71, 1033, 1976.
60. Donowitz, M., Ca^{++} in the control of active intestinal Na and Cl transport: involvement in neurohumoral action, *Am. J. Physiol.*, 245, G165, 1983.
61. Gaginella, T. S., Rimele, T. J., and Wietecha, M., Studies on rat intestinal epithelial cell receptors for serotonin and opiates, *J. Physiol.*, 355, 101, 1983.
62. Zimmerman, T. and Binder, H., Serotonin-induced alteration of colonic electrolyte transport in the rat, *Gastroenterology*, 86, 310, 1984.
63. Richardson, P. D. I., Drug induced changes in capillary filtration coefficient and blood flow in the innervated small intestine of the anaesthetized cat, *Br. J. Pharmacol.*, 52, 481, 1974.
64. Biber, B., Fara, J., and Lundgren, O., Vascular reactions in the small intestine during vasodilation, *Acta Physiol. Scand.*, 89, 449, 1973.
65. Fara, J., Mesenteric vasodilator effect of 5-hydroxytryptamine: possible enteric neuron mediation, *Arch. Int. Pharmacodyn. Ther.*, 221, 235, 1976.
66. Fasth, S., Hedland, H., Hulten, L., Nordgren, S., and Oresland, T., The effects of 5-hydroxytryptamine on large intestinal motility and blood flow in the cat, *Acta Physiol. Scand.*, 118, 329, 1983.
67. Biber, B., Vasodilator mechanisms of the small intestine, *Acta Physiol. Scand. Suppl.*, 401, 1, 1973.
68. Donowitz, M., Wicklein, D., Reynolds, D., Hynes, R., Charney, A., and Zinner, M., Effect of altered intestinal water transport on rabbit ileal blood flow, *Am. J. Physiol.*, 236, E482, 1979.
69. Doyle, H., Greeley, G. H., Mate, L., Sakamoto, T., Townsend, C. M., and Thompson, J. C., Distribution of neurotensin in the canine gastrointestinal tract, *Surgery*, 97, 337, 1985.
70. Al-Saffar, A., Theodorsson-Norheim, E., and Rosell, S., Nervous control of the release of neurotensin-like immunoreactivity from the small intestine of the rat, *Acta Physiol. Scand.*, 122, 1, 1984.
71. Reasbeck, P. G. and Barbezat, G. O., A role for neurotensin in the control of jejunal transport, *Proc. Otago Med. Sch.*, 59, 90, 1981.
72. Wiklund, B., Liljequist, L., and Rokaeus, A., Neurotensin increases net fluid secretion and transit rate in the small intestine of man, *Regul. Peptides*, 8, 33, 1984.
73. Mitchenere, P., Adrian, T. E., Kirk, R. M., and Bloom, S. R., Effect of gut regulatory peptides on intestinal luminal fluid in the rat, *Life Sci.*, 29, 1563, 1981.
74. Miller, R. J., Kachur, J. F., and Field, M., Neurohumoral control of ileal electrolyte transport, *Ann. N.Y. Acad. Sci.*, 372, 571, 1981.
75. Baca, I., Mittmann, U., Feurle, G. E., Haas, M., and Muller, T., Effect of neurotensin on regional intestinal blood flow in the dog, *Res. Exp. Med.*, 179, 53, 1981.
76. Harper, S. L., Barrowman, J. A., Kvietys, P. R., and Granger, D. N., Effect of neurotensin on intestinal capillary permeability and blood flow, *Am. J. Physiol.*, 247, G161, 1984.
77. Pansu, A., Bosshard, A., Dechelette, M. S., and Vagne, M., Effect of pentagastrin, secretin and cholecystokinin on intestinal water and sodium absorption in the rat, *Digestion*, 20, 201, 1980.
78. Matuchansky, C. P., Huet, P. M., Mary, J. Y., Rambaud, J. C., and Bernier, J. J., Effects of cholecystokinin and metoclopramide on jejunal movements of water and electrolytes and on transit time of luminal fluid in man, *Eur. J. Clin. Invest.*, 2, 169, 1972.
79. Bussjaeger, L. J. and Johnson, L. R., Evidence for hormonal regulation of intestinal absorption by cholecystokinin, *Am. J. Physiol.*, 244, 1276, 1973.
80. Teitelbaum, D. H., O'Dorisio, T. M., Gaginella, T. S., and Perkins, W. T., Effects of caerulein on rat small and large intestinal fluid transport in vivo, *Regul. Peptides*, 4, 97, 1982.
81. Barbezat, G. O. and Grossman, M. I., Effect of glucagon on water and electrolyte movement in jejunum and ileum of dog, *Gastroenterology*, 60, 762, 1971a.
82. Turner, S. G. and Barrowman, J. A., The effects of cholecystokinin and cholecystokinin-octapeptide on intestinal lymph flow in the rat, *Can. J. Physiol. Pharmacol.*, 55, 1393, 1977.
83. Fara, J. W. and Madden, K. S., Effect of secretin and cholecystokinin on small intestinal blood flow distribution, *Am. J. Physiol.*, 229, 1365, 1975.

84. Bowen, J., Pawlik, W., Fang, W., and Jacobson, E. D., Pharmacologic effects of gastrointestinal hormones on intestinal oxygen consumption and blood flow, *Surgery,* 78, 515, 1975.
85. Hubel, K. A., Effects of secretin and glucagon on intestinal transport of ions and water in rat, *Proc. Soc. Exp. Biol. Med.,* 139, 656, 1972.
86. Hicks, T. and Turnberg, L. A., Influence of glucagon on the human jejunum, *Gastroenterology,* 67, 1114, 1974.
87. Barbezat, G. O. and Grossman, M. I., Cholera-like diarrhea induced by glucagon plus gastrin, *Lancet,* 1, 1025, 1971b.
88. MacFerran, S. and Mailman, D., Effects of glucagon on canine intestinal sodium and water fluxes and regional blood flow, *J. Physiol.,* 266, 1, 1977.
89. Isaacs, P. E. T. and Turnberg, L. A., Failure of glucagon to influence ion transport across human jejunal and ileal mucosa in vitro, *Gut,* 18, 1059, 1977.
90. Yau, W. M. and Makhlouf, G. M., Different effects of hormonal peptides and cyclic 3′,5′-adenosine monophosphate on colonic transport in vitro, *Gastroenterology,* 67, 662, 1974.
91. Kaufman, M. E., Dinno, M., and Huang, K. C., Effect of glucagon on ion transport in mouse intestine, *Am. J. Physiol.,* 238, G491, 1980.
92. Klaveman, H. L., Conlon, T. P., Levy, A. G., and Gardner, J., Effects of gastrointestinal hormones on adenylate cyclase activity in human jejunal mucosa, *Gastroenterology,* 68, 667, 1975.
93. Kilander, A. F., Dotevall, G., Lindsteadt, G., and Lundberg, P. A., Plasma enteroglucagon related to malabsorption in coeliac disease, *Gut,* 25, 629, 1984.
94. Granger, D. N., Kvietys, P., Wilborn, N., and Taylor, A., Mechanism of glucagon-induced intestinal secretion, *Am. J. Physiol.,* 239, G30, 1980.
95. Cooke, H. J., Nemeth, P. R., and Wood, J. D., Histamine action on guinea pig ileal mucosa, *Am. J. Physiol.,* 246, G372, 1984.
96. Fromm, D. and Halpern, N., Effects of histamine receptor antagonists on ion transport by isolated ileum of the rabbit, *Gastroenterology,* 77, 1034, 1979.
97. McCabe, R. D. and Smith, P. L., Effects of histamine and histamine receptor antagonists on ion transport in rabbit descending colon, *Am. J. Physiol.,* 247, G411, 1984.
98. Linaker, B. J., McKay, J. S., Higgs, N. B., and Turnberg, L. A., Mechanisms of histamine-stimulated secretion in rabbit ileal mucosa, *Gut,* 22, 964, 1981.
99. Lee, J. S. and Silverberg, J. W., Effect of histamine on intestinal fluid secretion in the dog, *Am. J. Physiol.,* 231, 793, 1976.
100. Walus, K. M., Fondacaro, J. D., and Jacobson, E. D., Mesenteric vascular reactivity to histamine receptor agonists and antagonists, *Dig. Dis. Sci.,* 26, 438, 1981.
101. Guth, P. H. and Hirabayashi, K., The effect of histamine on microvascular permeability in the muscularis externa of the rat small intestine, *Microvasc. Res.,* 25, 322, 1983.
102. Mortillaro, N. A., Granger, D. N., Kvietys, P. R., Rutili, G., and Taylor, A. E., Effects of histamine and histamine antagonists on intestinal capillary permeability, *Am. J. Physiol.,* 240, G381, 1981.
103. Walling, M. W., Brasitus, T. A., and Kimberg, D. V., Effects of calcitonin and substance P on the transport of Ca, Na, and Cl across rat ileum in vitro, *Gastroenterology,* 73, 89, 1977.
104. Kachur, J. F., Miller, R. J., Field, M., and River, J., Neurohumoral control of ileal electrolyte transport. II. Neurotensin and substance P, *J. Pharmacol. Exp. Ther.,* 220, 456, 1982.
105. Premen, A. J., Dobbins, D. E., Soika, C. Y., and Dabney, J. M., Relationship between substance P, intestinal wall compliance and vascular resistance in the canine ileum, *Regul. Peptides,* 9, 119, 1984.
106. Yeo, C. J., Jaffe, B. M., and Zinner, M. J., Local regulation of blood flow in the feline jejunum, *J. Clin. Invest.,* 70, 1329, 1982.
107. Pierce, N. F., Carpenter, C. C. J., Elliott, H. L., and Greenough, W. B., Effects of prostaglandins, theophylline, and cholera exotoxin upon transmucosal water and electrolyte movement in the canine jejunum, *Gastroenterology,* 60, 22, 1971.
108. Matuchansky, C. and Bernier, J. J., Effect of prostaglandin E_1 on glucose, water, and electrolyte absorption in the human jejunum, *Gastroenterology,* 64, 1111, 1973.
109. Coupar, I. M. and McColl, I., Stimulation of water and sodium secretion and inhibition of glucose absorption from the rat jejunum during intraarterial infusions of prostaglandins, *Gut,* 16, 759, 1975.
110. Rush, B. D. and Ruwart, M. J., The role of accelerated colonic transit in prostaglandin-induced diarrhea and its inhibition by prostacyclin, *Br. J. Pharmacol.,* 83, 157, 1984.
111. Racusen, L. C. and Binder, H. J., Effect of prostaglandin on ion transport across isolated colonic mucosa, *Dig. Dis. Sci.,* 25, 900, 1980.
112. Kimberg, D. V., Field, M., Gershon, E., and Henderson, A., Effects of prostaglandins and cholera enterotoxin on intestinal mucosal cyclic AMP accumulation. Evidence against an essential role for prostaglandins in the action of toxin, *J. Clin. Invest.,* 53, 941, 1974.

113. Al-Awqati, Q. and Greenough, W. B., Prostaglandins inhibit intestinal sodium transport, *Nature (London), New Biol.*, 238, 26, 1972.
114. Bukhave, K. and Rask-Madsen, J., Saturation kinetics applied to in vitro effects of low prostaglandin E_2 and $F_{2\alpha}$ concentrations on ion transport across human jejunal mucosa, *Gastroenterology*, 78, 32, 1980.
115. Gallavan, R. H. and Jacobson, E. D., Prostaglandins and the splanchnic circulation, *Proc. Soc. Exp. Biol. Med.*, 170, 391, 1982.
116. Mangino, M. J. and Chou, C. C., Arachidonic acid and postprandial intestinal hyperemia, *Am. J. Physiol.*, 246, G521, 1984.
117. Beubler, E. and Juan, H., The function of prostaglandins in transmucosal water movement and blood flow in the rat jejunum, *Naunyn-Schmiedebergs Arch. Pharmakol.*, 299, 89, 1977.
118. Granger, D., Schackelford, J., and Taylor, A., PGE_1-induced intestinal secretion: mechanism of enhanced transmucosal protein efflux, *Am. J. Physiol.*, 236, E788, 1979.
119. Kvietys, P. R., Wilborn, W. H., and Granger, D. N., Effect of atropine on bile-oleic acid-induced alterations in dog jejunal hemodynamics, oxygenation, and net transmucosal water movement, *Gastroenterology*, 80, 31, 1981.
120. Sernka, T. J., Rood, R. P., Mah, M. Y., and Tseng, C. H., Antiabsorptive effects of 16,16-dimethyl prostaglandin E_2 in isolated rat colon, *Prostaglandin*, 23, 411, 1982.
121. Cassuto, J., Jodal, M., Tuttle, R., and Lundgren, O., On the role of intramural nerves in the pathogenesis of cholera toxin-induced intestinal secretion, *Scand. J. Gastroenterol.*, 16, 377, 1981.
122. Mailman, D., Effects of pentagastrin on intestinal absorption and blood flow, *J. Physiol.*, 307, 429, 1980.
123. Tapper, E. J., Local modulation of intestinal ion transport by enteric neurons, *Am. J. Physiol.*, 244, G457, 1983.
124. Dahlstrom, A., Newson, B., Naito, S., Ueda, T., and Ahlman, H., Further evidence for the presence of subepithelial nerve cells in the rat ileum — an immunohistochemical study, *Acta Physiol. Scand.*, 120, 1, 1984.
125. Zimmerman, T. W. and Binder, H. J., Muscarinic receptors on rat isolated colonic epithelial cells, *Gastroenterology*, 83, 1244, 1982.
126. Gaginella, T. S., Neuromodulation of intestinal ion transport. Cholinergic modulation of transport, *Fed. Proc., Fed. Am. Soc. Exp. Biol.*, 43, 2929, 1984.
127. Isaacs, P. E. T., Whitehead, J. S., and Kim, Y. S., Muscarinic acetylcholine receptors of the small intestine and pancreas of the rat: distribution and the effects of vagotomy, *Clin. Sci.*, 62, 203, 1982.
128. Rimele, T. J. and Gaginella, T. S., In vivo identification of muscarinic receptors on rat colonic epithelial cells: binding of (^{3}H)-quinuclidinyl benzilate, *Naunyn-Schmiedebergs Arch. Pharmakol.*, 319, 18, 1982.
129. Isaacs, P. E. T., Corbett, C. L., Riley, A. K., Hawker, P. C., and Turnberg, L. A., The influence of acetylcholine on ion transport, *J. Clin. Invest.*, 58, 535, 1979.
130. Buckley, N. and Burnstock, G., Autoradiographic localization of muscarinic receptors in guinea-pig intestine: distribution of high and low affinity agonist binding sites, *Brain Res.*, 294, 15, 1984.
131. Thomas, E. M. and Munday, K. A., Noradrenergic innervation of the villus, *Scand. J. Gastroenterol. Suppl.*, 17, 157, 1982.
132. Morris, A. and Turnberg, L., The influence of a parasympathetic agonist and antagonist on human intestinal transport in vivo, *Gastroenterology*, 79, 861, 1980.
133. Hubel, K. A., Intestinal ion transport: effect of norepinephrine, pilocarpine, and atropine, *Am. J. Physiol.*, 231, 252, 1976.
134. Wright, R., Jennings, M., Florey, H., and Lium, R., The influence of nerves and drugs on secretion by the small intestine and investigation of the enzymes of intestinal juice, *Q. J. Exp. Phys.*, 30, 73, 1940.
135. Tidball, C. S., Active chloride transport during intestinal secretion, *Am. J. Physiol.*, 200, 309, 1961.
136. Morris, A. I. and Turnberg, L. A., Influence of isoproterenol and propranolol on human intestinal transport in vivo, *Gastroenterology*, 81, 1076, 1981.
137. Hubel, K. A., Effects of scorpion venom on electrolyte transport by rabbit ileum, *Am. J. Physiol.*, 244, G501, 1983.
138. Cooke, H. J., Influence of enteric cholinergic neurons on mucosal transport in guinea pig ileum, *Am. J. Physiol.*, 246, G263, 1984.
139. Cooke, H. J., Shonnard, K., Highison, G., and Wood, J. D., Effects of neurotransmitter release on mucosal transport in guinea pig ileum, *Am. J. Physiol.*, 245, G745, 1983.
140. Hubel, K. A., The effects of electrical field stimulation and tetrodotoxin on ion transport by the isolated rabbit ileum, *J. Clin. Invest.*, 62, 1039, 1978.
141. Hubel, K. A. and Shirazi, S., Human ileal ion transport in vitro: changes with electrical field stimulation and tetrodotoxin, *Gastroenterology*, 83, 63, 1982.

142. Hubel, K. A., Neuromodulation of intestinal ion transport, EFS studies, *Fed. Proc., Fed. Am. Soc. Exp. Biol.*, 43, 2929, 1984.
143. Greenwood, B., Read, N. W., Hardcastle, P. T., and Hardcastle, J., Effect of secoverine and atropine on intestinal secretion and motor activity in the rat small intestine in-vivo, *J. Pharm. Pharmacol.*, 36, 100, 1984.
144. Powell, D. W. and Tapper, E. J., Intestinal ion transport: cholinergic adrenergic interactions, in *Mechanisms of Intestinal Secretion*, Binder, H. J., Ed., Alan R. Liss, New York, 1979, 175.
145. Zimmerman, T. W. and Binder, H. J., Effect of tetrodotoxin on cholinergic agonist-mediated colonic electrolyte transport, *Am. J. Physiol.*, 244, G386, 1983.
146. Sparso, B. H., Frederiksen, H. J. B., Malchon-Moller, A., Henriksen, J. H., and Krag, E., Mucosal function of the perfused ileum in patients with and without diarrhoea and dumping after vagotomy and pyloroplasty, *Scand. J. Gastroenterol.*, 18, 669, 1983.
147. Fondacaro, J. D., Intestinal blood flow and motility, in *Physiology of the Intestinal Circulation*, Shepherd, A. P. and Granger, D. N., Eds., Raven Press, New York, 1984, 107.
148. Wells, H. S. and Johnson, R. G., The intestinal villi and their circulation in relation to absorption and secretion of fluid, *Am. J. Physiol.*, 109, 387, 1934.
149. Padula, R., Noble, P., and Camishion, R., Vascularity of the mucosa of the small intestine after vagotomy and splanchnicectomy, *Surg. Gynecol. Obstet.*, 122, 41, 1968.
150. Winne, D., Role of blood flow in intestinal permeation, in *Handbook of Experimental Pharmacology*, Vol. 70 (Part 2), Csaky, T. Z., Ed., Springer-Verlag, Basel, 1984, 301.
151. Mailman, D., Effects of atropine and guanethidine on canine intestinal absorption and blood flow, *Life Sci.*, 34, 1309, 1984.
152. Giraud, G. D. and MacCannell, K. L., Decreased nutrient blood flow during dopamine- and epinephrine-induced intestinal vasodilation, *J. Pharmacol. Exp. Ther.*, 230, 214, 1984.
153. Granger, D. N., Valleau, J. D., Parker, R. I., Cane, R. S., and Taylor, A. E., Effects of adenosine on vascular hemodynamics, oxygen delivery and capillary fluid exchange in the feline small intestine, *Am. J. Physiol.*, 235, H707, 1978.
154. Grasl, M. and Turnheim, K., Stimulation of electrolyte secretion in rabbit colon by adenosine, *J. Physiol.*, 346, 93, 1984.
155. Shepherd, A. P., Riedel, G. L., Maxwell, L. C., and Kiel, J. W., Selective vasodilators redistribute intestinal blood flow and depress oxygen uptake, *Am. J. Physiol.*, 247, G377, 1984.
156. El Masri, S. H., Lewin, M. R., and Clark, C. G., In vitro effects of gastrin on the movement of electrolytes across the human colon, *Scand. J. Gastroenterol.*, 12, 999, 1977.
157. Gardner, J. D., Peskin, G. W., Certa, J. J., and Brooks, F. P., Alterations of in vitro fluid and electrolyte absorption by gastrointestinal hormones, *Am. J. Surg.*, 113, 57, 1967.
158. Yau, W. M. and Makhlouf, G. M., Different effects of hormonal peptides and cyclic 3′,5′-adenosine monophosphate on colonic transport in vitro, *Gastroenterology*, 67, 662, 1974.
159. Rambaud, J. C., Modigliani, R., Emonts, P., Matuchansky, C., Vidon, N., Recherche, M., Besterman, H., and Bernier, J., Fluid secretion in the duodenum and intestinal handling of water and electrolytes in Zollinger-Ellison syndrome, *Am. J. Dig. Dis.*, 23, 1089, 1978.
160. Gingell, J. C., Davies, M. W., and Shields, R., Effect of a synthetic gastrin-like pentapeptide upon the intestinal transport of sodium, potassium, and water, *Gut*, 9, 111, 1968.
161. Bynum, T. E., Jacobson, E. D., and Johnson, L. R., Gastrin inhibition of intestinal absorption in dogs, *Gastroenterology*, 61, 858, 1971.
162. Musch, M. W., Kachur, J. F., Miller, R. J., and Field, M., Bradykinin-stimulated electrolyte secretion in rabbit and guinea pig intestine, *J. Clin. Invest.*, 71, 1073, 1983.
163. Crocker, A. D. and Willavoys, S. P., Effect of bradykinin on transepithelial transfer of sodium and water in vitro, *J. Physiol.*, 253, 401, 1975.
164. Granger, D. N., Richardson, P. D. I., and Taylor, A. E., The effect of isoprenaline and bradykinin on capillary filtration in the cat small intestine, *Br. J. Pharmacol.*, 67, 361, 1979.
165. Gutniak, M., Rosenquist, U., Grimelius, L., Lundberg, J. M., Hokfelt, T., Rokaeus, A., Rosell, S., Lundquist, G., Fahrenkrug, J., Sundblad, R., and Gutniak, E., Report on a patient with watery diarrhea syndrome caused by a pancreatic tumor containing neurotensin, enkephalin and calcitonin, *Acta Med. Scand.*, 208, 95, 1980.
166. Viale, G., Dell'Orto, P., Moro, E., Cozzaglio, L., and Coggi, G., Vasoactive intestinal polypeptide-, somatostatin-, and calcitonin-producing adrenal pheochromocytoma associated with the watery diarrhea (WDHH) syndrome, *Cancer*, 55, 1099, 1985.
167. Booth, I. W., Fenton, T. R., Milla, P. J., and Harries, J. T., A pathophysiological study of the intestinal manifestations of a vasoactive intestinal peptide, calcitonin, and catecholamine-secreting tumor, *Gut*, 24, 954, 1983.
168. Gray, T. K., Brannon, P., Juan, D., et al., Ion transport changes during calcitonin-induced intestinal secretion in man, *Gastroenterology*, 71, 392, 1976.

169. Kisloff, B. and Moore, E. W., Effects of intravenous calcitonin on water, electrolyte, and calcium movement across in vivo rabbit jejunum and ileum, *Gastroenterology,* 72, 462, 1977.
170. Gray, T. K., Juan, D., and Powell, D. W., Salmon calcitonin and water and electrolyte transport in rabbit ileum, *Proc. Soc. Exp. Biol. Med.,* 150, 151, 1975.
171. Barbezat, G. O. and Reasbeck, P. G., Effect of bombesin, calcitonin, and enkephalin on canine jejunal water and electrolyte transport, *Dig. Dis. Sci.,* 28, 273, 1983.
172. Pierce, N. F., Greenough, W. B., and Carpenter, C. C. J., *Vibrio cholerae* enterotoxin and its mode of action, *Bacteriol. Rev.,* 35, 1, 1971.
173. Moore, W. L., Bieberdorf, F. A., and Morawski, S. G., Ion transport during cholera-induced ileal secretion in the dog, *J. Clin. Invest.,* 50, 312, 1971.
174. Al-Awqati, Q., Cameron, J. L., and Greenough, W. B., Electrolyte transport in human ileum: effect of purified cholera exotoxin, *Am. J. Physiol.,* 224, 818, 1973.
175. Kimberg, D. V., Field, M., Gershon, E., Schooley, R. T., and Henderson, A., Effects of cyclohex-imide on the response of intestinal mucosa to cholera enterotoxin, *J. Clin. Invest.,* 52, 1376, 1973.
176. Desjeux, J. F., Tai, Y. H., Powell, D. W., and Curran, P. F., Effects of cholera toxin on cellular and paracellular sodium fluxes in rabbit ileum, *Biochim. Biophys. Acta,* 44, 352, 1976.
177. Iber, F. L., McGonagle, T., Serebro, H. A., Luebbers, E., Bayless, T. M., and Hendrix, T. R., Unidirectional sodium flux in small intestine in experimental canine cholera, *Am. J. Med. Sci.,* 258, 340, 1969.
178. Forsyth, G. W., Hamilton, D. L., Goertz, K. E., and Johnson, M. R., Cholera toxin effects on fluid secretion, adenylate cyclase, and cyclic AMP in porcine small intestine, *Infect. Immun.,* 21, 373, 1978.
179. Sheerin, H. E. and Field, M., Ileal mucosal cyclic AMP and Cl secretion: serosal vs. mucosal addition of cholera toxin, *Am. J. Physiol.,* 232, E210, 1977.
180. Cedgard, S., Hallback, D. A., Jodal, M., Lundgren, O., and Redfors, S., The effects of cholera toxin on intramural blood flow distribution and capillary hydraulic conductivity on the cat small intestine, *Acta Physiol. Scand.,* 102, 148, 1978.
181. Mailman, D. and Goldschmidt, M., Effects of *E. coli* enterotoxin on canine intestinal Na and H_2O fluxes and blood flow, *Microvasc. Res.,* 17 (Abstr.), 514, 1980.
182. Carpenter, C. C. J., Greenough, W. B., and Sack, R. B., The relationship of superior mesenteric artery blood flow to gut electrolyte loss in experimental cholera, *J. Infect. Dis.,* 119, 182, 1969.
183. Elliott, H. L., Carpenter, C. C. J., Sack, R. B., and Yardley, J. H., Small bowel morphology in experimental canine cholera, *Lab. Invest.,* 22, 112, 1970.
184. Granger, D. N., Mortillaro, N. A., and Taylor, A. E., Interactions of intestinal lymph flow and secretion, *Am. J. Physiol.,* 232, E13, 1977.
185. Binder, H. J., Pharmacology of laxatives, *Ann. Rev. Pharmacol. Toxicol.,* 17, 355, 1977.
186. Powell, D. W., Johnson, P. T., Bryson, J. C., Orlando, R. C., and Fan, C. C., Effect of phenol-phthalein on monkey intestinal water and electrolyte transport, *Am. J. Physiol.,* 243, G268, 1982.
187. Powell, D. W., Lawrence, B. A., Morris, S. M., and Etheridge, D. R., Effect of phenolphthalein on in vivo rabbit ileal electrolyte transport, *Gsatroenterology,* 78, 454, 1980.
188. Beubler, E. and Juan, H., Effect of ricinoleic acid and other laxatives on net water flux and prosta-glandin E release by the rat colon, *J. Pharm. Pharmacol.,* 31, 681, 1979.
189. Maenz, D. D. and Forsyth, G. W., Ricinoleate and deoxycholate are calcium ionophores in jejunal brush border vesicles, *J. Membr. Biol.,* 70, 125, 1982.
190. Oddsson, E., Rask-Madsen, J., and Krag, E., Effect of glycochenodeoxycholic acid on unidirectional transepithelial fluxes of electrolytes in the perfused human ileum, *Scand. J. Gastroenterol.,* 12, 199, 1977.
191. Gullikson, G. W., Cline, W. S., Lorenzsonn, V., Benz, L., Olsen, W. A., and Bass, P., Effects of anionic surfactants on hamster small intestinal membrane structure and function: relationship to surface activity, *Gastroenterology,* 73, 501, 1977.
192. Landsverk, T., O'Hedal, E., and Sund, R. B., Studies on hydragogue drugs: light and electron mi-croscopic examination of the isolated rat colonic mucosa exposed to deoxycholic acid and synthetic surfactants, *Acta Pharmacol. Toxicol.,* 54, 22, 1984.
193. Chadwick, V. S., Gaginella, T. S., Carlson, G. L., Debongnie, J. C., Phillips, S. F., and Hofmann, A. F., Effect of molecular structure on bile acid-induced alterations in absorptive function, permea-bility, and morphology in the perfused rabbit colon, *J. Lab. Clin. Med.,* 94, 661, 1979.
194. Gaginella, T. S., Lewis, J. C., and Phillips, S. F., Ricinoleic acid effects on rabbit intestine, *Mayo Clin. Proc.,* 51, 569, 1976.
195. Goerg, K. J., Nell, G., and Rummel, W., Effect of deoxycholate on the perfused rat colon, *Digestion,* 26, 105, 1983.
196. Farack, V. M., Nell, G., and Rummel, W., Differentiation of secretagogue drugs by chlorpromazine in rat intestine in vivo, *Naunyn-Schmiedebergs Arch. Pharmakol.,* 324, 70, 1983.

197. Sund, R. B., The effect of dodecylsulphate upon net sodium and water transport from tied jejunal loops in anaesthetized rats, *Acta Pharmacol. Toxicol.*, 37, 282, 1975.
198. Farack, V. M. and Loeschke, K., Inhibition by loperamide of deoxycholic acid induced intestinal secretion, *Naunyn-Schmiedebergs Arch. Pharmakol.*, 325, 286, 1984.
199. Bright-Asare, P. and Binder, H. J., Stimulation of colonic secretion of water and electrolytes by hydroxy fatty acids, *Gastroenterology*, 64, 81, 1973.
200. Gaginella, T. S., Chadwick, V. S., Debongnie, J. C., Lewis, J. C., and Phillips, S. F., Perfusion of rabbit colon with ricinoleic acid. Dose related mucosal injury, fluid secretion and increased permeability, *Gastroenterology*, 73, 95, 1977.
201. Shepherd, A. P. and Riedel, G. L., Laser-Doppler blood flowmetry of intestinal mucosal hyperemia induced by glucose and bile, *Am. J. Physiol.*, 248, G393, 1985.
202. Karlstrom, L., Cassuto, J., Jodal, M., and Lundgren, O., The effect of hexamethonium on the secretion induced by sodium deoxycholate in the rat jejunum, *Experientia*, 37, 991, 1981.
203. Reichelderfer, M., Pero, B., Lorenzsonn, V., and Olsen, W. A., Magnesium sulfate-induced water secretion in hamster small intestine, *Proc. Soc. Exp. Biol. Med.*, 176, 8, 1984.
204. Levine, S. E., Granger, D. N., Brace, R. A., and Taylor, A. E., Effect of hyperosmolality on vascular resistance and lymph flow in the cat ileum, *Am. J. Physiol.*, 234, H14, 1978.
205. Moss, G., Malabsorption associated with extreme malnutrition. Importance of replacing plasma albumin, *J. Am. Coll. Nutr.*, 1, 89, 1982.
206. Granger, D. N. and Barrowman, J. A., Microcirculation of the alimentary tract. II. Pathophysiology of edema, *Gastroenterology*, 84, 1035, 1983.
207. Benoit, J. N., Barrowman, J. A., Harper, S. L., Kvietys, P. R., and Granger, D. N., Role of humoral factors in the intestinal hyperemia associated with chronic portal hypertension, *Am. J. Physiol.*, 247, G486, 1984.
208. Barrowman, J. A. and Granger, D. N., Effect of experimental cirrhosis on splanchnic microvascular fluid and solute exchange in the rat, *Gastroenterology*, 87, 165, 1984.
209. Norman, D. A., Atkins, J. A., Sielig, L. I., Gomez-Sanchez, C., and Krejs, G., Water and electrolyte movement and mucosal morphology in the jejunum of patients with portal hypertension, *Gastroenterology*, 79, 707, 1980.
210. Lepper, K. G., A Physiological and Ultrastructural Examination of Rat Jejunum, M.S. thesis, University of Houston, Texas, 1976.
211. Witte, C. L., Myers, J. F., Witte, M. H., and Katz, M. A., Transcapillary water and protein fluxes in the canine intestine with acute and chronic extra hepatic portal hypertension, *Circ. Res.*, 53, 622, 1983.
212. Shields, R., The absorption and secretion of fluid and electrolyte by the obstructed bowel, *Br. J. Surg.*, 52, 774, 1965.
213. Sung, D. T. W. and Williams, L. F., Intestinal secretion after intravenous fluid infusion in small bowel obstruction, *Am. J. Surg.*, 121, 91, 1971.
214. Lee, J. S., Intraluminal distension pressure on intestinal lymph flow, serosal transudation and fluid transport in rat, *J. Physiol.*, 355, 399, 1984.
215. Caren, J., Meyer, J., and Grossman, M., Canine intestinal secretion during and after distension of small bowel, *Am. J. Physiol.*, 227, 183, 1974.
216. Mishra, N. K., Appert, H. E., and Howard, J. M., The effects of distension and obstruction on the accumulation of fluid in the lumen of small bowel of dogs, *Ann. Surg.*, 180, 791, 1974.
217. Swabb, E. A., Hynes, R. A., and Donowitz, M., Elevated intraluminal pressure alters rabbit small intestinal transport *in vivo*, *Am. J. Physiol.*, 242, G58, 1982.
218. Mirkovitch, V., Menge, H., and Robinson, J. W. L., The effect of intraluminal hydrostatic pressure on intestinal absorption in vivo, *Experientia*, 30, 912, 1974.
219. Wangensteen, O. H., *Intestinal Obstructions*, 3rd ed., Charles C Thomas, Springfield, Ill., 1955, chap. 1.
220. Ohman, U., Studies on small intestinal obstruction. III. Circulatory effects of artificial small bowel distension, *Acta Chir. Scand.*, 141, 536, 1975.
221. Bury, K. D., McClure, O. N., and Wright, H. K., Reversal of colonic net absorption to net secretion, *Arch. Surg.*, 108, 854, 1974.
222. Wright, H. K., O'Brien, J. J., and Tilson, M. D., Water absorption in experimental closed segment obstruction of the ileum in man, *Am. J. Surg.*, 121, 96, 1971.
223. Ruf, W., Suehiro, G. T., Suehiro, A., Pressler, V., and McNamara, J. J., Intestinal blood flow at various intraluminal pressures in the piglet with closed abdomen, *Ann. Surg.*, 191, 157, 1980.
224. Mizonishi, T. and Semba, T., Effect of distension on mesenteric blood flow and O_2 saturation of venous blood in the dog intestinal loop, *Jpn. J. Physiol.*, 29, 627, 1979.

225. Yamamoto, M., Plessow, B., Koch, H. K., and Oehlert, W., Electron microscopic studies on the small intestinal mucosa of rats after mechanical intestinal obstruction and ischemia, *Virchows Arch. B,* 32, 157, 1980.
226. Bookstein, J. J., Non-occlusive ischemic colitis-angiographic aspects in a canine model, *Invest. Radiol.,* 13, 506, 1978.
227. Granger, D. N., Kvietys, P. R., Mortillaro, N. A., and Taylor, A. E., Effect of luminal distension on intestinal transcapillary fluid exchange, *Am. J. Physiol.,* 239, G516, 1980.
228. Enochsson, L., Nylander, G., and Ohman, U., Effects of intraluminal pressure on regional blood flow in obstructed and unobstructed small intestines in the rat, *Am. J. Surg.,* 144, 558, 1982.
229. Shields, R. and Code, C. F., Effect of increased portal pressure on absorption of water and sodium from the ileum of dogs, *Am. J. Physiol.,* 200, 755, 1961.
230. Mailman, D., unpublished observations.

Chapter 10

ROLE OF THE CIRCULATION IN ACUTE PANCREATITIS

Miklós Papp

TABLE OF CONTENTS

I. INTRODUCTION

This chapter addresses the question, why does an initial inflammatory and autodigestive process characterized by interstitial edema progress into hemorrhagic necrosis of the pancreas? The former form is reversible, while the latter one is a severe, often lethal disease. It is suggested that among the causes of the progression, functional and pathological changes of the local vasculature are present which impair the metabolism of the pancreas. We consider also whether in the development of acute hemorrhagic necrotic pancreatitis the "vascular factor" is a primary pathogenic component, or merely a secondary contributory factor.

II. HISTORICAL AND GENERAL SURVEY

The vascular concept of the etiology of acute pancreatitis (a.p.) is based on the assumption that vascular disturbances of the gland may result in hemorrhage of the pancreas. Embolization of the pancreatic vascular tree can lead to pancreatic hemorrhage and necrosis.[1-5] Ligation of the splenic artery is followed by infarcts of the pancreas.[6,7] Ischemia of the gland induced by obstruction of the arterial blood supply, combined with ductal ligation, results in the progression of pancreatic edema to necrosis.[8-10] Venous congestion induced by ligation of pancreatic veins, with or without ductal obstruction, produces the same results.[10-12] Stimulation of the sympathetic nervous system decreases pancreatic blood flow (PBF)[13,14] and seems to aggravate the pancreatitis.[15,16] Postganglionic sympathectomy increases pancreatic perfusion and reduces the severity of experimental a.p.[17] In experimental a.p., changes in lobular arteries (reduced caliber, segmental spasm, etc.), transient vasodilation, increased capillary permeability, capillary stasis, and extravasation of plasma can be demonstrated. Due to damage of pancreatic vasculature, PBF decreases in experimental a.p. The degree of ischemia exceeds the extent of acinar necrosis.[18] Impairment of local blood supply in a.p. may also be due to alterations in systemic hemodynamics, induced by circulatory shock, for example. Circulatory shock may result from intrapancreatic formation of vasoactive substances or escape of digestive enzymes from pancreatic interstices into the systemic circulation. The vasoactive substances entering the blood lead to a diminution of circulating plasma volume and a fall in cardiac output and blood pressure. Among the digestive enzymes the most important are trypsin,[19,20] elastase,[21,22] and phospholipase A.[23,24] These enzymes also damage the wall of pancreatic vessels, eliciting arteritis, phlebitis, hemorrhages, and impairment of the microcirculation.[25] Bile salts damage acinar parenchyma and pancreatic vessel walls through their detergent properties.[26-29] Their effects result in decreased oxygen uptake of the inflamed gland and in a reduction of total pancreatic phosphate content.

The increase in the amount of the extravasated fluid, together with the juice escaping from the pancreatic excretory ducts, leads to pancreatic edema. The transport of the extravasated protein from the interstitium is the function of the local lymphatics. The activity of pancreatic digestive enzymes is elevated in the thoracic duct or in the pancreatico-duodenal lymph by obstructing pancreatic juice flow. Due to ductal obstruction the activity of digestive enzymes in the pancreatic interstitial fluid may reach one third of the enzymatic activity of the stimulated pancreatic juice collected before obstruction. The close anatomical and functional relation between acini and lymph capillaries has been demonstrated.[30] Simultaneous ligation of the pancreatic ducts and the thoracic duct increases the extension and severity of pancreatic damage.

III. INCIDENCE OF VASCULAR DISEASE ASSOCIATED WITH HUMAN ACUTE PANCREATITIS

It is well known that the most frequent etiological factors in human a.p. are biliary tract disease and chronic alcoholism. Their incidence associated with a.p. is 41 and 27%, respectively. In the etiology of the disease, the incidence of vascular disease is 4.5%.[31]

The relationship between pancreatic infarcts and hemorrhagic a.p. is not clear. Occlusive local vascular lesions promote the development of pancreatic infarcts, and reduced PBF may be associated with hemorrhagic pancreatitis. Pancreatic hemorrhages develop due to ruptures of diseased arterial walls. The question is whether hemorrhages are causes or consequences of the pathological process.[2,32,33] In old age, alterations of arteries due to arteriosclerosis are very frequent. Atheromas have been demonstrated in small and large pancreatic arteries.[34,35] Hyaline accumulation in the media narrows and sometimes occludes the pancreatic arterioles. The extent of vessel wall alteration seems to correspond to the reduction in acinar parenchyma.[36] The first pancreatic infarct due to arteriosclerosis and endarteritis was described by Chiari (see Reference 37). In the pancreas of patients suffering from periarteritis nodosa, anemic infarcts can be demonstrated.[38] Occurrence of pancreatic infarcts was studied in the absence of acute necrotizing pancreatitis. In 80% of the cases the infarcts were associated with thrombosis or embolization of pancreatic arteries due to periarteritis nodosa, hypertension, etc. In 20% of the cases shock or heart failure was a contributory factor.[37] Gerlei[39] observed 13 focal or extended necroses in an examination of the pancreas in 30 patients suffering from cardiac failure. The incidence of a.p. was 20% at autopsy following cardiac surgery.[40] It is well known that severe pancreatic arteriosclerosis occurs in malignant hypertension. In a hundred cases of malignant hypertension, the incidence of pancreatic lesions was studied. In none of these 100 cases was diffuse hemorrhagic pancreatitis or pancreatic necrosis found at necropsy. Atheromatous embolization of pancreatic arteries,[41,42] diffuse intravascular coagulation,[43] and fat emboli due to hyperlipemia[44] may play a role in the development of a.p. The occurrence of a.p. in a group of patients with longstanding diabetes mellitus was also analyzed. Besides the involvement of pancreatic vessels, a functional ischemia of the gland was suggested when anatomical lesions were not demonstrable.[45] Alteration of local vessel walls caused by arteriosclerosis or venous thrombosis often occurs in a.p. Examination of 44 patients who died from a.p. revealed 26 thromboses in pancreatic and peripancreatic vessels, 2 emboli and 3 pancreatic hemorrhages.[4] Baer and New[46] observed microthrombi in blood vessels of the pancreas associated with a.p. It was suggested that ischemia was a common factor in the production of pancreatic necrosis or infarction. The rate of development of ischemia determines which of these lesions will be produced.[47]

IV. BLOOD AND NERVE SUPPLY OF THE PANCREAS

The pancreas consists of head, neck, body, and tail. The arteries supplying the gland show rich anastomoses with each other. The arterial supply of the gland is provided by arterial arcades.[48] Extensive anastomosis exists between the superior and inferior pancreatico-duodenal arteries. The splenic artery takes part in supplying the body of the gland. The splenic and the superior pancreatico-duodenal arteries originate (via common hepatic and gastroduodenal arteries) from the celiac, while the inferior pancreatico-duodenal arteries arise from the superior mesenteric artery.[49] The arterial branches form an interlobular plexus; from it a single intralobular artery enters each lobule and forms a capillary plexus among the acini or the islets of Langerhans.[50,51] Capillaries supplying and then leaving the islets subsequently perfuse the acini.[50,52-54] The neurotransmitter regulating the caliber of arteries is norepinephrine.[55] The pancreatic capillaries are fenestrated.[56] Histamine-type agents augment their filtration and diffusion capacity.[57] The veins draining the pancreas course along the arteries and finally flow into the portal vein.[51]

The pancreas is innervated both by sympathetic and parasympathetic fibers of the autonomic nervous system.[51,58] Efferent sympathetic fibers from thoracic ganglia reach the pancreas directly or via the celiac and superior mesenteric plexus. After synapsing in the ganglia, the fibers enter the pancreas together with the arteries. The afferent sympathetic fibers leaving the pancreas reach their ganglion cells via splanchnic nerves and the sympathetic trunk. The sympathetic nerve fibers mediate pain of pancreatic origin, with the gastroduodenal plexus playing a very important role. The efferent parasympathetic axons originate from cells of the dorsal vagal nucleus and pass into the posterior vagal trunk, and fibers from there enter the celiac plexus. Without synapsing they reach the pancreas in the vascular plexuses which accompany the arteries supplying the pancreas; they synapse in intraglandular ganglia, the cells of which integrate impulses of different nerves. There are also direct fibers to the pancreas. Afferent fibers leaving the pancreas enter the dorsal vagal nucleus. The vagus nerves are the secretory nerves of the pancreas. Cholinergic fibers and parasympathomimetic agents induce pancreatic vasodilation, acting on presynaptic receptors and inhibiting in this way the release of norepinephrine.[55]

V. RESPONSE OF THE PANCREAS TO ISCHEMIA

The severity of changes in the pancreas induced by normothermic ischemia is proportional to the duration of the ischemia. Dog and rat pancreas can tolerate periods of total ischemia lasting 40 to 60 min,[59-64] while the ischemic tolerance time of swine pancreas is longer.[65] Pancreatic ischemia lasting for 1 hr is followed by a hyperemia, while 2 hr of ischemia induces pancreatic edema.[64] Reperfusion of the ischemic pancreas results in death of the animals after 2[62] or 5 hr.[59] When ischemia is combined with ductal obstruction the ischemia tolerance time is shorter and hemorrhagic a.p. develops.[65,66] In the cat pancreas, necrosis of acinar cells starts to develop following ligation of splenic artery for 1 hr; the necrosis is complete after 24 hr.[6,7] Damage to canine acinar cells can be demonstrated by electron microscopy soon after induction of ischemia.[59] In acinar cells of rat pancreatic slices, damage of mitochondria develops and is followed within 4 hr by necrosis of the cells.[67] In the rat, ischemia of the gland increases the number of islets of Langerhans.[68]

Norepinephrine dramatically reduces blood flow to the intact pancreas. Norepinephrine or epinephrine released in states such as asphyxia and hypoxia augments the damaging effect of intraductally injected bile.[69] In another study, however, MacPhedran and Lee[70] could not confirm these results; they induced pancreatitis and noted that the ischemia induced by norepinephrine was not an aggravating factor in the experimental hemorrhagic a.p.

VI. AGENTS AFFECTING PBF

Catecholamines (norepinephrine, epinephrine),[55,71-74] large doses of dopamine,[75] vasopressin,[76-79] ethanol,[80,81] and somatostatin[82,83] decrease PBF. When administered systemically, prostaglandins decrease PBF;[84,85] when given directly into the pancreatic circulation they increase PBF.[86] *Escherichia coli* endotoxin reduces PBF.[87] Sympathetic stimulation[13,14,88] also decreases blood flow to the pancreas, as does hypothermia.[89]

Kinins, serotonin,[90] histamine,[90-92] and caerulein[86,93] increase PBF. Glucagon alone increases PBF,[86] while in combination with secretin it reduces it.[94] A sudden increase in pancreatic intraductal pressure also increases PBF.[95,96] Clinically it is important to note that vasopressin reduces the extent of retroperitoneal edema, inhibits capillary sludging in the pancreas, and increases oxygen extraction of the gland, while decreasing pancreatic arterial flow. These effects of vasopressin may counteract the effect of the decrease in PBF in a.p.[76] Some investigators contend that low-molecular-weight dextran improves the impaired pancreatic microcirculation and counteracts the decrease in PBF during a.p.[97-99] Others have not confirmed the beneficial effect of dextran in experimental a.p.[100]

VII. PBF IN EXPERIMENTAL ACUTE PANCREATITIS

The changes in PBF during a.p. have been examined in various experimental animal models; the most frequently used species was the dog. In the early phase of the induction of experimental a.p., at least two components have to be taken into consideration: (1) the chemical properties of the inducing agent(s) and (2) the response of the pancreas. The provoking agents, e.g., bile salts, digestive enzymes (lipase, phospholipase A, trypsin, elastase), damage the glandular parenchyma and its vasculature. Moreover, they initiate an inflammatory reaction. In the development of the inflammatory reaction, vasoactive substances released within the gland play a role. These vasoactive agents cause an early transient local vasodilation, increased capillary blood flow, and an increase in the number of opened capillaries. Furthermore, they provoke an increased leakage of plasma proteins into the interstitium.[101] These changes are followed by capillary and venous stasis and outflow.[102] In the course of a.p., the initial vascular reaction is a hyperemia,[23,96,103] which when coupled to injury of blood vessels results in pancreatic edema. The injury of blood vessels (the "vascular factor") seems to be significant. Whether the capillaries are obstructed by edema, by vascular spasm, or by capillary stasis, the severity of the vascular factor will determine whether an edematous pancreatitis will go into a much more severe form of the disease, i.e., hemorrhagic a.p.[20,104] Vasoactive substances entering blood may cause systemic hypotension and in this way exacerbate the pancreatic ischemia.

It is generally accepted that a.p. or a focal form of a.p. cannot result from prolonged pancreatic ischemia alone. However, when the blood supply of an edematous pancreas is interrupted, severe hemorrhagic a.p. develops,[5-10,12] suggesting that ischemia diminishes the resistance of acinar cells to the damaging effects of digestive enzymes present in the edema fluid. Some authors contend that impairment of the blood supply to the pancreas is not the significant initiating factor in the etiology of a.p.;[105] rather, several factors such as ductal obstruction and passage of digestive enzymes into the pancreatic interstitium, together with obstruction of the pancreatic blood supply, are the main etiological factors. Others suggest that intrapancreatic vascular injury determines the type of lesion that will be produced in the gland.[20]

Table 1 summarizes the normal values of PBF obtained by different methods in different species. The values vary over a wide range, presumably due to the methods and species used and whether they were anesthetized or awake. Lower values were measured in anesthetized animals. Long-term obliteration of pancreatic ducts or pancreatic fibrosis did not significantly alter the basal PBF,[106-108] most certainly because the arterial flow to the islets is well maintained despite the reduced blood flow to the acini.[106]

Table 2 summarizes the changes in PBF during experimental a.p. With pancreatic edema, PBF increases.[97,109] In the early phase of necrotic a.p., a transient rise in PBF

Table 1
VALUES OF PBF MEASURED BY DIFFERENT METHODS

Animal	Awake	Anesthetized	Method	Value[a]	Ref.
Dog	−	+	Stromuhr	80	163
	−	+	Venous outflow	60—70	95
	−	+		57	109
	−	+		12—28	164
	−	+		22 mℓ/min/pancreas	76
	−	+	^{42}K clearance	100	165
	−	+	^{86}Rb clearance	60—63	71, 166, 167
Rat	−	+		50	168
Dog	−	+		75.5	139
	−	+		65.2	97
Cat	+	−	^{86}Rb clearance	136	169
Dog	−	+		90	113
Rat	−	+		56—65	170
Dog	−	+	^{133}Xe washout technique	26 mℓ/min/pancreas	96
	−	+		106	171
	−	+		107	172
	−	+		85	146
	+	−	H_2 gas clearance	76	173
	−	+		42.8	173
	−	+		45.6—48.5	106
Man	+	−		87.8	174
Dog	−	+	Flow probe	18.5	89
	−	+		22 mℓ/min/a.p. duod. sup.	96
	−	+		100—156	175
	−	+		45	176
	−	+		43.9 mℓ/min/pancreas	141
	−	+		48	112
	−	+		61	111
Swine	−	+		23.4 mℓ/min/pancreas	107
Dog	−	+		40 mℓ/min/a.p. duod. sup.	78
	−	+		15.3 mℓ/min/pancreas	79
	+	−	Radioactive microspheres	64	73
	+	−		131 mℓ/min/pancreas	111a, 177
	−	+		33—35 mℓ/min/pancreas	
	−	+		45—50	87
	+	−		172	80
	+	−		173	81
	−	+		54	
	−	+		27—38	178
	+	−		77	83

[a] All values in mℓ/min/100 g except where otherwise noted.

is measured[96,97,103,110] which is subsequently followed by a definite reduction in PBF; the arteriovenous shunt flow is not increased.[100] In contrast to the normal pancreas, in the inflamed gland the arteriovenous oxygen difference does not increase when PBF decreases.[111] Thus, oxygen uptake of the inflamed pancreas is reduced,[98,100] and high-energy phosphate stores will be depleted.[111a] Hypotension-induced ischemia decreased pancreatic oxygen uptake without a concomitant rise in lactate output.[112] The study of

Table 2
CHANGES OF PBF AND OXYGEN UPTAKE DURING ACUTE EXPERIMENTAL PANCREATITIS

		Pancreatic edema				Pancreatic necrosis				
Animal	Agent	Blood flow (mℓ/gland)	Perfusion rate (mℓ/min/100 g)	% of cardiac output	O_2 uptake per gland	Blood flow (mℓ/gland)	Perfusion rate (mℓ/min/100 g)	% of cardiac output	O_2 uptake per gland	Ref.
Dog	Bile	—	—	—	—	D	—	—	—	110
	Bile	—	—	—	—	NS	D	D	—	139
	Trypsin	—	—	—	—	NS	D	NS	—	139
	Bile	—	NS	—	NS	—	—	—	—	109
	Bile	I	D	I	—	D	D	D	—	97
	Bile	—	—	—	—	D	—	—	—	76
	Bile	NS	NS	—	—	D	D	—	—	179
	Bile	—	—	—	—	D	—	D	D	98, 141
	Bile + trypsin	—	—	—	—	—	D	—	—	111a
Rat	Closed duod. loop	—	—	—	—	—	NS	I	—	170
Dog	Bile	—	—	—	—	—	—	D	—	103
	Trypsin	—	—	—	—	D	—	NS	D	100

Note: (—) Not studied; (I) significant increase vs. control; (D) Significant decrease vs. control; (NS) not significant.

Kvietys et al.[111] was very instructive regarding PBF, oxygen uptake, and reactive hyperemia induced by temporary arterial occlusion. The magnitude of the postocclusion reactive hyperemia was proportional to the duration of arterial occlusion. Both reduction in arterial pressure and elevation in venous pressure of the totally isolated, normal canine pancreas decreased PBF. The pancreatic oxygen uptake was not altered by a reduction in arterial flow because of the increase in arteriovenous oxygen difference, which compensated for the reduction in PBF only at arterial pressures greater than 40 mmHg. These results indicate that in the normal pancreas the oxygen uptake is maintained due to the interaction between resistance (blood flow) and exchange (perfused capillary density) vessels. In necrotic a.p., deterioration of both glandular microcirculation and systemic blood circulation (hypotension) is responsible for the reduced blood flow. Vasoactive agents pass into blood circulation and provoke its deterioration. Thus, a chain reaction is started which leads to hypoxia of the pancreas, which further reduces PBF[113] and potentiates bile-induced damage to the pancreas.[69]

VIII. CHANGES OF INTRAPANCREATIC VASCULAR PATTERN IN ACUTE PANCREATITIS

The behavior of large blood vessels supplying the pancreas can be demonstrated in vivo by angiography. Due to inflammation of the gland an early increase in PBF is expected. The findings are, however, highly variable in man. These include an increase in the diameter of arteries, hypervascularity, arterial deformations, hypovascularity, occlusion, or signs of impeded venous outflow.[114-116] In experimental a.p., reduced caliber and segmental spasm of the lobular arteries, their obstruction and compression, opening of new arteriovenous anastomoses, deficient filling of precapillaries, and venous stasis have been observed[117,118] by vascular filling[119,120] and by angiography.[121]

While deficient filling of pancreatic precapillaries was demonstrated in a.p., the filling of precapillaries supplying the duodenum was complete.[119,120] Early dilation of pancreatic capillaries followed by an increased permeability with extravasation of plasma resulting in capillary stasis has been demonstrated by transillumination, capillary microscopy, and vascular filling during development of a.p.[30,117,119,120,122-124] Obstruction of the pancreatic duct results in pancreatic edema, which slows capillary blood flow, separates plasma and erythrocytes, widens the pericapillary space, and leads to ischemia, hemorrhage, and venous stasis.[125] Microangiographic findings confirmed the course of development of pancreatic microvascular abnormalities, with peripheral areas of the damage showing increased circulation.[126] In the establishment of the above changes the damaging effect of the agents inducing pancreatitis, compression of capillaries due to pancreatic edema, and neural mechanisms has a part. Figure 1 demonstrates the phases of capillary damage in a.p.

IX. VASOACTIVE AGENTS IN ACUTE PANCREATITIS

In the production of systemic circulatory and local pancreatic vascular changes and inflammatory reactions, vasoactive substances which are released by the inflamed pancreas take part. Thus, these vasoactive substances can be demonstrated in the pancreatic exudate, pancreatic venous, and peripheral blood. The agents entering the blood circulation provoke hypovolemia, hypotension, and shock; locally they affect PBF, increase capillary permeability, provoke ascites formation, and induce capillary vasodilation, edema, inflammation, and pain. Such vasoactive substances are the amines (histamine, serotinin), kinins (bradykinin, kallidin), prostaglandins, myocardial depressant factor (MDF), enzymes, etc. It has been demonstrated that pancreatic

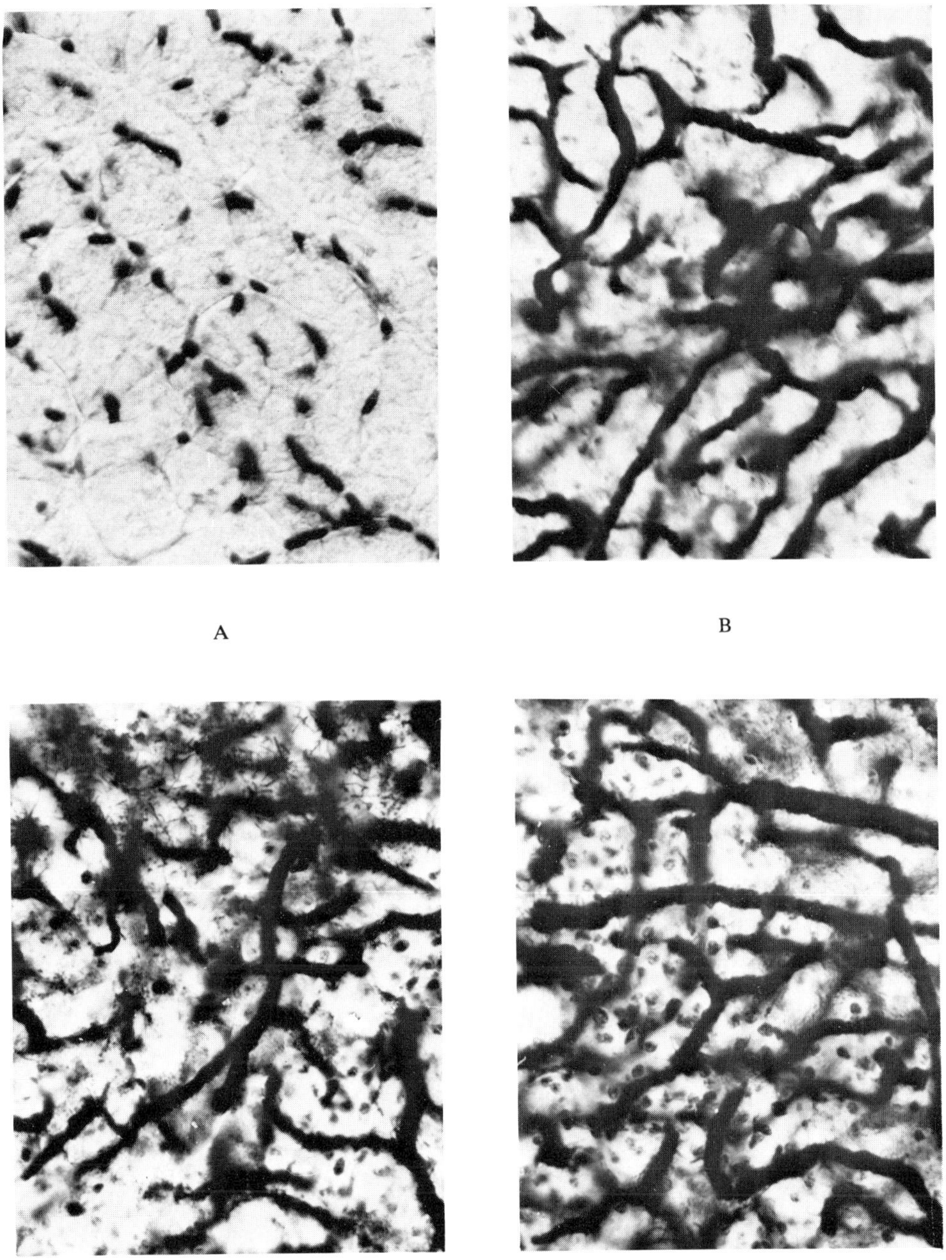

FIGURE 1. Erythrocytes in capillaries of dog pancreas demonstrated by benzidine reaction (sections of 40 μm); photos 2 to 6, sections after intraductal (i.d.) bile injection. (A) Intact pancreas; short, not confluent capillary segments (magnification × 350). (B) 10 min after i.d. bile; network of dilated confluent capillaries (magnification × 350). (C) 30 min after i.d. bile; as in Photo 2, but increased cellular reaction in pancreatic interstices (magnification × 350). (D) 60 min after i.d. bile; enormously dilated capillary network with definitely marked cellular reaction (magnification × 350). (E) 3 hr after i.d. bile; capillaries are constricted or compressed (magnification × 140). (F) 24 hr after i.d. bile; failure of capillary filling; only the filling of a vessel with greater caliber and that of a group of capillaries could be demonstrated (magnification × 140). (Reprinted from Papp, M., Ungvari, Gy., Nemeth, P. E., Munkacsi, I., and Zubek, L., *Scand. J. Gastroenterol.*, 4, 681, 1969. With permission of Universitetsforlaget, Oslo.)

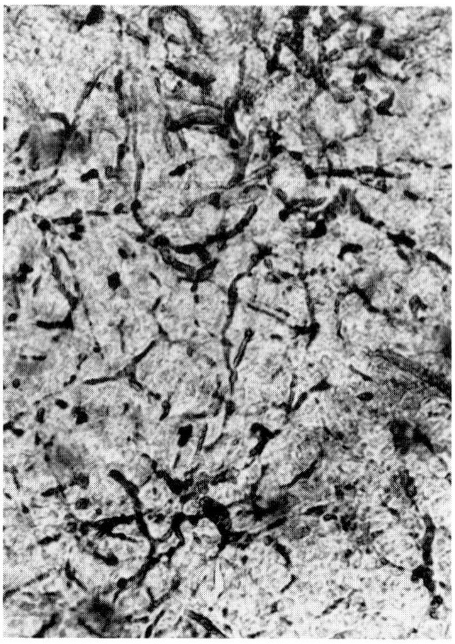

FIGURE 1E

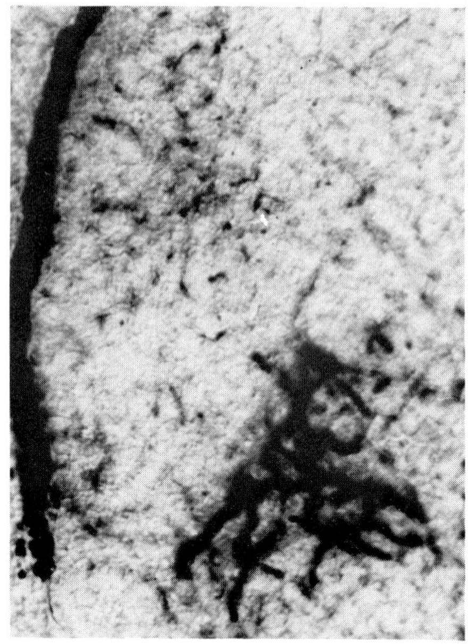

FIGURE 1F

exudate induces hypovolemia,[118,127] and the hypotensive effect is due to the presence of vasoactive[121,128] or other agents in the exudate which act through histamine release.[129,130] In the above pathological changes, formation of kinins of pancreatic origin and the plasma kinin system take part.[130-133] Bradykinin infused intraductally induces pancreatic edema and leukocyte infiltration.[134] Prostaglandins may play a role in affecting arterial flow into the pancreas, inasmuch as indomethacin reduces it.[135] In a.p., prostaglandin activity in pancreatic venous blood rises significantly, suggesting enhanced prostaglandin synthesis and secretion.[136] Due to hypoperfusion and ischemia of the pancreas, shock-producing factors such as MDF[137] and lysosomal enzymes[138] are released into the blood and pancreatic transudate.

X. SYSTEMIC HEMODYNAMIC CONSEQUENCES OF ACUTE PANCREATITIS

Deterioration of systemic blood circulation due to the disease is characterized by a fall in cardiac output and arterial blood pressure and an elevation of portal venous pressure.[97,110,118,121,127,140-142] The above hemodynamic changes result in a reduced perfusion of the pancreas. Others, however, have found an elevation of the cardiac index in a.p.[143,144] Reduction of blood volume due to hemorrhage results in diminished perfusion of the pancreas, the degree of which is greater than the fall in arterial blood pressure.[145] Oligemic shock also reduces PBF.[137,146] From a clinical point of view it is interesting to note that the incidence of a.p. is increased by circulatory shock; in cardiogenic shock it was found to be 10%,[147] and in severe shock, 50%.[148] Arterial hypotension aggravated the histological damage to the pancreas in experimental a.p. and increased its mortality.[149] The incidence of severe arterial hypoxia was twice as high in a.p. as in control patients with acute abdominal pains.[150] Hypoxia decreased PBF[113] and augmented the damage to the pancreas.

XI. THE LYMPHATIC SYSTEM IN ACUTE PANCREATITIS

Both blood and lymph capillaries drain the pancreatic interstitium, transferring protein, enzymes, and fluid. The enhanced lymphatic transport of enzymes from the pancreatic interstitium during obstruction of the pancreatic duct(s) and a.p. suggests that the digestive enzyme activity in the interstitial (edema) fluid is elevated. The enzyme activity within the interstitium can reach 20 to 30% of that secreted in the stimulated canine or rat pancreatic juice collected before duct ligation or induction of a.p. for 60 min. The enzyme activity in the edema fluid decreases during the course of a.p.[151] Enzyme activity in the thoracic duct rises following pancreatic ductal ligation,[152-154] pharmacological obstruction of pancreatic juice outflow,[155] pancreatic stimulation,[152,156] and intraductal injection of a.p.-inducing agents.[110,152,157,158] The concentration of labeled albumin infused into the pancreatic duct was higher in the thoracic duct lymph than in pancreatic venous plasma. The lymphatic system in the pancreas functions as a "safety valve";[30,155] in other words, there is a lymphatic pathway for pancreatic enzymes. Stimulation of the pancreas combined with ligation of the pancreatic duct and the thoracic duct results in the progression of pancreatic edema to focal pancreatic necrosis.[153,159] The pattern of extrapancreatic fat necroses corresponds to the course of the abdominal lymphatics.[153] Ligation of the thoracic duct in the rat increases the severity and extension of the damage of the pancreas and the mortality of trypsin-induced a.p.[124,149] Thoracic duct drainage seems to be effective in the treatment of a.p.[160] During a.p., changes in lymph flow from the pancreas are not reflected in thoracic duct lymph flow, since pancreatico-duodenal lymph flow does not change in the early phase of experimental a.p.[161] During a.p., lymphatic transport of enzymes from the pancreas may be impeded by erythrocytes entering local lymphatics due to inflammation.[31,159] Thus, lymphatic obstruction in a.p. has to be considered as a secondary, aggravating factor.[162]

XII. CONCLUSION

A survey of the literature suggests that when acute edematous pancreatitis is progressing into a hemorrhagic necrotic form, local vascular injury is an aggravating factor. Deterioration of the local circulation results in metabolic impairment of the acinar parenchyma, increasing the intensity and severity of the pathological process in the pancreas.

REFERENCES

1. Panum, P. L., Experimentelle Beitraege zur Lehre von der Embolie, *Virchows Arch. Pathol. Anat. Physiol.*, 25, 308, 1862.
2. Bunge, B., Zur Pathogenese und Therapie der akuten Pankreashaemorrhagie und abdominalen Fettgewebsnekrosen, *Langenbecks Arch. Chir.*, 71, 726, 1903.
3. MacKenzie, W. C., Pancreatitis, *Ann. R. Coll. Surg. Engl.*, 15, 220, 1954.
4. Smyth, C. J., Etiology of acute hemorrhagic pancreatitis with special reference to vascular factors; analysis of autopsies and experimental investigation, *Arch. Pathol.*, 30, 651, 1940.
5. Pfeffer, R. B., Lazzarini-Robertson, A., Safadi, D., Mixter, G., Jr., Secoy, C. F., and Hinton, J. W., Gradations of pancreatitis, edematous through hemorrhagic experimentally produced by controlled injections of microspheres into blood vessels in dogs, *Surgery*, 51, 764, 1962.
6. Schmitz-Moormann, P., Fruehveraenderungen bei der experimentellen partiellen permanenten Ischaemie des Katzen-Pankreas, *Virchows Arch. A*, 348, 249, 1969.

7. Schmitz-Moormann, P., Spaetveraenderungen bei der experimentellen partiellen permanenten Ischaemie des Katzen-Pankreas, *Virchows Arch. A,* 348, 260, 1969.
8. Popper, H. L., Necheles, H., and Russel, K. C., Transition of pancreatic edema into pancreatic necrosis, *Surg. Gynecol. Obstet.,* 87, 79, 1948.
9. Block, M. A., Wakim, K. G., and Baggenstoss, A. H., Experimental studies concerning factors in the pathogenesis of acute pancreatitis, *Surg. Gynecol. Obstet.,* 99, 83, 1954.
10. Menguy, R. B., Hallenbeck, G. A., Bollman, J. L., and Grindley, J. H., Ductal and vascular factors in the etiology of experimentally induced acute pancreatitis, *Arch. Surg. (Chicago),* 74, 881, 1957.
11. Adams, T. W. and Musselman, M. M., Pancreatic venous thrombosis as an etiologic factor in acute necrotizing hemorrhagic pancreatitis, *Surg. Forum,* 4, 401, 1953.
12. Anderson, M. C., Venous stasis in the transition of edematous pancreatitis to necrosis, *JAMA,* 183, 534, 1963.
13. Barlow, T. E., Greenwell, J. R., Harper, A. A., and Scratcherd, T., The influence of the splanchnic nerves on the external secretion, blood flow and electrical conductance of the cat pancreas, *J. Physiol. (London),* 236, 421, 1974.
14. Varga, B., Folly, G., and Papp, M., L'effet de l'excitation electrique du ganglion coeliaque sur le debit sanguin du pancreas, *Lyon Chir.,* 70, 168, 1974.
15. Mallet-Guy, P., Feroldi, J., and Reboul, E., Recherches experimentales sur la pathogenie des pancreatites aigues. Leur provocation par l'excitation du nerf splanchnique gauche, *Lyon Chir.,* 44, 281, 1949.
16. Gilsdorf, R. B., Long, D., Moberg, A., and Leonard, A. S., Central-nervous-system influence on experimentally induced pancreatitis, *JAMA,* 192, 394, 1965.
17. Goodhead, B. and Wright, P. W., The effect of postganglionic sympathectomy on the development of hemorrhagic pancreatitis in the dog, *Ann. Surg.,* 170, 951, 1969.
18. Aho, H. J., Nevalainen, T. J., and Aho, A. J., Experimental pancreatitis in the rat, *Eur. Surg. Res.,* 15, 28, 1983.
19. Polya, E., Die Wirking des Trypsins auf das lebende Pankreas, *Pfluegers Arch.,* 121, 483, 1908.
20. Anderson, M. C. and Bergan, J. J., The significance of vascular injury as a factor in the pathogenesis of pancreatitis, *Ann. Surg.,* 154, 58, 1961.
21. Geokas, M. C., The role of elastase in acute pancreatitis. II. Intrapancreatic elastolytic activity in trypsin-induced acute pancreatitis in dogs, *Arch. Pathol.,* 86, 127, 1968.
22. Molnar, J. J., Schneider, I. J., Tindel, S., Shapira, D., and State, D., Hemorrhagic pancreatitis induced by elastase, *Acta Morphol. Acad. Sci. Hung.,* 16, 213, 1968.
23. Anderson, M. C., Neddleman, S. B., Gramatica, L., Toranto, I. R., and Briggs, D. R., Further inquiry into the pathogenesis of acute pancreatitis, *Arch. Surg. (Chicago),* 99, 185, 1969.
24. Nevalainen, T. J., The role of phospholipase A in acute pancreatitis, *Scand. J. Gastroenterol.,* 15, 641, 1980.
25. Anderson, M. C., Pancreatic hemorrhage. Relationship to necrotizing pancreatitis, *Arch. Surg. (Chicago),* 83, 467, 1961.
26. Wanke, M., *Experimentelle Pankreatitis,* Georg Thieme Verlag, Stuttgart, 1968.
27. Sum, P. T., Bencosme, A., and Beck, I. T., Pathogenesis of bile-induced acute pancreatitis in the dog, experiments with detergents, *Am. J. Dig. Dis.,* 15, 637, 1970.
28. Nagy, A., Papp, M., and Balint, A., Vascular injury associated with acute pancreatitis induced by oil or Na-deoxycholate, *Acta Morphol. Acad. Sci. Hung.,* 19, 175, 1971.
29. Papp, M., Nagy, A., and Fodor, I., Ultrastructure of pancreatic acinar parenchyma in acute experimental pancreatitis of the pigeon, *Acta Morphol. Acad. Sci. Hung.,* 19, 377, 1971.
30. Anderson, M. C. and Schiller, W. R., Microvasculatory dynamics in the normal and inflamed pancreas, *Am. J. Surg.,* 115, 118, 1968.
31. Duerr, G. H.-K., Acute pancreatitis, in *The Exocrine Pancreas,* Howat, H. T. and Sarles, H., Eds., W. B. Saunders, Philadelphia, 1979, 352.
32. Loewenthal, K., Pathogenese der akuten Pankreasnekrose, *Dtsch. Med. Wochenschr.,* 58, 1209, 1932.
33. Balo, J., Zur Frage der Entstehungsursache der Pankreasnekrose, *Beitr. Pathol. Anat. Allg. Pathol.,* 92, 14, 1933.
34. Houcke, E., Houcke, M., and Leblois, J., Le pancreas du vieillard. Etude histologique, *Presse Med.,* 72, 1887, 1964.
35. Stumpf, H. H., Microatheromas of very small arteries, *Hum. Pathol.,* 14, 1039, 1983.
36. Kaiser, G. and Hommel, G., Morphometric-statistical analysis of pancreatic arteries in chronic pancreatitis, *Virchows Arch.,* 365, 103, 1975.
37. MacKay, J. W., Baggenstoss, A. H., and Wollaeger, E. E., Infarcts of the pancreas, *Gastroenterology,* 35, 256, 1958.

38. Roessle, R., Beitraege zur Kenntnis der gesunden und der kranken Bauchspeicheldruese, *Beitr. Pathol. Anat. Allg. Pathol.*, 69, 163, 1921.
39. Gerlei, F., Ueber die Veraenderung der Bauchspeicheldruese bei Herzkranken, *Virchows Arch. Pathol. Anat. Physiol.*, 276, 148, 1930.
40. Feiner, H., Pancreatitis after cardiac surgery, *Am. J. Surg.*, 131, 684, 1976.
41. Probstein, J. G., Joshi, R. A., and Blumanthal, H., Atheromatous embolisation an etiology of acute pancreatitis, *Arch. Surg., (Chicago)*, 75, 566, 1957.
42. Moberg, A., Svenhamn, K., and Wagermark, J., Acute idiopathic pancreatitis, *Acta Chir. Scand.*, 134, 369, 1968.
43. Muggia, F. M., Vascular factors in acute pancreatitis, *Lancet*, 1, 245, 1970.
44. Klatskin, G. and Gordon, M., Relationship between relapsing pancreatitis and essential hyperlipemia, *Am. J. Med.*, 12, 3, 1952.
45. Bossak, E. T. and Joelson, R. H., Acute pancreatitis complicating diabetes mellitus, *Arch. Intern. Med.*, 97, 201, 1956.
46. Baer, L. and New, H. C., Intravascular clotting and acute pancreatitis in primary hyperparathyroidism, *Ann. Intern. Med.*, 64, 1062, 1966.
47. Hranilovich, G. T. and Baggenstoss, A. H., Lesions of the pancreas in malignant hypertension; review of one hundred cases at necropsy, *AMA Arch. Pathol.*, 55, 443, 1953.
48. Woodburne, R. and Olsen, L., The arteries of the pancreas, *Anat. Rec.*, 111, 255, 1951.
49. Pierson, J. M., The arterial blood supply of the pancreas, *Surg. Gynecol. Obstet.*, 77, 426, 1943.
50. Wharton, G., The blood supply of the pancreas with special reference to that of the islands of Langerhans, *Anat. Rec.*, 53, 55, 1932.
51. Harris, P. F., Anatomy, in *The Exocrine Pancreas*, Howat, H. T. and Sarles, H., Eds., W. B. Saunders, Philadelphia, 1979, 15.
52. Oppenheimer, M. J. and Mann, F. C., The intralobular pancreatic circulation, *Gastroenterology*, 3, 218, 1944.
53. Fujita, T., Insulo-acinar portal system in the horse pancreas, *Arch. Histol. Jpn.*, 35, 161, 1973.
54. Ohtani, O., Microcirculation of the pancreas: a correlative study of intravital microscopy of vascular corrosion casts, *Arch. Histol. Jpn.*, 46, 315, 1983.
55. Varga, G., Papp, M., Harsing, L. G., Jr., Toth, E. I., Gaal, Gy., Somogy, G. T., and Vizi, E. S., Neuroeffector transmission of the hepatic and pancreatico-duodenal isolated arteries of the dog, *Gastroenterology*, 87, 1056, 1984.
56. Kvietys, P. R., Perry, M. A., and Granger, D. N., Permeability of pancreatic capillaries to small molecules, *Am. J. Physiol.*, 245, G519, 1983.
57. Haraldsson, B., Rippe, B., Moxham, B. J., and Folkow, B., Permeability of fenestrated capillaries in the isolated pig pancreas, with effects of bradykinin and histamine, as studied by simultaneous registration of filtration and diffusion capacities, *Acta Physiol. Scand.*, 114, 67, 1982.
58. Richins, C. A., Innervation of the pancreas, *J. Comp. Neurol.*, 83, 223, 1945.
59. Moser, R., Meili, H. U., and Largiader, F., The ischemia tolerance of pancreas, *Z. Gesamte Exp. Med.*, 143, 266, 1967.
60. Largiader, F., Hegglin, J., Jacob, A., and Meili, H. U., Erhaltene exocrine Funktion als Voraussetzung fuer den Erfolg der Pankreastransplantation, *Helv. Chir. Acta*, 35, 321, 1968.
61. Inou, T., Ota, K., and Mori, S., Manifestations of rejection of pancreatico-duodenal allografts, *Transplantation*, 6, 503, 1968.
62. Binder, P. S., Heiskell, C. A., Adams, J. R., Cerra, F. B., Eilbert, J. B., and Bergan, J. J., Pancreatic function after normothermic ischemia. I. In vivo ischemia, *Am. J. Surg.*, 120, 687, 1970.
63. Slater, D. N., Bradsley, D., Magnall, Y., Smythe, A., and Fox, M., Pancreatic ischemia; sensitivity and reversibility of the changes, *Br. J. Exp. Pathol.*, 56, 530, 1975.
64. Broe, J. P., Zuidema, G. D., and Cameron, J. L., The role of ischemia in acute pancreatitis: studies with an isolated perfused canine pancreas, *Surgery*, 91, 377, 1982.
65. Zimmermann, G., Die Beeinflussung der Funktion des Pankreas durch Stoerungen der Blut- und Lymphzirkulation, *Wien. Med. Wochenschr.*, 126, 307, 1976.
66. Fleischer, G. M., Herden, P., and Spormann, H., Tierexperimentelle Untersuchungen zur Rolle der Ischaemie in der Pathogenese der akuten Pankreatitis, *Z. Exp. Chir. Transplant.*, 17, 179, 1984.
67. Jones, R. T. and Trump, B. F., Cellular and subcellular effects of ischemia on the pancreatic acinar cell: in vitro studies of rat tissue, *Virchows Arch. B*, 19, 325, 1975.
68. Adams, D. J. and Harrison, R. G., The vascularization of the rat pancreas and the effect of ischemia on the islets of Langerhans, *J. Anat.*,. 87, 257, 1953.
69. Day, S. B., Griffer, W. O., Castaneda, A., Nicoloff, D., Doberneck, R. C., and Stone, N. H., Potentiating influence of apnea, hypoxia and hypercapnia on bile-induced hemorrhagic pancreatic necrosis, *Surg. Gynecol. Obstet.*, 111, 304, 1960.

70. MacPhedran, N. T. and Lee, S. B., Effect of intraductal or intravascular norepinephrine infusion on the development of acute hemorrhagic pancreatitis, *Surgery,* 53, 490, 1964.
71. Delanay, J. P. and Grim, E., Drug influences on pancreatic blood flow, *Fed. Proc., Fed. Am. Soc. Exp. Biol.,* 23, 252, 1964.
72. Barlow, T. E., Greenwell, J. R., Harper, A. A., and Scratcherd, T., The effect of adrenaline and noradrenaline on the blood flow, electrical conductance and external secretion of the pancreas, *J. Physiol. (London),* 217, 665, 1971.
73. Polansky, D. B. and Safaie-Shirazi, S., Simultaneous measurement of pancreatic blood flow, endocrine and exocrine secretion in conscious dogs, *Surg. Forum,* 28, 91, 1977.
74. Vaysse, N., Bastie, J. M., Pascal, J. P., Martinel, C., Fourtainier, G., and Ribet, A., Effects of catecholamines and their inhibitors on the isolated canine pancreas, *Gastroenterology,* 72, 711, 1977.
75. Bastie, J. M., Vaysse, N., Brenac, B., Pascal, J. P., and Ribert, A., Effects of catecholamines and their inhibitors on the isolated canine pancreas. II. Dopamine, *Gastroenterology,* 72, 619, 1977.
76. Pissiotis, C. A., Condon, R. E., and Nyhus, L. M., Effect of vasopressin on pancreatic blood flow in acute hemorrhagic pancreatitis, *Am. J. Surg.,* 123, 203, 1972.
77. Schuurkes, J. A. J., Bronwers, H. A. A., Beijer, H. J. M., Charbon, G. A., and Schapiro, H., Lysine-vasopressin: hemodynamic effects in the anaesthetized dogs, *Am. J. Dig. Dis.,* 21, 1021, 1976.
78. Papp, M., Varga, B., and Varga, G., Pancreatic secretion: effects of vasopressin and glucagon on pancreatic blood flow and secretion, *Mt. Sinai J. Med., N.Y.,* 50, 439, 1983.
79. Beijer, H. J. M., Maas, A. H., and Charbon, A., A vasopressin-induced decrease in pancreatic blood flow and in pancreatic secretion in the anaesthetized dog, *Pfluegers Arch.,* 400, 324, 1984.
80. Horwitz, L. D. and Myers, J. H., Ethanol-induced alterations in pancreatic blood flow in conscious dogs, *Circ. Res.,* 50, 250, 1982.
81. Friedman, H. S., Lowery, R., Shaughnessy, E., and Scorza, J., The effect of ethanol on pancreatic blood flow in awake and anaesthetized dogs, *Proc. Soc. Exp. Biol. Med.,* 174, 377, 1983.
82. Samnegard, H., Thulin, L., Andreen, M., Tyden, G., Hallberg, D., and Efendic, S., Circulatory effects of somatostatin in anaesthetized dogs, *Acta Chir. Scand.,* 145, 209, 1979.
83. Price, B. A., Jaffe, B. M., and Zinner, M. J., Effect of exogenous somatostatin infusion on gastrointestinal blood flow and hormones in conscious dogs, *Gastroenterology,* 88, 80, 1985.
84. Saunders, R. N. and Moser, C. A., Increased vascular resistance by prostaglandins B1 and B2 in the isolated rat pancreas, *Nature (London) New Biol.,* 237, 285, 1972.
85. Case, R. M. and Scratcherd, T., Prostaglandin action on pancreatic blood flow and enzyme secretion by exocrine pancreas in vivo and in vitro, *J. Physiol. (London),* 226, 393, 1972.
86. Papp, M., Feher, S., Varga, B., and Folly, G., Humoral influences on local blood flow and external secretion of the resting dog pancreas, *Acta Med. Acad. Sci. Hung.,* 34, 185, 1977.
87. Spitzer, J. J., Ferguson, J. L., Hirsch, H. J., Loo, S., and Gabbay, K. H., Effects of *E. coli* endotoxin on pancreatic hormones and blood flow, *Circ. Shock,* 7, 353, 1980.
88. Gilsdorf, R. B., Urdatena, L. F., Delanay, J. P., and Leonard, A. S., Central nervous system influences on pancreatic secretion, sphincteric mechanisms and blood flow and their role in the course of pancreatitis, *Surgery,* 62, 581, 1967.
89. Eichelter, P. and Schenk, W. G., The influence of hypothermia on pancreatic secretion and blood flow, *Arch. Surg. (Chicago),* 96, 883, 1968.
90. Papp, M., Makra, G. B., and Varga, B., Effets de la bradykinine, de la kallidine, de la serotonine et de l'histamine sur le flux sanguin du pancreas, *Arch. Int. Pharmacodyn. Ther.,* 165, 31, 1967.
91. Papp, M., Varga, B., and Folly, G., Effect of secretin, pancreozymin, histamine and Decholin on canine pancreatic blood flow, *Pfluegers Arch.,* 340, 349, 1973.
92. Pascal, J. P., Vaysse, N., Boucard, J. P., Laval, J., and Ribet, A., Effets de l'histamine exogene et endogene et des antihistaminiques sur la vaso-motriciate et sur la secretion du pancreas isole perfuse du chien, *Biol. Gastro-Enterol.,* 4, 279, 1971.
93. Homma, T. and Malik, K. U., Effect of secretin and caerulein in canine pancreas: relation to prostaglandins, *Am. J. Physiol.,* 244, G660, 1983.
94. Takeshima, T., Miyamoto, J., Iwasaki, Y., and Dreiling, D. A., Relationships between pancreatic blood flow and secretion in the dog, *Mt. Sinai J. Med., N.Y.,* 48, 1, 1981.
95. Bennett, A. L. and Still, E. W., A study of the relation of pancreatic duct pressure to the rate of blood flow through the pancreas, *Am. J. Physiol.,* 106, 454, 1933.
96. Mallet-Guy, P., Papp, M., Switalska, Ch., Ungvary, Gy., and Varga, B., Les modifications precoces du debit sanguin dans les pancreatites aigues experimentales, *Lyon Chir.,* 67, 21, 1971.
97. Goodhead, B., Acute pancreatitis and pancreatic blood flow, *Surg. Gynecol. Obstet.,* 129, 331, 1969.
98. Donaldson, L. A. and Schenk, W. G., Jr., Experimental acute pancreatitis. The changes in pancreatic oxygen consumption and the effect of dextran 40, *Ann. Surg.,* 190, 728, 1979.
99. Donaldson, L. A. and Schenk, W. G., Jr., Acute pancreatitis — ischemia or hyperemia?, *Med. Hypothes.,* 6, 329, 1980.

100. Knol, J. A., Edgcomb, L. P., Inman, M. G., and Eckhauser, F. E., Low molecular weight dextran in experimental pancreatitis, *J. Surg. Res.*, 35, 73, 1983.
101. Ascheim, E. and Zweifach, B. W., Quantitative studies of protein and water shifts during inflammation, *Am. J. Physiol.*, 202, 534, 1962.
102. Zweifach, B. W., Microvascular aspects of tissue injury, in *The Inflammatory Process*, Zweifach, B. W., Grant, C., and McCluskey, R. T., Eds., Academic Press, Orlando, Fla., 1965, 161.
103. Wells, A. D., Imahori, S. C., and Schenk, W. G., Jr., Does edematous pancreatitis exist in biliary-related pancreatitis?, *Arch. Surg.*, 118, 1277, 1983.
104. Nemir, P., Jr. and Drabkin, D. J., The pathogenesis of acute necrotizing hemorrhagic pancreatitis: an experimental study, *Surgery*, 40, 171, 1956.
105. Ivy, A. C. and Gibbs, G. E., Pancreatitis: a review, *Surgery*, 31, 614, 1952.
106. Inoue, K., Kawano, T., Shima, K., Suzuki, T. K. T., Tobe, T., and Yajima, H., Relationship between development of fibrosis and hemodynamic changes of the pancreas in dogs, *Gastroenterology*, 81, 37, 1981.
107. Wayand, W., Pattermann, M., Umlauft, M., and Schur, W., Measurement of pancreatic blood supply before and after duct occlusion, *Z. Exp. Chir.*, 15, 14, 1982.
108. Gooszen, H. G., van Schilfgaarde, R., and Terpstra, J. L., Arterial blood supply of the left lobe of the canine pancreas. II. Electromagnetic flow measurements, *Surgery*, 93, 549, 1983.
109. Hermreck, A. S., Smith, L., and Thal, A. P., Acute edematous pancreatitis: metabolic and hemodynamic studies, *Surg. Forum*, 19, 368, 1968.
110. Egdahl, R. H., Mechanism of blood enzyme changes following the production of experimental pancreatitis, *Ann. Surg.*, 148, 389, 1958.
111. Kvietys, P. R., McLendon, J. M., Bulkley, G. B., Perry, M. A., and Granger, D. N., Pancreatic circulation: intrinsic regulation, *Am. J. Physiol.*, 242, G596, 1982.
111a. Becker, H., Vinten-Johansen, J., Buckberg, G. D., and Bugyi, H. I., Correlation of pancreatic blood flow and high-energy phosphates during experimental pancreatitis, *Eur. Surg. Res.*, 14, 203, 1982.
112. Alteveer, R. J., Jaffe, M. J., and van Dam, J., Hemodynamics and metabolism of the in vivo vascularly isolated canine pancreas, *Am. J. Physiol.*, 236, E626, 1979.
113. Broadie, T. A., Devedas, M., Rysavy, J., Leonard, A. S., and Delanay, J. P., The effect of hypoxia and hypercapnia on canine pancreatic blood flow, *J. Surg. Res.*, 27, 114, 1979.
114. Aakhus, T., Hofsli, M., and Vestad, E., Angiography in acute pancreatitis, *Acta Radiol. Diagn.*, 8, 119, 1969.
115. Wenz, W., Angiographische Befunde bei der Pankreatitis, *Chirurg*, 43, 250, 1972.
116. Roe, M. and Greenough, W. G., Marked hypervascularity and arteriovenous shunting in acute pancreatitis, *Radiology*, 113, 47, 1974.
117. Thal, A., Studies on pancreatitis. IV. The pathogenesis of bile pancreatitis, *Surg. Forum*, 5, 391, 1954.
118. Anderson, M. C., Schoenfeld, F. B., Iams, W. B., and Suwa, M., Circulatory changes in acute pancreatitis, *Surg. Clin. N. Am.*, 47, 127, 1967.
119. Papp, M., Ungvari, Gy., Nemeth, E. P., Munkacsi, I., and Zubek, L., The effect of bile-induced pancreatitis on the intrapancreatic vascular pattern in dogs, *Scand. J. Gastroenterol.*, 4, 681, 1969.
120. Schiller, W. R. and Anderson, M. C., Microcirculation of the normal and inflamed canine pancreas, *Ann. Surg.*, 181, 466, 1975.
121. Skjennald, A., Angiography in acute experimental pancreatitis correlated to hemodynamic changes, *Scand. J. Gastroenterol.*, 17 (Suppl. 71), 1, 1982.
122. Schoenbach, G., Sailer, F. X., Moeller, H. D., and Ammann, K., Capillarmikroskopische Beobachtungen am normal und krankhaft veraenderten Pankreas, *Langenbecks Arch. Chir.*, 313, 242, 1965.
123. Galletti, G., Cavallari, A., Battisti, C., and Pierangeli, M., La pancreatite acuta sperimentale di ansa duodenale chiusa, *Riv. Gastro-Enterol.*, 19 (Suppl. 6), 675, 1967.
124. Papp, M., Csaki, L., and Ormai, S., The total intraorganic plasma protein space in rats under normal conditions and in acute pancreatitis, *Acta Med. Acad. Sci. Hung.*, 28, 243, 1971.
125. Morris, R. E., Studies on the development of pancreatic necrosis in the living mouse, *Bull. Johns Hopkins Hosp.*, 114, 212, 1964.
126. Kivisaari, L., The effect of experimental pancreatitis and diabetes on the microvasculature of the rat pancreas, *Scand. J. Gastroenterol.*, 14, 689, 1979.
127. Carey, L. C. and Rodgers, R. E., Pathophysiologic alterations in experimental pancreatitis, *Surgery*, 60, 171, 1966.
128. Ellison, E. C., Pappas, T. N., Johnson, J. A., Fabri, P. J., and Carey, L. C., Demonstration and characterization of the hemoconcentrating effect of ascitic fluid that accumulates during hemorrhagic pancreatitis, *J. Surg. Res.*, 30, 241, 1981.
129. Amundsen, E., Histamine release during experimental acute hemorrhagic pancreatitis in dogs, *Ann. Chir. Gynaecol. Fenn.*, 61, 251, 1972.

130. Ofstad, E., Formation and destruction of plasma kinins during experimental acute hemorrhagic pancreatitis in dogs, *Scand. J. Gastroenterol.*, 5 (Suppl. 5), 1970.
131. Thal, A. P., Kobold, E. E., and Hollenberg, M. J., The release of vasoactive substances in acute pancreatitis, *Am. J. Surg.*, 105, 708, 1963.
132. Satake, K., Rozmanith, J., Appert, H., and Howard, J. M., Hemodynamic changes and bradykinin levels in plasma and lymph during experimental acute pancreatitis in dogs, *Ann. Surg.*, 178, 659, 1973.
133. Takasugi, S. and Kanno, T., Increase in content and release of kallikreinogen in acute experimental pancreatitis in rats, *Hiroshima J. Med. Sci.*, 31, 45, 1982.
134. Papp, M., Fodor, I., and Makara, G. B., Bradykinin-induced histological changes in the pancreas, *Z. Gesamte Exp. Med.*, 147, 264, 1968.
135. Studley, J. G., Lee, J. B., and Schenk, W. G., Jr., Pathophysiology of acute pancreatitis: evaluation of the effects and mode of action of indomethacin in experimental pancreatitis in dogs, *J. Surg. Res.*, 32, 563, 1982.
136. Glazer, G. and Bennette, A., Prostaglandin release in canine hemorrhagic pancreatitis, *Gut*, 17, 22, 1976.
137. Lefer, A. M. and Spath, D. A., Pancreatic hypoperfusion and the production of myocardial depressant factor in hemorrhagic shock, *Ann. Surg.*, 179, 868, 1974.
138. Ferguson, W. W., Glenn, T. M., and Lefer, A. M., Mechanism of production of circulatory shock factors in isolated perfused pancreas, *Am. J. Physiol.*, 222, 450, 1972.
139. Papp, M., Makara, G. B., Hajtman, B., and Csaki, L., A quantitative study of pancreatic blood flow in experimental pancreatitis, *Gastroenterology*, 51, 524, 1966.
140. Castiglioni, G. C. and Lojacono, L., Circulatory changes in acute pancreatitis, *Surg. Italy*, 1, 23, 1971.
141. Donaldson, L. A., Williams, R. W., and Schenk, W. G., Jr., Experimental pancreatitis: effect of plasma and dextran on pancreatic blood flow, *Surgery*, 84, 313, 1978.
142. Wells, A. D. and Schenk, W. G., Jr., Beneficial effect of ethamsylate on the relative blood flow of the pancreas in acute canine necrotizing pancreatitis, *Surg. Gynecol. Obstet.*, 155, 673, 1982.
143. Di Carlo, V., Nespoli, A., Chiesa, R., Staudacher, C., Cristallo, M., Bevilacqua, G., and Staudacher, V., Hemodynamic and metabolic impairment in acute pancreatitis, *World J. Surg.*, 5, 329, 1981.
144. Bradley, E. L., Hall, J. R., Luitz, J., Hamner, L., and Lattouf, O., Hemodynamic consequences of severe pancreatitis, *Ann. Surg.*, 198, 130, 1983.
145. Forsyth, R. P., Hoffbrand, B. I., and Melmon, K. L., The distribution of cardiac output during hemorrhage in the unanesthetized monkey, *Circ. Res.*, 27, 311, 1970.
146. Bor, N. M., Alvur, M., Ercan, M. T., Oener, G., and Bekdik, C. F., Pancreatic blood flow in hemorrhagic shock, *Pfluegers Arch.*, 386, 277, 1980.
147. White, T. T., Murat, J. E., and Morgan, A., Pancreatitis I: review of 733 cases of pancreatitis from three Seattle hospitals, *Northwest Med.*, 67, 374, 1968.
148. Warshaw, A. L. and O'Hara, P. J., Susceptibility of the pancreas to ischemic injury in shock, *Ann. Surg.*, 188, 197, 1978.
149. Nemeth, E. P., Fodor, I., Folly, G., and Papp, M., Arterial hypotension as a factor aggravating the histological damage in experimental acute hemorrhagic pancreatitis, *Acta Morphol. Acad. Sci. Hung.*, 21, 319, 1973.
150. Imrie, C. W., Ferguson, J. C., Murphy, D., and Blumgart, L. H., Arterial hypoxia in acute pancreatitis, *Br. J. Surg.*, 64, 185, 1977.
151. Papp, M., Fodor, I., Varga, G., and Folly, G., Pancreatic edema: its effect on the function and morphology of the pancreas in dogs and rats, *Mt. Sinai J. Med., N.Y.*, 49, 456, 1982.
152. Popper, H. L. and Necheles, H., Pathways of enzymes into the blood in acute damage of the pancreas, *Proc. Soc. Exp. Biol. Med.*, 43, 220, 1940.
153. Papp, M., Nemeth, E. P., Feuer, L., and Fodor, I., Effect of impairment of lymph flow in experimental acute pancreatitis, *Acta Med. Acad. Sci. Hung.*, 11, 203, 1958.
154. Dreiling, D. A., The lymphatics, pancreatic ascites and pancreatic inflammatory disease, *Am. J. Gastroenterol.*, 53, 119, 1970.
155. Dumont, A. E., Martelli, A. B., and Mulholland, J. H., Lymphatic pathway of pancreatic secretion in man, *Ann. Surg.*, 152, 403, 1960.
156. Papp, M., Feher, S., Nemeth, E. P., Somogyi, J., and Folly, G., Exit routes for secretory proteins from the dog pancreas, *Acta Physiol. Acad. Sci. Hung.*, 56, 401, 1980.
157. Sim, D. N., Duprez, A., and Anderson, M. C., Alterations of the lymphatic circulation during acute experimental pancreatitis, *Surgery*, 60, 1775, 1966.
158. Papp, M., Ormai, S., and Csaki, L., The share of pancreatic lymph and blood circulation in pancreatic self-digestion, *Z. Gesamte Exp. Med.*, 147, 285, 1968.

159. Duprez, A., Dupont, J. M., and Litvine, J., Le facteur lymphatique dans les pancreatites experimentales, *Acta Chir. Belg.*, 64, 687, 1964.
160. Bartos, V. and Brzek, V., Drainage of thoracic duct in patients with diseases of the pancreas, in *Progress in Lymphology*, Vol. 2, Viamonte, M. et al., Eds., Georg Thieme Verlag, Stuttgart, 64, 1970.
161. Papp, M., Nemeth, E. P., and Horvath, E. J., Pancreatico-duodenal lymph flow and lipase activity in acute experimental pancreatitis, *Lymphology*, 4, 48, 1971.
162. Granger, D. N. and Barrowman, J. A., Microcirculation of the alimentary tract, *Gastroenterology*, 84, 1035, 1983.
163. Burton-Opitz, R., Ueber die Stroemung des Blutes in dem Gebiete der Pfortader. V. Die Blutversorgung des Pfortaders und Pankreas, *Arch. Gesamte Physiol.*, 146, 344, 1912.
164. Rappaport, A. M., Ohira, S., Coodling, J. A., Empey, G., Kalnius, A., Lin, B. J., and Haist, R. E., Effect on insulin output and on pancreatic blood flow of exogenous insulin infusion into an in situ isolated portion of the pancreas, *Endocrinology*, 91, 168, 1972.
165. Sapirstein, L., Regional blood flow by fractional distribution of indicators, *Am. J. Physiol.*, 193, 161, 1958.
166. Delanay, J. P. and Custer, J., Gastrointestinal blood flow in the dog, *Circ. Res.*, 17, 394, 1965.
167. Delanay, J. P. and Grim, E., Influence of hormones and drugs on canine pancreatic blood flow, *Am. J. Physiol.*, 1398, 1966.
168. Steiner, S. H. and Mueller, G. C. E., Distribution of blood flow in the digestive tract of the rat, *Circ. Res.*, 9, 99, 1961.
169. Gilsdorf, R. B., Urdatena, L. F., Leonard, A. S., et al., Posterior hypothalamic effect on gastrointestinal blood flow in conscious cat, *Proc. Soc. Exp. Biol. Med.*, 143, 329, 1973.
170. Berry, A. R., Millar, A. M., and Taylor, T. V., Pancreatic blood flow in experimental acute pancreatitis, *Dig. Dis. Sci.*, 27, 444, 1982.
171. Ercan, M. T., Bor, N. A., Bekdik, C. F., and Oener, G., Measurement of pancreatic blood flow in dog by 133 Xe clearance technique, *Pfluegers Arch.*, 348, 51, 1974.
172. Bor, N. A., Ercan, M. T., Alvur, M., Bekdik, C., and Oener, G., Calculation of net insulin secretion and pancreatic blood flow, *Pfluegers Arch.*, 352, 179, 1974.
173. Aune, S. and Semb, L. S., The effect of secretin and pancreozymin on pancreatic blood flow in conscious and anaesthetized dog, *Acta Physiol. Scand.*, 76, 406, 1969.
174. Ishida, H., Makino, T., Kobayashi, M., and Tsuneoka, K., Laparoscopic measurement of pancreatic blood flow, *Endoscopy*, 15, 107, 1983.
175. Rappaport, A. M., Kawamura, T., Davidson, J. K., Lin, B. J., Ohira, S., Zeigler, M., Coodling, J. A., Henderson, J., and Haist, R. E., Effects of hormones and of blood flow on insulin output of isolated pancreas in situ, *Am. J. Physiol.*, 221, 343, 1971.
176. Spath, J. A., Gorczynski, R. J., and Lefer, A. M., Pancreatic perfusion in the pathophysiology of hemorrhagic shock, *Am. J. Physiol.*, 226, 443, 1974.
177. Becker, H., Manganaro, A., Lazar, H., Mulder, D. G., and Buckberg, G. D., Limitations of studying splanchnic blood flow during anaesthesia, *Surg. Forum*, 30, 347, 1979.
178. Chung, R. S. and Safaie-Shirazi, S., The effect of secretin on pancreatic blood flow in the awake and anaesthetized dog, *Proc. Soc. Exp. Biol. Med.*, 173, 620, 1983.
179. Valente, U., Prior, C., Casaccia, M., Campisi, C., Arcuri, V., Pellicci, R., and Barabino, C., Osservazioni preliminari sulla modificazioni del flusso sanguino pancreatico, mediante l'uso de rubido Rb86 nelle pancreatiti acute sperimentale, *Minerva Chir.*, 31, 167, 1976.

INDEX

A

B

C

D

E

F

G

H

I

J

K

L

M

N

O

P

R

S

T

U

V

W

X

Y